GCSE AQA
Mathematics
Higher Level

Complete Revision and Practice

Contents

The columns for Units 1-3 on these pages might be useful if you're studying AQA's 'Mathematics A' Specification (the one divided into units — ask your teacher if you're not sure which one you do). They show which units the pages cover.

Throughout this book you'll see grade stamps like these:
You can use these to focus your revision on easier or harder work.
But remember — to get a top grade you have to know **everything**, not just the hardest topics.

(A*) (C) (B) (A)

Contents

Published by CGP

From original material by Richard Parsons

Updated by: Sharon Keeley-Holden, Paul Jordin, Kirstie McHale, Sarah Oxley, Alison Palin, Andy Park, Caley Simpson, Ruth Wilbourne

Contributors: Rosie Hanson, Alan Mason

With thanks to Simon Little and Alastair Duncombe for the proofreading

ISBN: 978 1 84762 177 1

Printed by Elanders Ltd, Newcastle upon Tyne.
Clipart from Corel®

Calculating Tips

Welcome to GCSE Maths — not always fun, but stuff you have to learn. Thankfully there are some nifty exam tricks you can learn, which could get you marks in your exams. Read on...

BODMAS — **Brackets, Other, Division, Multiplication, Addition, Subtraction**

BODMAS tells you the ORDER in which these operations should be done:
Work out Brackets first, then Other things like squaring, then Divide / Multiply groups of numbers before Adding or Subtracting them.

This set of rules works really well, so remember the word BODMAS.

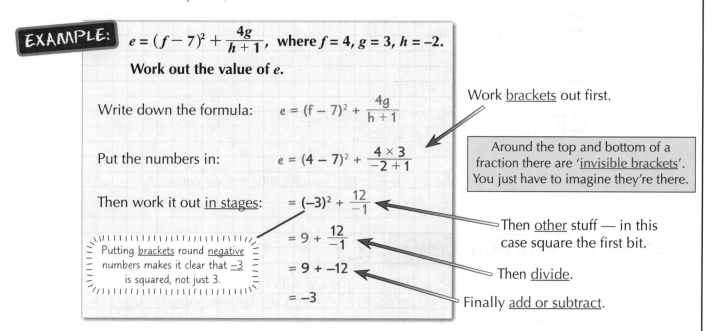

EXAMPLE: $e = (f - 7)^2 + \dfrac{4g}{h + 1}$, where $f = 4$, $g = 3$, $h = -2$.

Work out the value of e.

Write down the formula: $e = (f - 7)^2 + \dfrac{4g}{h + 1}$

Put the numbers in: $e = (4 - 7)^2 + \dfrac{4 \times 3}{-2 + 1}$

Then work it out in stages: $= (-3)^2 + \dfrac{12}{-1}$

> Putting brackets round negative numbers makes it clear that -3 is squared, not just 3.

$= 9 + \dfrac{12}{-1}$

$= 9 + -12$

$= -3$

Work **brackets** out first.

Around the top and bottom of a fraction there are 'invisible brackets'. You just have to imagine they're there.

Then *other* stuff — in this case square the first bit.

Then divide.

Finally add or subtract.

Don't Be Scared of *Wordy Questions*

A lot of the marks in your exam are for answering wordy, real-life questions. For these you don't just have to do the maths — you've got to work out what the question's asking you to do. Relax and work through them step by step.

1) **READ** the question **carefully**. Work out **what bit of maths** you need to answer it.

2) **Underline** the **INFORMATION YOU NEED** to answer the question — you might not have to use **all** the numbers they give you.

3) Write out the question **IN MATHS** and answer it, showing all your **working** clearly.

EXAMPLE: The table shows rates of **depreciation** over a three year period for three different motorbikes. Helen bought a B260 for **£6300** three years ago. How much is the motorbike worth now?.

Model	Depreciation over 3 years
A125	37%
B260	45%
F400	42%

1) The word "depreciation" tells you this is a percentages question.

2) You need the initial value of £6300 and the B260 depreciation of 45%.

3) "Depreciation" is a percentage decrease, so in maths: 0.45 × £6300 = £2835

£6300 − £2835 = £3465

Calculating Tips

You're allowed to use a calculator in some of your exams, so make sure you know how it can help you, and watch the marks roll in. Here are just a few things you'll end up using all the time.

Know Your *Buttons*

x^{-1} The <u>reciprocal</u> button. The reciprocal of a number is <u>1 divided by it</u>. So the reciprocal of 2 is ½.

Ans This uses your <u>last answer</u> in your current calculation. Super useful.

$\sqrt[3]{\Box}$ The <u>cube root</u> button. You might have to press <u>shift</u> first.

S⇔D Flips your answer from a <u>fraction or surd</u> to a <u>decimal</u> and vice versa.

Look for these buttons on <u>your</u> calculator — they might be a bit different on yours.

BODMAS on Your Calculator

BODMAS questions on the <u>calculator paper</u> will be packed with <u>tricky decimals</u> and maybe a <u>square root</u> and <u>sin/cos/tan</u>. You <u>could</u> do it on your calculator in one go, but that runs the risk of losing precious marks.

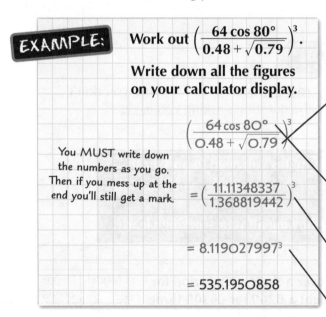

EXAMPLE: Work out $\left(\dfrac{64\cos 80°}{0.48+\sqrt{0.79}}\right)^3$.

Write down all the figures on your calculator display.

You MUST write down the numbers as you go. Then if you mess up at the end you'll still get a mark.

$$\left(\frac{64\cos 80°}{0.48+\sqrt{0.79}}\right)^3$$

$$=\left(\frac{11.11348337}{1.368819442}\right)^3$$

$$= 8.119027997^3$$

$$= 535.1950858$$

There are lots of <u>slightly different ways</u> of working out this type of calculation. Here's one:

1) Work out the <u>bottom</u> of the fraction:
   0.48 + √ 0.79 =
   Write the answer down and store it in the <u>memory</u> by pressing: STO M+

2) Now work out the <u>top</u> of the fraction:
   64 cos 80 =

3) Do the division: Ans ÷ RCL M+ =
   This gets the value of the bottom of the fraction out of the memory.

4) And cube: Ans $x^{\Box}$ 3 =

Calculators are a great help — as long as you use them properly

Calculators can give you quick, accurate answers — but only if you know how to use them properly. Make sure you know what the important buttons do and how to use them.

Calculating Tips

Here are some important <u>checks</u> to help you spot <u>mistakes</u> and make sure you give the correct <u>final answer</u>.

Check *Your Answer using* **Brackets** (*and*)

<u>Check your answer</u> to a question like the one on the previous page by plugging it into your calculator <u>in fewer steps</u>.

1) To work out $\dfrac{64\cos 80°}{0.48 + \sqrt{0.79}}$ you <u>CAN'T</u> just press `64` `cos` `80` `÷` `0.48` `+` `√☐` `0.79` `=`

2) The calculator follows BODMAS, so it'll think you mean $\dfrac{64\cos 80°}{0.48} + \sqrt{0.79}$.

3) The secret is to <u>OVERRIDE</u> the automatic <u>BODMAS</u> using the <u>BRACKETS BUTTONS</u>.

4) The calculator will do the bits in brackets first. So you'd press:

`(` `64` `cos` `80` `)` `÷` `(` `0.48` `+` `√☐` `0.79` `)` `=`

(Cube this to check the question on p2.)

Your calculator might need you to add an extra ")" here. See the note below.

And maybe an extra ")" or a <u>right arrow nudge</u> here.

 NOTE:
1) On some calculators, a <u>bracket</u> opens when you use a <u>trig function</u> or the square/cube root function. So to enter something like tan 40° + 1, you have to <u>close the bracket</u>: `tan` `40` `)` `+` `1`

2) On some calculators, the cursor stays <u>under the square root bar</u> until you nudge it out by pressing the <u>right arrow</u>.

Make Sure You Know What Your Answer **Means**

It's taken 2 minutes of frenzied button pressing and finally your calculator screen looks like this.

> 3.6

Before you merrily jot down 3.6 as your answer, think about <u>what it means</u> — 3.6 what? Pipers piping? It sounds silly, but it can lose you easy marks in the exam.

E.g. If you're answering a money question, 3.6 won't get you any marks — you really need to write <u>£3.60</u>.

Learn these three pages, store, then recall...

Learn this stuff — it can really help you get marks in your exams. It's really important that you get used to using <u>your</u> calculator — you don't need any extra worries when it comes to your exam.

Types of Number

This section is about numbers, so before we get stuck into the maths,
there are a few definitions of different types of number that you need to know.

Integers:

You need to make sure you know the <u>meaning</u> of this word — it'll come up <u>all the time</u> in GCSE Maths.
An <u>integer</u> is another name for a <u>whole number</u> — either a positive or negative number, or zero.

> **Examples:**
>
> **1) Integers**
>
> $-365, \quad 0, \quad 1, \quad 17, \quad 989, \quad 1\ 234\ 567\ 890$
>
> **2) Not integers**
>
> $0.5, \quad \frac{2}{3}, \quad \sqrt{7}, \quad 13\frac{3}{4}, \quad -1000.1, \quad 66.66, \quad \pi$

Rational and Irrational Numbers:

All numbers fall into one of these two categories.
<u>Rational numbers</u> can be written as <u>fractions</u>. Most numbers you deal with are rational.

> **Rational numbers come in 3 different forms:**
>
> **1** <u>Integers</u> e.g. $4\ (= \frac{4}{1})$, $-5\ (= \frac{-5}{1})$, $-12\ (= \frac{-12}{1})$
>
> **2** <u>Fractions</u> p/q, where p and q are (non-zero) integers, e.g. $\frac{1}{4}$, $-\frac{1}{2}$, $\frac{3}{4}$
>
> **3** <u>Terminating or recurring decimals</u> e.g. $0.125\ (= \frac{1}{8})$, $0.33333333...\ (= \frac{1}{3})$, $0.143143143...\ (= \frac{143}{999})$

- <u>Irrational numbers</u> are messy. They <u>can't</u> be written as fractions — they're <u>never-ending</u>, <u>non-repeating decimals</u>.

- <u>Roots</u> of +ve integers are either integers or irrational (e.g. $\sqrt{2}$, $\sqrt{3}$, $\sqrt[3]{2}$ are all irrational, but $\sqrt{4} = 2$ isn't).

- <u>Surds</u> (see p45) are numbers or expressions containing irrational roots. π is also irrational.

An integer can be positive, negative or zero

Remember that <u>all</u> numbers are either rational or irrational. It's really important that you know these different types of number and understand what they are — otherwise you'll run into trouble further on.

Types of Number

Here are a few more types of number for you to get your head around.

Squares and Cubes:

Make sure you know these <u>squares</u> and <u>cubes by heart</u> — they could come up on a non-calculator paper.

THE SQUARES:

1^2	2^2	3^2	4^2	5^2	6^2	7^2	8^2	9^2	10^2	11^2	12^2	13^2	14^2	15^2
1	4	9	16	25	36	49	64	81	100	121	144	169	196	225
(1×1)	(2×2)	(3×3)	(4×4)	(5×5)	(6×6)	(7×7)	(8×8)	(9×9)	(10×10)	(11×11)	(12×12)	(13×13)	(14×14)	(15×15)

THE CUBES:

1^3	2^3	3^3	4^3	5^3	10^3
1	8	27	64	125	1000
(1×1×1)	(2×2×2)	(3×3×3)	(4×4×4)	(5×5×5)	(10×10×10)

Prime Numbers:

2	3	5	7	11	13	17
19	23	29	31	37	41	43...

1) A <u>prime number</u> is a number which <u>doesn't divide by anything</u> — apart from itself and 1. (The only exception is <u>1</u>, which is <u>NOT</u> a prime number.)

2) Apart from 2 and 5, <u>ALL PRIMES END IN 1, 3, 7, OR 9</u>.

So <u>POSSIBLE</u> primes would be 71, 73, 77, 79, 101, 103, 107, 109, etc. But <u>not all of these</u> are primes — you need to check carefully that they don't divide by anything.

EXAMPLE: **Show that 77 is not a prime number.**

Just find a way to make 77 using multiplication, other than 1 × 77:   7 × 11 = 77

77 divides by numbers other than 1 and 77, so it isn't a prime number.

All these types of number just need learning

These types of number will all appear again and again, so you need to be able to spot the different types from a mile away. Keep writing down the definitions and learn the square and cube numbers on this page.

Multiples, Factors and Prime Factors

You need to know what multiples, factors and prime factors are — and how to find them.

Multiples and Factors

The MULTIPLES of a number are just its <u>times table</u>.

EXAMPLE: **Find the first 8 multiples of 13.**
You just need to find the first 8 numbers in the <u>13 times table</u>:
13 26 39 52 65 78 91 104

The FACTORS of a number are all the numbers that <u>divide into it</u>.

There's a method that guarantees you'll find them all:

1) Start off with 1 × the number itself, then try 2 ×, then 3 × and so on, listing the pairs in rows.

2) Try each one in turn. Cross out the row if it doesn't divide exactly.

3) Eventually, when you get a number <u>repeated</u>, <u>stop</u>.

4) The numbers in the rows you haven't crossed out make up the list of factors.

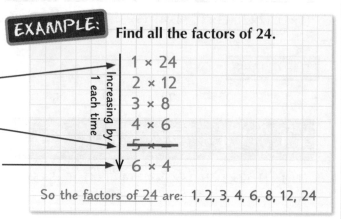

EXAMPLE: **Find all the factors of 24.**

1 × 24
2 × 12
3 × 8
4 × 6
~~5 ×~~
6 × 4

So the <u>factors of 24</u> are: 1, 2, 3, 4, 6, 8, 12, 24

Finding **Prime Factors** — The **Factor Tree**

<u>Any number</u> can be broken down into a string of prime numbers all multiplied together — this is called '<u>expressing it as a product of prime factors</u>'.

EXAMPLE: **Express 420 as a product of prime factors.**

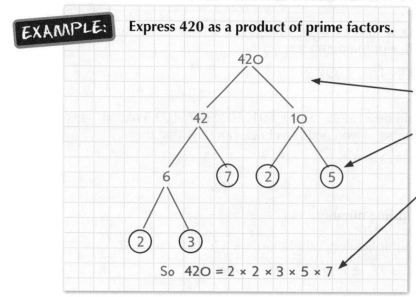

So 420 = 2 × 2 × 3 × 5 × 7

To write a number as a product of its prime factors, use the mildly entertaining <u>Factor Tree</u> method:

1) Start with the number at the top, and <u>split</u> it into <u>factors</u> as shown.

2) Every time you get a prime, <u>ring it</u>.

3) Keep going until you can't go further (i.e. you're just left with primes), then write the primes out <u>in order</u>.

Factors and multiples are easy marks

Factor and multiple questions are simple multiplications and divisions so there's no reason to lose marks. Practise doing them quickly and accurately and make sure you know what all the words mean.

LCM and HCF

You'll need to know about <u>multiples</u> and <u>factors</u> from the previous page before you have a go at this one...

LCM — 'Lowest Common Multiple'

'<u>Lowest Common Multiple</u>' — all it means is <u>this</u>:

The <u>SMALLEST</u> number that will <u>DIVIDE BY ALL</u> the numbers in question.

METHOD: 1) <u>LIST</u> the <u>MULTIPLES</u> of <u>ALL</u> the numbers.
2) Find the <u>SMALLEST</u> one that's in <u>ALL the lists</u>.
3) That's the LCM.

> The LCM is sometimes called the Least (instead of 'Lowest') Common Multiple.

EXAMPLE: **Find the lowest common multiple (LCM) of 12 and 15.**

Multiples of 12 are: 12, 24, 36, 48, (60), 72, 84, 96, ...
Multiples of 15 are: 15, 30, 45, (60), 75, 90, 105, ...

So the <u>lowest common multiple</u> (LCM) of 12 and 15 is **60**.

HCF — 'Highest Common Factor'

'<u>Highest Common Factor</u>' — all it means is <u>this</u>:

The <u>BIGGEST</u> number that will <u>DIVIDE INTO ALL</u> the numbers in question.

METHOD: 1) <u>LIST</u> the <u>FACTORS</u> of <u>ALL</u> the numbers.
2) Find the <u>BIGGEST</u> one that's in <u>ALL the lists</u>.
3) That's the HCF.

EXAMPLE: **Find the highest common factor (HCF) of 36, 54, and 72.**

Factors of 36 are: 1, 2, 3, 4, 6, 9, 12, (18), 36
Factors of 54 are: 1, 2, 3, 6, 9, (18), 27, 54
Factors of 72 are: 1, 2, 3, 4, 6, 8, 9, 12, (18), 24, 36, 72

So the <u>highest common factor</u> (HCF) of 36, 54 and 72 is **18**.

Just <u>take care</u> listing the factors — make sure you use the <u>proper method</u> (as shown on the previous page) or you'll miss one and blow the whole thing out of the water.

Don't be put off by the fancy names

Lowest common multiple and highest common factor questions can be a bit intimidating in the exam — but they're easy enough if you take them step by step. It's just multiplication and division again.

Warm-up and Worked Exam Questions

This stuff is pretty straightforward, but that doesn't mean you can get away without learning the facts and practising the questions. You should have learnt the facts already — try these and we'll see.

Warm-up Questions

1) Choose from the numbers 1, 2, 3, 4, 5, 6, 7, 8, 9, 10:
   Which numbers are   a) square?   b) cube?   c) prime?
2) Repeat Question 1 using the numbers 30-40 inclusive.
3) Explain why 231 is not a prime number.
4) Find all the factors of 40.
5) Write 40 as a product of its prime factors.

Worked Exam Questions

Take a look at these worked exam questions. They're not too hard, but they should give you a good idea of what to write. Make the most of the handy hints now — they won't be there in the exam.

1   Find: **(C)**

a) 48 as a product of its prime factors.

Draw a factor tree...

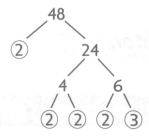

You could also write this as $48 = 2^4 \times 3$

$48 = 2 \times 2 \times 2 \times 2 \times 3$

[2 marks]

b) the highest common factor (HCF) of 48 and 108.

List all the factors of each number, then find the largest one that appears in both lists.

Factors of 48 are: 1, 2, 3, 4, 6, 8, ⑫, 16, 24, 48

Factors of 108 are: 1, 2, 3, 4, 6, 9, ⑫, 18, 27, 36, 54, 108

HCF = 12

[1 mark]

2   Find the LCM of 6, 8 and 10. **(C)**

List all the multiples of each number until you find one that appears in all three lists.

Multiples of 6 are: 6, 12, 18, 24, 30, 36, 42, 48, 54, 60, 66, 72, 78, 84, 90, 96, 102, 108, 114, ⑫⓪, 126, ...

Multiples of 8 are: 8, 16, 24, 32, 40, 48, 56, 64, 72, 80, 88, 96, 104, 112, ⑫⓪, 128, ...

Multiples of 10 are: 10, 20, 30, 40, 50, 60, 70, 80, 90, 100, 110, ⑫⓪, 130, ...

LCM = 120

[2 marks]

Exam Questions

3 If *a* and *b* are prime numbers, give an example to show that each of the following statements is false:

Remember — 1 is not a prime number.

a) *a* + *b* is always even.

....
[1 mark]

b) *a* × *b* is always odd.

....
[1 mark]

c) $a^2 + b^2$ is always even.

....
[1 mark]

4 Express:

a) 210 as a product of its prime factors.

....
[2 marks]

b) 105^2 as a product of its prime factors.

....
[2 marks]

5 Find:

a) 72 as a product of its prime factors.

....
[2 marks]

b) the HCF of 54 and 72.

....
[1 mark]

6 Two remote-control cars start at the same time from the start line on a track.

One car takes half a minute to complete a circuit.
The other car takes 1 minute 10 seconds to complete a circuit.

If they start side by side, how long will it be before they are next side by side on the start line? State the units in your answer.

....
[2 marks]

Fractions

These pages show you how to cope with fraction calculations without your <u>calculator</u>.

1) *Cancelling down* — *easy*

To <u>cancel down</u> or <u>simplify</u> a fraction, <u>divide top and bottom by the same number</u>, till they won't go further:

EXAMPLE: Simplify $\frac{18}{24}$.

Cancel down in a series of <u>easy steps</u> — keep going till the top and bottom don't have <u>any</u> common factors.

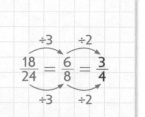

$$\frac{18}{24} = \frac{6}{8} = \frac{3}{4}$$

The number on the top of the fraction is the <u>numerator</u>, and the number on the bottom is the <u>denominator</u>.

2) *Mixed numbers* — *quite easy*

<u>Mixed numbers</u> are things like $3\frac{1}{3}$, with an integer part and a fraction part. <u>Improper fractions</u> are ones where the top number is larger than the bottom number. You need to be able to convert between the two.

EXAMPLES: **1.** Write $4\frac{2}{3}$ as an improper fraction.

1) Think of the <u>mixed number</u> as an <u>addition</u>:

$$4\frac{2}{3} = 4 + \frac{2}{3}$$

2) Turn the <u>integer part</u> into a <u>fraction</u>:

$$4 + \frac{2}{3} = \frac{12}{3} + \frac{2}{3} = \frac{12+2}{3} = \frac{14}{3}$$

2. Write $\frac{31}{4}$ as a mixed number.

<u>Divide</u> the top number by the bottom.
1) The <u>answer</u> gives the <u>whole number part</u>.
2) The <u>remainder</u> goes <u>on top</u> of the fraction.

$$31 \div 4 = 7 \text{ remainder } 3 \quad \text{so} \quad \frac{31}{4} = 7\frac{3}{4}$$

3) *Multiplying* — *easy*

Multiply top and bottom separately. It usually helps to cancel down first if you can.

EXAMPLE: Find $\frac{8}{15} \times \frac{5}{12}$.

<u>Cancel down</u> by dividing top and bottom by any common factors you find in <u>either</u> fraction:

Now multiply the top and bottom numbers <u>separately</u>:

8 and 12 both divide by 4

15 and 5 both divide by 5

$$\frac{{}^{2}8}{15} \times \frac{5}{{}_{3}12} = \frac{2}{15_{3}} \times \frac{{}^{1}5}{3}$$

$$= \frac{2}{3} \times \frac{1}{3} = \frac{2 \times 1}{3 \times 3} = \frac{2}{9}$$

Fractions

Here are some more tricks for dealing with fractions:

4) Dividing — quite easy

Turn the second fraction UNDERLINED and then <u>multiply</u>:

> **EXAMPLE:** Find $2\frac{1}{3} \div 3\frac{1}{2}$.
>
> Rewrite the <u>mixed numbers</u> as <u>fractions</u>: $\quad 2\frac{1}{3} \div 3\frac{1}{2} = \frac{7}{3} \div \frac{7}{2}$
>
> Turn $\frac{7}{2}$ <u>upside down</u> and <u>multiply</u>: $\qquad\qquad = \frac{7}{3} \times \frac{2}{7}$
>
> <u>Simplify</u> by cancelling the 7s: $\qquad\qquad = \frac{1}{3} \times \frac{2}{1} = \frac{2}{3}$

Look back at the previous page to see how to convert mixed numbers to improper fractions.

> When you're multiplying or dividing with <u>mixed numbers</u>,
> <u>always</u> turn them into <u>improper fractions</u> first.

5) Common denominators — slightly trickier

This comes in handy for <u>ordering fractions</u> by size, and for <u>adding</u> or <u>subtracting</u> fractions (see the next page). You need to find a number that <u>all</u> the denominators <u>divide into</u> — this will be your <u>common denominator</u>.

The simplest way is to find the <u>lowest common multiple</u> of the denominators:

> **EXAMPLE:** Put the fractions below in ascending order of size:
>
> $$\frac{8}{3} \qquad \frac{5}{4} \qquad \frac{12}{5}$$
>
> The <u>LCM</u> of 3, 4 and 5 is 60,
> so make 60 the <u>common denominator</u>:
>
> $$\overset{\times 20}{\frac{8}{3} = \frac{160}{60}} \qquad \overset{\times 15}{\frac{5}{4} = \frac{75}{60}} \qquad \overset{\times 12}{\frac{12}{5} = \frac{144}{60}}$$
>
> *Don't forget to use the original fractions in the final answer.*
>
> So the correct order is $\dfrac{75}{60}, \dfrac{144}{60}, \dfrac{160}{60}$ i.e. $\dfrac{5}{4}, \dfrac{12}{5}, \dfrac{8}{3}$

Don't be put off by mixed numbers

You can easily turn mixed numbers into 'normal' fractions. Finding a common denominator will often come in handy too — if you need a reminder on how to find the LCM, flick back to p7.

Fractions

There are <u>two important steps</u> to take when <u>adding</u> or <u>subtracting</u> fractions.

6) *Adding*, *subtracting* — *sort the denominators first*

> 1) Make sure the denominators are <u>the same</u> (see p11).

> 2) Add (or subtract) the top lines (numerators) <u>only</u>.

If you're adding or subtracting <u>mixed numbers</u>, it usually helps to convert them to improper fractions first.

> **EXAMPLE:** Calculate $2\frac{1}{5} - 1\frac{1}{2}$.
>
> Rewrite the <u>mixed numbers</u> as <u>fractions</u>: $\quad 2\frac{1}{5} - 1\frac{1}{2} = \frac{11}{5} - \frac{3}{2}$
>
> Find a <u>common denominator</u>: $\quad\quad\quad\quad = \frac{22}{10} - \frac{15}{10}$
>
> Combine the <u>top lines</u>: $\quad\quad\quad\quad\quad = \frac{22 - 15}{10} = \frac{7}{10}$

> People usually find <u>adding and subtracting fractions</u> harder than multiplying and dividing — but it's actually <u>pretty easy</u> as long as you remember to <u>make sure the denominators are the same</u>.

7) *Finding a fraction of something* — *just multiply*

> <u>Multiply</u> the 'something' by the <u>TOP</u> of the fraction, and <u>divide</u> it by the <u>BOTTOM</u>.

It doesn't matter which order you do those two steps in — just start with whatever's easiest.

> **EXAMPLE:** What is $\frac{9}{20}$ of £360?
>
> Start by dividing by 20, that's easiest:
>
> $\frac{9}{20}$ of £360 = (£360 ÷ 20) × 9
>
> $\quad\quad\quad\quad\quad = £18 × 9$
>
> $\quad\quad\quad\quad\quad = £162$

You have to learn to handle fractions in these 7 situations

If you've learnt how to find a common denominator (p11), then adding and subtracting fractions should be dead easy. To find one thing as a fraction of another, carry out the two steps whichever way's easiest.

Fractions, Decimals and Percentages

The one word that describes all these three is <u>PROPORTION</u>. Fractions, decimals and percentages are simply <u>three different ways</u> of expressing a <u>proportion</u> of something — and it's pretty important you should see them as <u>closely related and completely interchangeable</u> with each other. This table shows the really common conversions which you should know straight off without having to work them out:

Fraction	Decimal	Percentage
$\frac{1}{2}$	0.5	50%
$\frac{1}{4}$	0.25	25%
$\frac{3}{4}$	0.75	75%
$\frac{1}{3}$	0.333333...	$33\frac{1}{3}\%$
$\frac{2}{3}$	0.666666...	$66\frac{2}{3}\%$
$\frac{1}{10}$	0.1	10%
$\frac{2}{10}$	0.2	20%
$\frac{1}{5}$	0.2	20%
$\frac{2}{5}$	0.4	40%

The more of those conversions you learn, the better — but for those that you <u>don't know</u>, you must <u>also learn</u> how to <u>convert</u> between the three types. These are the methods:

Fraction $\xrightarrow{\text{Divide}}$ Decimal $\xrightarrow{\times \text{ by } 100}$ Percentage

E.g. $\frac{7}{20}$ is $7 \div 20$ $= 0.35$ e.g. 0.35×100 $= 35\%$

Fraction $\longleftarrow$ Decimal $\longleftarrow$ Percentage

The awkward one $\div$ by 100

<u>Converting decimals to fractions</u> is awkward, because it's different for different types of decimal. There are two different methods you need to learn:

1) <u>Terminating decimals</u> to fractions — this is fairly easy. The digits after the decimal point go on the top, and a <u>power of 10</u> on the bottom — with the same number of zeros as there were decimal places.

$$0.6 = \frac{6}{10} \qquad 0.3 = \frac{3}{10} \qquad 0.7 = \frac{7}{10} \qquad \text{etc.}$$

$$0.12 = \frac{12}{100} \qquad 0.78 = \frac{78}{100} \qquad 0.05 = \frac{5}{100} \qquad \text{etc.}$$

$$0.345 = \frac{345}{1000} \qquad 0.908 = \frac{908}{1000} \qquad 0.024 = \frac{24}{1000} \qquad \text{etc.}$$

These can often be <u>cancelled down</u> — see p10.

2) <u>Recurring decimals</u> to fractions — this is trickier. See next page...

Fractions, decimals and percentages are interchangeable

It's important you remember that a fraction, decimal or percentage can be converted into either of the other two forms. And it's even more important that you learn how to do it.

Fractions and Recurring Decimals

Recurring and terminating decimals can always be written as fractions.

Recurring or Terminating...

1) Recurring decimals have a pattern of numbers which repeats forever, e.g. $\frac{1}{3}$ is the decimal 0.333333...
   Note, it doesn't have to be a single digit that repeats. You could have, for instance: 0.143143143...

2) The repeating part is usually marked with dots or a bar on top of the number. If there's one dot, then only one digit is repeated. If there are two dots, then everything from the first dot to the second dot is the repeating bit. E.g. $0.2\dot{5} = 0.2555555...$, $0.\dot{2}\dot{5} = 0.25252525...$, $0.2\dot{5}\dot{5} = 0.255255255...$

3) Terminating decimals are finite (they come to an end), e.g $\frac{1}{20}$ is the decimal 0.05.

> The denominator (bottom number) of a fraction in its simplest form tells you if it converts to a recurring or terminating decimal. Fractions where the denominator has prime factors of only 2 or 5 will give terminating decimals. All other fractions will give recurring decimals.
>
> | | Only prime factors: 2 and 5 | | | | Also other prime factors | | | |
> |---|---|---|---|---|---|---|---|---|
> | FRACTION | $\frac{1}{5}$ | $\frac{1}{125}$ | $\frac{1}{2}$ | $\frac{1}{20}$ | $\frac{1}{7}$ | $\frac{1}{35}$ | $\frac{1}{3}$ | $\frac{1}{6}$ |
> | EQUIVALENT DECIMAL | 0.2 | 0.008 | 0.5 | 0.05 | $0.\dot{1}4285\dot{7}$ | $0.0\dot{2}8571\dot{4}$ | $0.\dot{3}$ | $0.1\dot{6}$ |
> | | Terminating decimals | | | | Recurring decimals | | | |

For prime factors, see p6.

Converting terminating decimals into fractions was covered on the previous page.
Converting recurring decimals is quite a bit harder — but you'll be OK once you've learnt the method...

Recurring Decimals into Fractions

1) Basic Ones

Turning a recurring decimal into a fraction uses a really clever trick. Just watch this...

EXAMPLE: Write $0.\dot{2}3\dot{4}$ as a fraction.

1) Name your decimal — I've called it *r*.
   Let $r = 0.\dot{2}3\dot{4}$

2) Multiply *r* by a power of ten to move it past the decimal point by one full repeated lump — here that's 1000:
   $1000r = 234.\dot{2}3\dot{4}$

3) Now you can subtract to get rid of the decimal part:
   $$\begin{aligned} 1000r &= 234.\dot{2}3\dot{4} \\ - \quad r &= 0.\dot{2}3\dot{4} \\ \hline 999r &= 234 \end{aligned}$$

4) Then just divide to leave *r*, and cancel if possible:
   $r = \dfrac{234}{999} = \dfrac{26}{111}$

The 'Just Learning the Result' Method:

1) For converting recurring decimals to fractions, you could just learn the result that the fraction always has the repeating unit on the top and the same number of nines on the bottom...

2) BUT this only works if the repeating bit starts straight after the decimal point (see the next page for an example where it doesn't).

3) AND some exam questions will ask you to 'show that' or 'prove' that a fraction and a recurring decimal are equivalent — and that means you have to use the proper method.

Fractions and Recurring Decimals

2) The *Trickier* Type

If the recurring bit doesn't come right after the decimal point,
things are slightly trickier — but only slightly.

EXAMPLE:

Write $0.1\dot{6}$ as a fraction.

1) Name your decimal.

   Let $r = 0.1\dot{6}$

2) Multiply r by a <u>power of ten</u> to move the <u>non-repeating part</u> past the decimal point.

   $10r = 1.\dot{6}$

3) Now multiply again to move <u>one full repeated lump</u> past the decimal point.

   $100r = 16.\dot{6}$

4) <u>Subtract</u> to <u>get rid</u> of the decimal part:

   $$100r = 16.\dot{6}$$
   $$-\quad 10r = 1.\dot{6}$$
   $$\overline{90r = 15}$$

5) <u>Divide</u> to leave r, and <u>cancel</u> if possible:

   $r = \dfrac{15}{90} = \dfrac{1}{6}$

Fractions *into* Recurring Decimals

You might find this cropping up in your exam too — and if they're being really unpleasant,
they'll stick it in a <u>non-calculator</u> paper.

EXAMPLE:

Write $\dfrac{8}{33}$ as a recurring decimal.

There are <u>two ways</u> you can do this:

1 Find an equivalent fraction with <u>all nines</u> on the bottom.
The number on the top will tell you the <u>recurring part</u>.

$$\overset{\times 3}{\frac{8}{33}} = \frac{24}{99} \atop \times 3$$

> Watch out — the <u>number of nines</u> on the bottom
> tells you the <u>number of digits</u> in the recurring part.
> E.g. $\frac{24}{99} = 0.\dot{2}\dot{4}$, but $\frac{24}{999} = 0.\dot{0}2\dot{4}$

$\dfrac{24}{99} = 0.\dot{2}\dot{4}$

2 Remember, $\dfrac{8}{33}$ means $8 \div 33$, so you could just <u>do the division</u>:

$8 \div 33 = 0.24242424...$

(This is OK if you're allowed your calculator, but could be a
bit of a nightmare if not... you <u>could</u> use <u>long division</u> if you're
feeling bold, but I recommend sticking with <u>method 1</u> instead.)

$\dfrac{8}{33} = 0.\dot{2}\dot{4}$

You could be asked to convert any recurring decimal into a fraction

So you need to learn how to turn basic and tricky recurring decimals into fractions. You should
practise turning fractions into recurring decimals too. If you're not sure which method you prefer,
have a go at both to see which you feel more comfortable with (I definitely recommend method 1).

Warm-up and Worked Exam Questions

These warm-up questions will help to check that you've learnt the basics from the last few pages — if you're struggling with any of them, go and look back over that page before you go any further.

Warm-up Questions

1) Work these out, then simplify your answers:

   a) $\frac{2}{5} \times \frac{2}{3}$ b) $\frac{2}{5} \div \frac{2}{3}$ c) $\frac{2}{5} + \frac{2}{3}$ d) $\frac{2}{3} - \frac{2}{5}$

2) What percentage is the same as $\frac{2}{5}$?

3) What percentage is the same as $\frac{2}{3}$?

4) a) What fraction is the same as 0.4?
   b) What fraction is the same as 0.444444...?
   c) What fraction is the same as 0.45454545...?

5) a) What decimal is the same as $\frac{7}{10}$?   b) What decimal is the same as $\frac{7}{9}$?

Worked Exam Question

Make sure you understand what's going on in this question before trying the next page for yourself.

1   Lisa is rearranging her wardrobe. She has 24 dresses.

$\frac{1}{3}$ of her dresses are black.

$\frac{1}{6}$ of her dresses are red.

$\frac{1}{4}$ of her dresses are blue.

a) What fraction of her dresses are not black, red or blue?
   Give your answer in its simplest form.

   Put over a common denominator and add.

   Fraction of dresses that are black, red and blue $= \frac{1}{3} + \frac{1}{6} + \frac{1}{4}$

   $= \frac{4}{12} + \frac{2}{12} + \frac{3}{12} = \frac{9}{12}$

   Fraction of dresses that are not black, red or blue $= 1 - \frac{9}{12} = \frac{3}{12} = \frac{1}{4}$

   Remember to give your answer in its simplest form.

   ......$\frac{1}{4}$......
   [3 marks]

b) How many of her dresses are not black, red or blue?

   $24 \times \frac{1}{4} = \frac{24}{4} = 6$

   ......6......
   [2 marks]

Exam Questions

2 Express £12 as a fraction of £60 in its simplest form.

....
[2 marks]

3 Express 0.725 as a fraction in its simplest form.

....
[2 marks]

4 Work out:

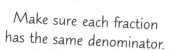
Make sure each fraction has the same denominator.

a) $3\frac{1}{2} + 2\frac{3}{5}$

....
[3 marks]

b) $3\frac{3}{4} - 2\frac{1}{3}$

....
[3 marks]

5 Work out the following, giving your answers as fractions in their simplest form.

a) $1\frac{2}{3} \times \frac{9}{10}$

....
[3 marks]

b) $3\frac{1}{2} \div 1\frac{3}{4}$

....
[3 marks]

6 Write $1.3\dot{6}$ in the form $\frac{a}{b}$. Simplify your answer as far as possible.

....
[4 marks]

7 Show that $0.5\dot{9}\dot{0} = \frac{13}{22}$ **B**

Hint: start by trying to get only the non-repeating part before the decimal point.

....
[3 marks]

Percentages

Make sure you know the <u>proper method</u> for each type of percentage question.

Three **Simple** *Question Types*

Type 1 — "Find *x*% of *y*"

Turn the percentage into a <u>decimal</u>, then <u>multiply</u>.

> **EXAMPLE:**
> **Find 15% of £46.**
> 1) Write 15% as a <u>decimal</u>:   15% = 15 ÷ 100 = 0.15
> 2) <u>Multiply</u> £46 by 0.15:   0.15 × £46 = £6.90

Type 2 — "Find the new amount after a % increase/decrease"

Turn the percentage into a <u>decimal</u>, then <u>multiply</u>. Add this on to (or subtract from) the original value.

> **EXAMPLE:**
> **A toaster is reduced in price by 40% in the sales.**
> **It originally cost £68. What is the new price of the toaster?**
>
> 1) Write 40% as a <u>decimal</u>:   40% = 40 ÷ 100 = 0.4
> 2) <u>Multiply</u> to find 40% <u>of</u> £68:   0.4 × £68 = £27.20
> 3) It's a decrease, so subtract from the original: £68 − £27.20 = £40.80
>
> If you prefer, you can use the <u>multiplier</u> method:
> multiplier = 1 − 0.4 = 0.6
> 68 × 0.6 = £40.80

Type 3 — "Express *x* as a percentage of *y*"

<u>Divide</u> *x* by *y*, then multiply by <u>100</u>.

> **EXAMPLE:**
> **Give 40p as a percentage of £3.34.**
>
> 1) Make sure both amounts are in the <u>same units</u> — convert £3.34 to pence: £3.34 = 334p
> 2) <u>Divide</u> 40p by 334p, <u>then multiply</u> by 100:   (40 ÷ 334) × 100 = 12.0% (1 d.p.)

Three **Trickier** *Question Types*

Type 1 — Finding the percentage change

1) This is the formula for giving a <u>change in value</u> as a <u>percentage</u> — <u>LEARN IT, AND USE IT</u>:

$$\text{PERCENTAGE 'CHANGE'} = \frac{\text{'CHANGE'}}{\text{ORIGINAL}} \times 100$$

2) This is similar to Type 3 above, because you end up with a <u>percentage</u> rather than an amount.
3) Typical questions will ask 'Find the percentage <u>increase</u>/<u>profit</u>/<u>error</u>' or 'Calculate the percentage <u>decrease</u>/<u>loss</u>/<u>discount</u>', etc.

> **EXAMPLE:**
> **A trader buys watches for £5 and sells them for £7. Find his profit as a percentage.**
>
> 1) Here the 'change' is <u>profit</u>, so the formula looks like this: $\text{percentage profit} = \frac{\text{profit}}{\text{original}} \times 100$
> 2) Work out the <u>actual value</u> of the profit: profit = £7 − £5 = £2
> 3) Calculate the <u>percentage</u> profit: $\text{percentage profit} = \frac{2}{5} \times 100 = 40\%$

Percentages

Three *Trickier* Question Types — Continued

Type 2 — Finding the original value

This is the type that <u>most people get wrong</u> — but only because they <u>don't recognise</u> it as this type and don't apply this simple method:

> 1) Write the amount in the question as a <u>percentage of the original value</u>.
> 2) <u>Divide</u> to find <u>1%</u> of the original value.
> 3) <u>Multiply by 100</u> to give the original value (= 100%).

EXAMPLE:

A house increases in value by 20% to £72 000.
Find what it was worth before the rise.

Note: The new, not the original value is given.

1) An <u>increase</u> of 20% means £72 000 represents <u>120% of the original</u> value.

2) Divide by 120 to find <u>1%</u> of the original value.

3) Then multiply by 100.

£72 000 = 120%
÷120
£600 = 1%
×100
£60 000 = 100%

If it was a decrease of 20%, then you'd put '£72 000 = 80%' and divide by 80 instead of 120.

So the original value was **£60 000**

Always set them out <u>exactly like this example</u>. The trickiest bit is deciding the top % figure on the right-hand side — the 2nd and 3rd rows are <u>always</u> 1% and 100%.

Type 3 — Simple Interest vs Compound Interest

Compound interest is covered on the next page.

1) There are two types of <u>interest</u> you could get asked about — <u>simple</u> and <u>compound</u>. Funnily enough, <u>simple interest</u> is the simpler of the two.

2) Simple interest means a certain percentage of the <u>original amount only</u> is paid at regular intervals (usually once a year). So the amount of interest is <u>the same every time</u> it's paid.

EXAMPLE:

Regina invests £380 in an account which pays 3% simple interest per annum.

How much interest will she earn in 4 years?

'Per annum' just means 'each year'.

1) Work out the amount of interest earned <u>in one year</u>:

3% = 3 ÷ 100 = 0.03
3% of £380 = 0.03 × £380 = £11.40

2) Multiply by 4 to get the <u>total interest</u> for <u>4 years</u>:

4 × £11.40 = £45.60

Percentages are one of the most useful things you'll ever learn

Whenever you open a newspaper, see an advert, watch TV or do a maths exam paper you will see percentages. So it's really important you get confident with using them — so practise.

Compound Growth and Decay

One more % type for you... Compound growth shows how a thing increases over time, e.g. money in a savings account. Compound decay shows the opposite, e.g. a shiny new car losing its value with age.

The Formula

This topic is simple if you LEARN THIS FORMULA. If you don't, it's pretty well impossible:

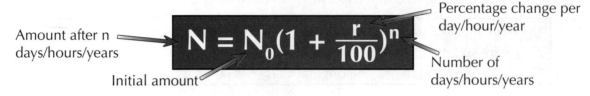

Percentage change per day/hour/year

Amount after n days/hours/years

$$N = N_0\left(1 + \frac{r}{100}\right)^n$$

Number of days/hours/years

Initial amount

Percentage Increase and Decrease

The $\left(1 + \frac{r}{100}\right)$ bit might look a bit confusing in the formula, but in practice it's really easy:

E.g. 5% increase will be 1.05   5% decrease will be 0.95 (= 1 − 0.05)
26% increase will be 1.26   26% decrease will be 0.74 (= 1 − 0.26)

3 Examples to show you how EASY it is:

The most popular context for these is compound interest. Compound interest means the interest is added on each time, and the next lot of interest is calculated using the new total rather than the original amount.

EXAMPLE: A man invests £1000 in a savings account which pays 8% compound interest per annum. How much will there be after 6 years?

'Per annum' just means 'each year'.

Use the formula: Amount = $1000(1.08)^6$ = £1586.87
initial amount   8% increase   6 years

Depreciation questions are about things (e.g. cars) which decrease in value over time.

EXAMPLE: Susan has just bought a car for £6500. If the car depreciates by 9% each year, how much will it be worth in 3 years' time?

Just use the formula again: Value = $6500(0.91)^3$ = £4898.21
initial value   9% decrease   3 years

The compound growth and decay formula isn't just used for money questions.

EXAMPLE: In a sample of bacteria, there are initially 500 cells and they increase in number by 15% each day. Find the formula relating the number of cells, c, and the number of days, d.

And again: $c = N_0(1 + 0.15)^d$ ⇒ $c = 500 \times (1.15)^d$

Compound growth and decay — percentages applied again and again

What this method does is to get the original value, increase it by the percentage, then increase that amount by the percentage, then take that amount and increase it by the percentage, then... get it?

Warm-up and Worked Exam Questions

Have a go at these warm-up questions and see how you get on — the exam questions will be a bit more tricky, so it's important that you can do these first.

Warm-up Questions

1) Find 15% of £90.

2) What is 37 out of 50 as a percentage?

3) Write 36 out of 80 as a percentage.

4) £200 is put in a bank account paying 2% simple interest (per year).
   Find the total amount in the account after 2 years if no money has been withdrawn.

5) £3000 is invested at 3% compound interest (per year).
   Work out how much money is in the account at the end of 4 years, to the nearest penny.

Worked Exam Question

I'd like an exam question, with the answers written in — and a surprise. Two out of three's not bad.

1 The population of fish in a lake is estimated to decrease by 8% every year.

    a) Approximately how many fish will be left after 15 years if the initial population is 2000?

Use the formula:

$$\text{Population after 15 years} = 2000 \times \left(1 - \frac{8}{100}\right)^{15}$$

$$= 2000 \times (0.92)^{15}$$

$$= 572.59\ldots$$

You need to round up, as it'll take more than 15 years for the population to fall to 572 fish.

..........573.......... fish

[3 marks]

    b) How many years will it take for the population of fish to be less than $\frac{3}{4}$ of the initial population?

$\frac{3}{4}$ of the initial population $= 2000 \times \frac{3}{4} = 1500$

You need to find the value of n for which the population drops below 1500.

n = 1: $2000 \times 0.92 = 1840$

n = 2: $2000 \times 0.92^2 = 1692.8$

n = 3: $2000 \times 0.92^3 = 1557.376$

n = 4: $2000 \times 0.92^4 = 1432.78592 < 1500$

So the population is less than $\frac{3}{4}$ of the initial population after 4 years.

..........4........ years

[2 marks]

Exam Questions

2 Ali has 40 micro pigs. 24 of them are female. (D)

What percentage of Ali's micro pigs are male?

.... %
[3 marks]

3 Kamal puts £2000 into a bank account. The account pays 3.2% per annum simple interest. (D)
After 2 years, what is the total amount of interest Kamal has earned?

£ ....
[3 marks]

4 A computer costs £927 plus VAT, where VAT is charged at 20%. (D)
Find the total cost of the computer.

£ ....
[3 marks]

5 After an 8% pay rise Mr Brown's salary was £15 714. (C)
What was his salary before the increase?

£ ....
[3 marks]

6 A new house cost £120 000, but increased in value by 15% each year. (C)
Work out its value after 5 years, to the nearest £1000.

£ ....
[3 marks]

7 Mrs Khan puts £2500 into a high interest savings account.
Interest is added to the account at the end of each year. (B)
After 2 years Mrs Khan's account contains £2704.

What is the interest rate on Mrs Khan's account?

.... %
[3 marks]

Ratios

Ratios can be a grisly subject, no doubt about it — but work your way through the examples on the next two pages, and the whole murky business should become crystal clear...

Reducing **Ratios** to their **Simplest Form**

To reduce a ratio to a simpler form, divide all the numbers in the ratio by the same thing (a bit like simplifying a fraction). It's in its simplest form when there's nothing left you can divide by.

> **EXAMPLE:**   **Write the ratio 15:18 in its simplest form.**
>
> For the ratio 15:18, both numbers have a factor of 3, so divide them by 3. $\div 3 \Big(\begin{array}{c} 15:18 \\ 5:6 \end{array} \Big) \div 3$
>
> We can't reduce this any further. So the simplest form of 15:18 is **5:6**.

A handy trick for the calculator paper — use the fraction button

If you enter a fraction with the button, the calculator automatically cancels it down when you press ⊟.

So for the ratio 8:12, just enter $\frac{8}{12}$ as a fraction, and you'll get the reduced fraction $\frac{2}{3}$.
Now you just change it back to ratio form, i.e. 2:3. Ace.

The More **Awkward Cases**: Ⓓ

① If the ratio contains decimals or fractions — multiply

> **EXAMPLES:**   **1. Simplify the ratio 2.4:3.6 as far as possible.**
>
> 1) Multiply both sides by 10 to get rid of the decimal parts. $\quad = {}^{\times 10} \Big(\begin{array}{c} 2.4:3.6 \\ 24:36 \end{array} \Big) {\times 10}$
>
> 2) Now divide to reduce the ratio to its simplest form. $\quad = {}^{\div 12} \Big(\begin{array}{c} \\ 2:3 \end{array} \Big) {\div 12}$

> **2. Give the ratio $\frac{5}{4} : \frac{7}{2}$ in its simplest form.**
>
> 1) Put the fractions over a common denominator (see p11). $\qquad \frac{5}{4} : \frac{7}{2}$
>
> 2) Multiply both sides by 4 to get rid of the fractions. $\qquad = {}_{\times 4}\big(\frac{5}{4} : \frac{14}{4} \big){\times 4}$
>
> 3) This ratio won't cancel further, so we're done. $\qquad = \quad \mathbf{5:14}$

② If the ratio has mixed units — convert to the smaller unit

> **EXAMPLE:**   **Reduce the ratio 24 mm : 7.2 cm to its simplest form.**
>
> 1) Convert 7.2 cm to millimetres. $\qquad\qquad\qquad$ 24 mm:7.2 cm
>
> 2) Simplify the resulting ratio. Once the units on both $\qquad$ = 24 mm:72 mm
> sides are the same, get rid of them for the final answer. $\quad ={}^{\div 24} \searrow 1:3 \swarrow {}^{\div 24}$

③ To get the form 1:n or n:1 — just divide

> **EXAMPLE:**   **Reduce 3:56 to the form 1:n.**
>
> Divide both sides by 3: $\quad {}_{\div 3}\Big(\begin{array}{c} 3:56 \\ 1:\frac{56}{3} \end{array} \Big){\div 3}$
> $\qquad\qquad\qquad\qquad = \quad 1:18\frac{2}{3}$ (or 1:18.6̇)

This form is often the most useful, since it shows the ratio very clearly.

Ratios

There's just so much <u>great stuff</u> to say about ratios. I couldn't possibly fit it onto only one page...

Scaling Up **Ratios**

If you know the <u>ratio between parts</u> and the actual size of <u>one part</u>,
you can <u>scale the ratio up</u> to find the other parts.

EXAMPLE: **Mortar is made from sand and cement in the ratio 7:2.**
If 21 buckets of sand are used, how much cement is needed?

You need to <u>multiply by 3</u> to go from 7 to 21 on
the left-hand side (LHS) — so do that to <u>both sides</u>:

$$\text{sand:cement}$$
$$= \ ^{\times 3}\!\!\left(\begin{array}{c}7:2\\21:6\end{array}\right)\!\!^{\times 3}$$

So **6 buckets** of cement are needed.

EXAMPLE: **Mrs Miggins owns tabby cats and ginger cats in the ratio 3:5.**
All her cats are either tabby or ginger, and she has 12 tabby cats.
How many cats does Mrs Miggins have in total?

Multiply <u>both sides</u> by 4 to go from
3 to 12 on the LHS:

$$\text{tabby:ginger}$$
$$= \ ^{\times 4}\!\!\left(\begin{array}{c}3:5\\12:20\end{array}\right)\!\!^{\times 4}$$

So Mrs Miggins has <u>12 tabby cats</u> and <u>20 ginger cats</u>.
So in total she has:

$$12 + 20 = 32 \text{ cats}$$

Proportional **Division**

In a <u>proportional division</u> question a <u>TOTAL AMOUNT</u> is split into parts <u>in a certain ratio</u>.
The key word here is <u>PARTS</u> — concentrate on 'parts' and it all becomes quite painless:

EXAMPLE: **Jess, Mo and Greg share £9100 in the ratio 2:4:7. How much does Mo get?**

1) <u>ADD UP THE PARTS</u>:
   The ratio 2:4:7 means there will be a total of 13 <u>parts</u>: $\quad 2 + 4 + 7 = 13$ parts

2) <u>DIVIDE TO FIND ONE "PART"</u>:
   Just divide the <u>total amount</u> by the number of <u>parts</u>: $\quad £9100 \div 13 = £700 \ \ (= 1 \text{ part})$

3) <u>MULTIPLY TO FIND THE AMOUNTS</u>:
   We want to know <u>Mo's share</u>, which is <u>4 parts</u>: $\quad 4 \text{ parts} = 4 \times £700 = £2800$

You need to know how to simplify all kinds of ratios

You should also understand how to scale up ratios and the three steps for proportional division.
If you're stuck, it's often really helpful to think about what one 'part' is and take it from there...

Warm-up and Worked Exam Questions

Warm-up questions first, then a worked example — then you're on your own.
So make the most of this page by working through everything carefully.

Warm-up Questions

1) Write these ratios in their simplest forms:
   a) $4:8$ b) $12:27$ c) $1.2:5.4$
   d) $\frac{8}{3}:\frac{7}{6}$ e) 0.5 litres : 400 ml

2) Reduce $5:22$ to the form $1:n$.

3) A recipe uses flour and sugar in the ratio $3:2$.
   How much flour do you need if you're using 300 g of sugar?

4) Divide 180 in the ratio $3:4:5$.

Worked Exam Question

I've gone through this worked example and written in the answer just like you'll do in the exam.
It should really help with the questions which follow, so don't say I never do anything for you.

*1   A ship is carrying first class passengers and second class passengers in the ratio $3:5$.
     There are 2928 passengers in total, and the total takings for all tickets were £666 120.
     Given that a second class ticket costs £190, how much does a first class ticket cost?

   1 part = 2928 ÷ (3 + 5) ——————   Start by finding how many
           = 2928 ÷ 8 = 366 passengers   passengers make up 1 'part'.

   number of second class passengers = 366 × 5
                                     = 1830 passengers

   number of first class passengers = 2928 − 1830
                                    = 1098 passengers

   second class ticket takings = 1830 × £190
                               = £347 700

   first class ticket takings = £666 120 − £347 700
                              = £318 420

   price of a first class ticket = £318 420 ÷ 1098   The * means you're being tested on the
                                 = £290   quality of your written communication —
                                                        so make sure your working is extra clear.

                                              £ ....290..........
                                                              [5 marks]

Exam Questions

2 Hannah is making some green paint to paint her kitchen wall.
She makes it by mixing together $3\frac{3}{4}$ tins of yellow paint and $1\frac{1}{2}$ tins of blue paint. **D**
The tins are all the same size.

a) Express this ratio in its simplest form.

....
[3 marks]

b) Hannah used 1355 ml of yellow paint. How much blue paint did she use?

.... ml
[2 marks]

3 Lucy, Peter, Edmund and Susan shared £120.
Edmund got twice as much money as Susan, Peter got three times as much **D**
money as Edmund, and Lucy got half as much money as Peter.

How much money did Lucy get?

TIP: assume Susan
gets 1 'part' of the
total amount.

£ ....
[3 marks]

4 Mr Tailor is going to his local garage to fill his car up with petrol for a journey.
Mrs Jones has just bought 25 litres of petrol from the same garage, and it cost her £31.25. **D**
The fuel tank in Mr Tailor's car has a maximum capacity of 52 litres.

How much will it cost Mr Tailor to completely fill his petrol tank from empty?

£ ....
[2 marks]

5 Here is a list of ingredients for making flapjacks. **D**

Simple Flapjack Recipe
(Makes 12)

250 g oats   150 g butter
75 g sugar   75 g syrup

a) Elenni is making 18 flapjacks. How much butter does she need?

.... g
[2 marks]

b) Jo has 300 g of syrup. What is the maximum number of flapjacks she can make?

....
[2 marks]

Rounding Numbers

There are <u>two different ways</u> of specifying <u>where</u> a number should be <u>rounded</u>.
They are: 'Decimal Places' and 'Significant Figures'.
We'll do decimal places first, but the basic method is the same for both...

Decimal Places (d.p.)

To round to a given number of <u>decimal places</u>:

1) <u>Identify</u> the position of the '<u>last digit</u>' from the number of decimal places.

   '<u>Last digit</u>' = last one in the <u>rounded version</u>, not the original number.

2) Then look at the next digit to the <u>right</u> — called <u>the decider</u>.

3) If the <u>decider</u> is <u>5 or more</u>, then <u>round up</u> the <u>last digit</u>.
   If the <u>decider</u> is <u>4 or less</u>, then leave the <u>last digit</u> as it is.

4) There must be <u>no more digits</u> after the last digit (not even zeros).

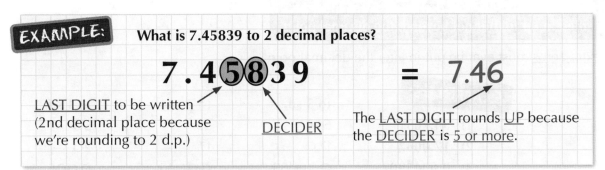

EXAMPLE: **What is 7.45839 to 2 decimal places?**

$$7.4\,\textcircled{5}\textcircled{8}39 \qquad = \qquad 7.46$$

<u>LAST DIGIT</u> to be written
(2nd decimal place because
we're rounding to 2 d.p.)

<u>DECIDER</u>

The <u>LAST DIGIT</u> rounds <u>UP</u> because
the <u>DECIDER</u> is <u>5 or more</u>.

Trickier cases with Pesky Nines

1) If you have to <u>round up</u> a <u>9</u> (to 10), replace the 9 with 0, and <u>carry 1</u> to the left.
2) Remember to keep enough <u>zeros</u> to fill the right number of decimal places.

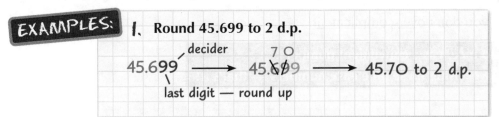

EXAMPLES: **1. Round 45.699 to 2 d.p.**

decider

45.699 ⟶ 45.6⁷⁰99 ⟶ 45.70 to 2 d.p.

last digit — round up

45.7 has the same value
as 45.70, but 45.7 isn't
rounded to 2 d.p. so it
would be marked wrong.

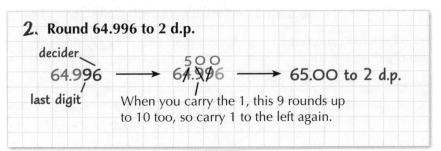

2. Round 64.996 to 2 d.p.

decider

64.996

last digit

64.⁵⁰⁰996 ⟶ 65.00 to 2 d.p.

When you carry the 1, this 9 rounds up
to 10 too, so carry 1 to the left again.

You'll need to round off a lot of your answers in the exam

Rounding is a really important skill, and you'll be throwing easy marks away if you get it wrong.
Make sure you're completely happy with the basic method, then get plenty of practice.

Rounding Numbers

The method for significant figures is <u>identical</u> to that for decimal places except that
locating the <u>last digit</u> is more difficult — it wouldn't be so bad, but for the <u>zeros</u>...

Significant Figures (s.f.)

1) The <u>1st significant figure</u> of any number is simply <u>the first digit which isn't a zero</u>.

2) The <u>2nd, 3rd, 4th, etc. significant figures</u> follow on immediately
   after the 1st, <u>regardless of being zeros or not zeros</u>.

$$0.002309 \qquad\qquad 2.03070$$

SIG. FIGS: 1st 2nd   3rd 4th   1st 2nd   3rd 4th

(If we're rounding to say, <u>3 s.f.</u>, then the <u>LAST DIGIT</u> is simply the <u>3rd sig. fig.</u>)

3) After <u>rounding</u> the <u>last digit</u>, <u>end zeros</u> must be
   filled in up to, <u>but not beyond</u>, the decimal point.

No <u>extra zeros</u> must ever be put in <u>after</u> the decimal point.

EXAMPLES:

		to 3 s.f.	to 2 s.f.	to 1 s.f.
1)	54.7651	54.8	55	50
2)	17.0067	17.0	17	20
3)	0.0045902	0.00459	0.0046	0.005
4)	30895.4	30900	31000	30000

Estimating

This is <u>very easy</u>, so long as you don't <u>over-complicate it</u>.

1) <u>Round everything off</u> to nice, easy, <u>convenient numbers</u>.
2) Then <u>work out the answer</u> using these nice easy numbers — that's it!

EXAMPLE:

Estimate the value of $\dfrac{127.8 + 41.9}{56.5 \times 3.2}$, showing all your working.

1) Round all the numbers to <u>easier ones</u>
   — <u>1 or 2 s.f.</u> usually does the trick.

2) You can <u>round again</u> to make later steps easier if you need to.

$$\frac{127.8 + 41.9}{56.5 \times 3.2} \approx \frac{130 + 40}{60 \times 3}$$
$$= \frac{170}{180} \approx 1$$

*In the exam you'll need to show all the steps,
to prove you didn't just use a calculator.*

Significant figures can be a bit tricky to get your head round

Decimal places are easy, but significant figures take a bit more thinking about. Learn the method
on this page for identifying significant figures, and make sure you really understand the examples.
Then do the examples again on a separate piece of paper and make sure you get the same answers.

Bounds

Rounding and bounds go hand in hand, so you need to understand the previous two pages before you tackle this one.

Upper and *Lower* Bounds

> **Whenever a measurement is <u>rounded</u> to a <u>given UNIT</u>, the <u>actual measurement</u> can be anything up to <u>HALF A UNIT bigger or smaller</u>.**

EXAMPLE: **A room is 9 m long to the nearest metre. Find upper and lower bounds for its length.**

The actual length could be <u>half a metre</u> either side of 9 m.

lower bound = 8.5 m
upper bound = 9.5 m

Note that the actual value is <u>greater than or equal to</u> the <u>lower bound</u> but <u>less than</u> the <u>upper bound</u>. In the example above, the actual length could be <u>exactly</u> 8.5 m, but if it was exactly 9.5 m it would <u>round up</u> to 10 m instead. Or, written as an inequality (see p63), 8.5 m ≤ actual length < 9.5 m.

EXAMPLE: **The mass of a cake is given as 2.4 kg to the nearest 0.1 kg. What are the upper and lower bounds for the actual mass of the cake?**

The <u>rounding unit</u> here is 0.1 kg, so the actual value could be anything between <u>2.4 kg ± 0.05 kg</u>.

lower bound = 2.4 − 0.05 = 2.35 kg
upper bound = 2.4 + 0.05 = 2.45 kg

Maximum and *Minimum* Values for Calculations (A)

When a calculation is done using rounded values there will be a <u>DISCREPANCY</u> between the <u>CALCULATED VALUE</u> and the <u>ACTUAL VALUE</u>:

EXAMPLES: **1. A floor is measured as being 5.3 m by 4.2 m, to the nearest 10 cm. Calculate minimum and maximum possible values for the area of the floor.**

The actual dimensions of the floor could be anything from <u>5.25 m to 5.35 m</u> and <u>4.15 m to 4.25 m</u>.

minimum possible floor area = 5.25 × 4.15
= 21.7875 m²

Find the <u>minimum</u> area by multiplying the <u>lower bounds</u>, and the <u>maximum</u> by multiplying the <u>upper bounds</u>.

maximum possible floor area = 5.35 × 4.25
= 22.7375 m²

2. a = 5.3 and b = 4.2, both given to 1 d.p. What are the maximum and minimum values of a ÷ b?

First find the <u>bounds</u> for a and b. ⟶ $5.25 \le a < 5.35$, $4.15 \le b < 4.25$

Now the tricky bit... The <u>bigger</u> the number you <u>divide by</u>, the <u>smaller</u> the answer, so:

max(a ÷ b) = max(a) ÷ min(b)

and min(a ÷ b) = min(a) ÷ max(b)

max. value of a ÷ b = 5.35 ÷ 4.15
= 1.289 (to 3 d.p.)

min. value of a ÷ b = 5.25 ÷ 4.25
= 1.235 (to 3 d.p.)

Bounds tell you the possible values of something that's been rounded

When you want to find the maximum or minimum value of a calculation, working out which bound to use for each bit can be pretty confusing — so make sure you always think about it very carefully.

Warm-up and Worked Exam Questions

Without a good warm-up you're likely to strain a brain cell or two. So take the time to run through these simple questions and get the basic facts straight before plunging into the exam questions.

Warm-up Questions

1) Round these numbers to the level of accuracy indicated:
   a) 40.218 to 2 d.p.   b) 39.888 to 3 s.f.   c) 27.91 to 2 s.f.

2) By rounding to 1 significant figure, estimate the answer to $\frac{94 \times 1.9}{0.328 + 0.201}$.

3) A distance is given as 14 km, to the nearest km.
   Find the upper and lower bounds for the distance.

4) $r = 6.3$ and $s = 2.9$, both to 1 d.p. Find the maximum and minimum possible values for:
   a) $r + s$ b) $r - s$
   c) $r \times s$ d) $r \div s$

Worked Exam Questions

With the answers written in, it's very easy to skim these worked examples and think you've understood. But that's not going to help you, so take the time to make sure you've really understood them.

1 Estimate the value of the fraction $\frac{215.7 \times 48.8}{460}$

Show all of your working.

Round each number to an easier one before doing the calculation.

$$\frac{215.7 \times 48.8}{460} \approx \frac{200 \times 50}{500} = \frac{10\,000}{500} = 20$$

.............20.............
[2 marks]

2 The width of a rectangular piece of paper is 23.6 centimetres, correct to 1 decimal place.
The length of the paper is 54.1 centimetres, correct to 1 decimal place.

a) Write down the lower bound for the length of the paper.

Lower bound for the length = 54.1 cm − 0.05 cm
                           = 54.05 cm

.............54.05............. cm
[1 mark]

b) Calculate the lower bound for the perimeter of the piece of paper.

Lower bound for the width = 23.6 cm − 0.05 cm
                         = 23.55 cm

Lower bound for the perimeter = (2 × 54.05 cm) + (2 × 23.55 cm)
                             = 108.1 cm + 47.1 cm = 155.2 cm

.............155.2............. cm
[2 marks]

Exam Questions

3 Use your calculator to work out $\dfrac{197.8}{\sqrt{0.01 + 0.23}}$

a) Write down all the figures on your calculator display.

....
[2 marks]

b) Write down your answer to part a) correct to 3 significant figures.

....
[1 mark]

4 Work out an estimate for $\sqrt{\dfrac{2321}{19.673 \times 3.81}}$

 Show all of your working.

....
[3 marks]

5 Here is a rectangle.
$x = 55$ mm to the nearest 5 mm.
$y = 30$ mm to the nearest 5 mm.

Calculate the upper bound for the area
of this rectangle.
Give your answer to 3 significant figures.

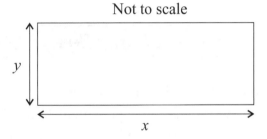

Not to scale

.... mm²
[3 marks]

*6 Dan runs 100 m, measured to the nearest metre. His time is 12.5 s to the nearest
tenth of a second. Use the formula below to find Dan's speed to a suitable
number of significant figures. Give a reason for your final answer.

Make sure your working is nice
and clear — the * means you're
being assessed on your quality
of written communication.

$$\text{speed (m/s)} = \frac{\text{distance (m)}}{\text{time (s)}}$$

TIP: compare
your upper and
lower bounds.

....
....
[5 marks]

Standard Form

Standard form (or 'standard index form') is useful for writing <u>VERY BIG</u> or <u>VERY SMALL</u> numbers in a more convenient way, e.g.

$56\,000\,000\,000$ would be 5.6×10^{10} in standard form.

$0.000\,000\,003\,45$ would be 3.45×10^{-9} in standard form.

But <u>ANY NUMBER</u> can be written in standard form and you need to know how to do it:

What it *Actually* is:

A number written in standard form must <u>always</u> be in <u>exactly</u> this form:

This <u>number</u> must <u>always</u> be <u>between 1 and 10</u>.

(The fancy way of saying this is $1 \le A < 10$)

$$A \times 10^n$$

This number is just the <u>number of places</u> the <u>decimal point</u> moves.

Learn the Three Rules:

1) The <u>front number</u> must always be <u>between 1 and 10</u>.

2) The power of 10, n, is <u>how far the decimal point moves</u>.

3) n is <u>positive for BIG numbers</u>, n is <u>negative for SMALL numbers</u>.
   (This is much better than rules based on which way the decimal point moves.)

Four *Important* Examples:

1 **Express 35 600 in standard form.**

1) <u>Move the decimal point</u> until 35 600 becomes 3.56 ($1 \le A < 10$)

2) The decimal point has moved <u>4 places</u> so n = 4, giving: 10^4

3) 35 600 is a <u>big number</u> so n is +4, not –4

3.5600

$= 3.56 \times 10^4$

2 **Express 0.0000623 in standard form.**

1) The decimal point must move <u>5 places</u> to give 6.23 ($1 \le A < 10$).
   So the power of 10 is 5.

2) Since 0.0000623 is a <u>small number</u> it must be 10^{-5} not 10^{+5}

0.0000623

$= 6.23 \times 10^{-5}$

3 **Express 4.95×10^{-3} as an ordinary number.**

1) The power of 10 is <u>negative</u>, so it's a <u>small number</u>
   — the answer will be less than 1.

2) The power is –3, so the decimal point moves <u>3 places</u>.

0004.95×10^{-3}

$= 0.00495$

4 **What is 146.3 million in standard form?**

Too many people get this type of question <u>wrong</u>.
Just take your time and do it in <u>two stages</u>:

146.3 million

$= 146\,300\,000$

$= 1.463 \times 10^8$

The two favourite <u>wrong answers</u> for this are:

146.3×10^6 — which is kind of right but it's not in <u>standard form</u>
because 146.3 is not between 1 and 10

1.463×10^6 — this one <u>is</u> in standard form but it's <u>not big enough</u>

Standard Form

You don't just need to be able to write numbers in standard form — you also need to be able to use them in calculations. Here's how...

Calculations with Standard Form

These are really popular <u>exam questions</u> — you might be asked to add, subtract, multiply or divide using numbers written in <u>standard form</u>.

Multiplying and Dividing — not too bad

> 1) Rearrange to put the <u>front numbers</u> and the <u>powers of 10 together</u>.
> 2) Multiply or divide the front numbers, and use the <u>power rules</u> (see p38) to multiply or divide the powers of 10.
> 3) Make sure your answer is still in <u>standard form</u>.

EXAMPLES:

1. Find $(2.24 \times 10^3) \times (6.75 \times 10^5)$. Give your answer in standard form.

Multiply front numbers and powers separately

$(2.24 \times 10^3) \times (6.75 \times 10^5)$
$= (2.24 \times 6.75) \times (10^3 \times 10^5)$
$= 15.12 \times 10^{3+5}$ ← Add the powers (see p38)
$= 15.12 \times 10^8$

Not in standard form — convert it
$= 1.512 \times 10 \times 10^8$
$= 1.512 \times 10^9$

2. Calculate $189\,000 \div (5.4 \times 10^{10})$. Give your answer in standard form.

Convert 189 000 to standard form
$189\,000 \div (5.4 \times 10^{10})$
$= \dfrac{1.89 \times 10^5}{5.4 \times 10^{10}} = \dfrac{1.89}{5.4} \times \dfrac{10^5}{10^{10}}$

Divide front numbers and powers separately
$= 0.35 \times 10^{5-10}$ ← Subtract the powers (see p38)
$= 0.35 \times 10^{-5}$

Not in standard form — convert it
$= 3.5 \times 10^{-1} \times 10^{-5}$
$= 3.5 \times 10^{-6}$

Adding and Subtracting — a bit trickier

> 1) Make sure the <u>powers of 10</u> are <u>the same</u> — you'll probably need to rewrite one of them.
> 2) Add or subtract the <u>front numbers</u>.
> 3) Convert the answer to <u>standard form</u> if necessary.

EXAMPLE:

Calculate $(9.8 \times 10^4) + (6.6 \times 10^3)$. Give your answer in standard form.

$(9.8 \times 10^4) + (6.6 \times 10^3)$

1) <u>Rewrite one number</u> so both powers of 10 are equal: $= (9.8 \times 10^4) + (0.66 \times 10^4)$

2) Now add the <u>front numbers</u>: $= (9.8 + 0.66) \times 10^4$

3) 10.46×10^4 isn't in standard form, so <u>convert it</u>: $= 10.46 \times 10^4 = 1.046 \times 10^5$

To put standard form numbers into your <u>calculator</u>, use the **EXP** or the **×10^x** button.

E.g. enter 2.67×10^{15} by pressing **2.67** **EXP** **15** **=** or **2.67** **×10^x** **15** **=** .

Your calculator might <u>display</u> an answer such as 7.986×10^{15} as $\boxed{7.986 \quad ^{15}}$. If so, <u>don't forget</u> to add in the "×10" bit when you write it down. Some calculators do display a little "×10" so check what yours does.

Remember, n tells you how far the decimal point moves

If you aren't a fan of the method above, you can add and subtract numbers in standard form by writing them as ordinary numbers, adding or subtracting as usual, then converting the answer back to standard form.

Warm-up and Worked Exam Questions

I know that you'll be champing at the bit to get into the exam questions, but these basic warm-up questions are invaluable for getting the basic facts straight first.

Warm-up Questions

1) The moon is about 240 000 miles away from Earth.
   Write this number in standard form.

2) The half-life of a chemical isotope is 0.0000027 seconds.
   Write this number in standard form.

3) An oxygen atom has a mass of 2.7×10^{-23} g. Write this as an ordinary number.

4) Work out $(4 \times 10^3) \times 30\,000$. Give your answer in standard form.

5) Find each of the following. Give your answers in standard form.
   a) $(3 \times 10^6) \times (8 \times 10^4)$
   b) $(8.4 \times 10^8) \div (4.2 \times 10^4)$
   c) $(7.65 \times 10^6) + (1.47 \times 10^5)$
   d) $(3.28 \times 10^{12}) - (7.12 \times 10^{10})$

Worked Exam Question

Instead of flicking past this worked exam question, go through it yourself — it'll help you to tackle the exam questions on the next page.

1   $A = 4.834 \times 10^9$, $B = 2.7 \times 10^5$, $C = 5.81 \times 10^3$

   a) Express A as an ordinary number.

   $A = 4.834 \times 10^9 = 4\,834\,000\,000$ —— Since n = 9, the decimal
   point moves 9 places.

   <u>4 834 000 000</u>
   [1 mark]

   b) Work out $B \times C$. Give your answer in standard form.

   Multiply the front numbers together and use the power rules on the powers of 10:

   $B \times C = (2.7 \times 10^5) \times (5.81 \times 10^3)$
   $= (2.7 \times 5.81) \times (10^5 \times 10^3)$
   $= 15.687 \times 10^8$
   $= 1.5687 \times 10^9$ —— Make sure the final answer
   is in standard form.

   <u>1.5687 × 10⁹</u>
   [2 marks]

   c) Put A, B and C in order from smallest to largest.

   In this question, each number has a different power of 10,
   so you can order them just by looking at these.

   <u>C</u> , <u>B</u> , <u>A</u>
   [1 mark]

Exam Questions

2 Express the following in standard form. Ⓑ

    a) 12 500

....
[1 mark]

    b) $\dfrac{2 \times 10^8}{8 \times 10^3}$

....
[2 marks]

    c) $(6 \times 10^4)^2$

....
[2 marks]

3 Light travels at approximately 1.86×10^5 miles per second.
The distance from the Earth to the Sun is approximately 9.3×10^7 miles.
How long will it take light to travel this distance? Ⓑ
Give your answer in standard form.

.... seconds
[3 marks]

4 A patient has been prescribed a dose of 4×10^{-4} grams of a certain drug to be given daily. Ⓑ

    a) The tablets that the hospital stocks each contain 8×10^{-5} grams of the drug.
       How many tablets should the patient be given each day?

.... tablets
[3 marks]

    b) The doctor increases the patient's daily dose of the drug by 6×10^{-5} grams.
       What is the patient's new daily dose of the drug?

TIP: you need matching powers to be able to add two numbers together in standard form.

.... grams per day
[3 marks]

Revision Questions for Section One

Well, that wraps up <u>Section One</u> — time to put yourself to the test and find out <u>how much you really know</u>.
- Try these questions and <u>tick off each one</u> when you <u>get it right</u>.
- When you've done <u>all the questions</u> for a topic and are <u>completely happy</u> with it, tick off the topic.

Types of Number, Factors and Multiples (p4-7) ☑

1) What are: a) integers   b) rational numbers   c) prime numbers?
2) Complete the following: a) $13^2 =$ __   b) __$^2 = 49$ c) __$^3 = 27$ d) $5^3 =$ __
3) Express each of these as a product of prime factors: a) 240   b) 1050
4) Find: a) the HCF of 42 and 28   b) the LCM of 8 and 10

Fractions (p10-12) ☑

5) How do you simplify a fraction?
6) a) Write $\frac{74}{9}$ as a mixed number   b) Write $4\frac{5}{7}$ as an improper fraction
7) What are the rules for multiplying, dividing and adding/subtracting fractions?
8) Calculate: a) $\frac{2}{11} \times \frac{7}{9}$ b) $5\frac{1}{2} \div 1\frac{3}{4}$ c) $\frac{5}{8} - \frac{1}{6}$ d) $3\frac{3}{10} + 4\frac{1}{4}$

Fractions, Decimals and Percentages (p13-15) ☑

9) How do you convert: a) a fraction to a decimal?   b) a terminating decimal to a fraction?
10) Write: a) 0.04 as: (i) a fraction   (ii) a percentage   b) 65% as: (i) a fraction   (ii) a decimal
11) How can you tell if a fraction will convert to a terminating or recurring decimal?
12) Show that $0.\dot{5}\dot{1} = \frac{17}{33}$

Percentages (p18-20) ☑

13) What's the method for finding one amount as a percentage of another?
14) What's the formula for finding a change in value as a percentage?
15) A tree's height has increased by 15% in the last year to 20.24 m. What was its height a year ago?
16) I have £850 to invest for 4 years. Which will pay more interest, and how much more:
    an account paying 6% simple interest, or an account paying 4% compound interest?

Ratios (p23-24) ☑

17) Sarah is in charge of ordering stock for a clothes shop. The shop usually sells red scarves and blue
    scarves in the ratio 5:8. Sarah orders 150 red scarves. How many blue scarves should she order?
18) What are the three steps of the method of proportional division?
19) Divide 3000 in the ratio $5:8:12$.

Rounding and Bounds (p27-29) ☑

20) Round 427.963 to: a) 2 d.p.   b) 1 d.p.   c) 2 s.f.   d) 4 s.f.
21) Estimate the value of $(124.6 + 87.1) \div 9.4$
22) How do you determine the upper and lower bounds of a rounded measurement?
23) A rectangle measures 15.6 m by 8.4 m, to the nearest 0.1 m. Find its maximum possible area.

Standard Form (p32-33) ☑

24) What are the three rules for writing numbers in standard form?
25) Write these numbers in standard form: a) 970 000   b) 3 560 000 000   c) 0.00000275
26) Calculate: a) $(2.54 \times 10^6) \div (1.6 \times 10^3)$ b) $(1.75 \times 10^{12}) + (9.89 \times 10^{11})$
    Give your answers in standard form.

Sequences

You'll often be asked to "find an <u>expression</u> for the <u>nth term</u> of a sequence" — this is just a formula with n in, like $5n - 3$. It gives you <u>every term in a sequence</u> when you put in different values for n.

Finding the **nth Term** of a **Sequence**

The two methods below work for sequences with a <u>common difference</u> — where the sequence <u>increases</u> or <u>decreases</u> by the <u>same number</u> each time (i.e. the difference between each pair of terms is the <u>same</u>).

EXAMPLE:

Find an expression for the nth term of the sequence that starts 5, 8, 11, 14, ...

n:	1	2	3	4
term:	5	8	11	14

+3   +3   +3

The common difference is <u>3</u>, so '<u>3n</u>' is in the formula.

3n:	3	6	9	12

+2   +2   +2   +2

term:	5	8	11	14

You have to $+ 2$ to get to the term.

So the expression for the nth term is **3n + 2**

Method 1 — Work it out

1) <u>Find the common difference</u> — this tells you what to multiply n by. So here, 3 gives '$3n$'.
2) <u>Work out what to add or subtract</u>. So for $n = 1$, '$3n$' is 3 so add 2 to get to the term (5).
3) <u>Put both bits together</u>. So you get $3n + 2$.

Always <u>check</u> your formula by putting the first few values of n back in, e.g. putting $n = 1$ into $3n + 2$ gives 5, $n = 2$ gives 8, etc. which is the <u>original sequence</u> you were given — hooray!

Method 2 — Learn the formula

The other approach is to simply <u>learn this formula</u> and stick in the values of $\underline{a}$ and $\underline{d}$ (you don't need to replace the n though):

$$n\text{th term} = dn + (a - d)$$

$\underline{d}$ is the <u>common difference</u> and $\underline{a}$ is the <u>first term</u>.

So for the example above, $d = 3$ and $a = 5$. Putting these in the formula gives:
nth term $= 3n + (5 - 3) = \underline{3n + 2}$. Again, <u>check</u> it by putting in values for n.

Deciding if a Term is in a Sequence

You might be given the nth term and asked if a <u>certain value</u> is in the sequence. The trick here is to <u>set the expression equal to that value</u> and solve to find n. If n is a <u>whole number</u>, the value is <u>in</u> the sequence.

EXAMPLE:

The nth term of a sequence is given by $n^2 - 2$.

Have a look at p48-49 for more on solving equations.

a) Find the 6th term in the sequence.

This is dead easy — just put $n = 6$ into the expression:

$6^2 - 2 = 36 - 2$
$\qquad = 34$

b) Is 45 a term in this sequence?

Set it equal to 45... $n^2 - 2 = 45$
$\qquad\qquad n^2 = 47$ ...and solve for n.
$\qquad\qquad n = \sqrt{47} = 6.8556...$

n is not a whole number, so 47 is **not** in the sequence $n^2 - 2$.

Look for the common difference

There are two methods for finding the nth term of a common difference sequence — pick your favourite and learn it. Both methods involve finding the common difference, so make sure you know how to find it.

Powers and Roots

Powers are a very useful <u>shorthand</u>:
$2 \times 2 \times 2 \times 2 \times 2 \times 2 \times 2 = 2^7$ ('two to the power 7')

That bit is easy to remember. Unfortunately, there are <u>ten special rules</u> for powers — seven easy ones (on this page) and three trickier ones (on the next page). They're not tremendously exciting, but you do need to know them for the exam:

The **Seven** Easy Rules:

1) When <u>MULTIPLYING</u>, you <u>ADD THE POWERS</u>.

   e.g. $3^4 \times 3^6 = 3^{6+4} = 3^{10}$, $a^2 \times a^7 = a^{2+7} = a^9$

   Warning: Rules 1 & 2 <u>don't</u> work for things like $2^3 \times 3^7$, only for powers of the <u>same number</u>.

2) When <u>DIVIDING</u>, you <u>SUBTRACT THE POWERS</u>.

   e.g. $5^4 \div 5^2 = 5^{4-2} = 5^2$, $b^8 \div b^5 = b^{8-5} = b^3$

3) When <u>RAISING</u> one power to another, you <u>MULTIPLY THEM</u>.

   e.g. $(3^2)^4 = 3^{2 \times 4} = 3^8$, $(c^3)^6 = c^{3 \times 6} = c^{18}$

4) $x^1 = x$, <u>ANYTHING</u> to the <u>POWER 1</u> is just <u>ITSELF</u>.

   e.g. $3^1 = 3$, $d \times d^3 = d^1 \times d^3 = d^{1+3} = d^4$

5) $x^0 = 1$, <u>ANYTHING</u> to the <u>POWER 0</u> is just <u>1</u>.

   e.g. $5^0 = 1$, $67^0 = 1$, $e^0 = 1$

6) $1^x = 1$, <u>1 TO ANY POWER</u> is <u>STILL JUST 1</u>.

   e.g. $1^{23} = 1$, $1^{89} = 1$, $1^2 = 1$

7) <u>FRACTIONS</u> — Apply the power to <u>both TOP and BOTTOM</u>.

   e.g. $\left(1\frac{3}{5}\right)^3 = \left(\frac{8}{5}\right)^3 = \frac{8^3}{5^3} = \frac{512}{125}$, $\left(\frac{u}{v}\right)^5 = \frac{u^5}{v^5}$

Remember that rules 1 & 2 only work for powers of the same number

If you can add, subtract and multiply, there's nothing on this page you can't do — as long as you learn the rules. Try copying them over and over until you can do it with your eyes closed.

Powers and Roots

The **Three** Tricky Rules:

---

8) <u>NEGATIVE Powers — Turn it Upside-Down</u>

People have real difficulty remembering this — whenever you see a negative power you need to immediately think: "Aha, that means turn it the other way up and make the power positive".

e.g. $7^{-2} = \dfrac{1}{7^2} = \dfrac{1}{49}$, $a^{-4} = \dfrac{1}{a^4}$, $\left(\dfrac{3}{5}\right)^{-2} = \left(\dfrac{5}{3}\right)^{+2} = \dfrac{5^2}{3^2} = \dfrac{25}{9}$

---

9) <u>FRACTIONAL POWERS</u>

The power $\frac{1}{2}$ means <u>Square Root</u>,
The power $\frac{1}{3}$ means <u>Cube Root</u>,
The power $\frac{1}{4}$ means <u>Fourth Root</u> etc.

e.g. $25^{\frac{1}{2}} = \sqrt{25} = 5$
$64^{\frac{1}{3}} = \sqrt[3]{64} = 4$
$81^{\frac{1}{4}} = \sqrt[4]{81} = 3$
$z^{\frac{1}{5}} = \sqrt[5]{z}$

The one to really watch is when you get a <u>negative fraction</u> — people get mixed up and think that the minus is the square root, and forget to turn it upside down as well.

e.g. $49^{-\frac{1}{2}} = \dfrac{1}{\sqrt{49}} = \dfrac{1}{7}$

---

10) <u>TWO-STAGE FRACTIONAL POWERS</u>

With fractional powers like $64^{\frac{5}{6}}$ always <u>split the fraction</u> into a <u>root</u> and a <u>power</u>, and do them in that order: <u>root</u> first, then <u>power</u>: $(64)^{\frac{1}{6} \times 5} = \left(64^{\frac{1}{6}}\right)^5 = (2)^5 = 32$.

EXAMPLE: **Simplify $28p^5q^3 \div 14p^3q^3$**

Just deal with each bit separately:

$= (28 \div 14)(p^5 \div p^3)(q^3 \div q^3)$

$= (28 \div 14)p^{5-3}q^{3-3}$ ⟶ $\boxed{q^{3-3} = q^0 = 1}$

$= 2p^2$

You simplify <u>algebraic fractions</u> using the <u>power rules</u> (though you might not realise it).

So if you had to simplify e.g. $\dfrac{p^3q^6}{p^2q^3}$, you'd just <u>cancel</u> using the power rules to get $p^{3-2}q^{6-3} = pq^3$.

These three rules might be a bit trickier — but they are essential

Because these are things which people often get muddled, examiners love to sneak them into the exam — so scribble down these rules and learn them. Then in the exam you'll have the last laugh.

Warm-up and Worked Exam Questions

Have a go at these warm-up questions and check that you're comfortable with them before moving on to the exam questions. If you find anything a bit tricky, go back and read over it until you understand it.

Warm-up Questions

1) a) Find the first 6 terms of the sequence whose nth term is $5n + 3$.
   b) Find the first 6 terms of the sequence whose nth term is $3n + 5$.

2) Find the nth term of the following sequences:
   a) 5, 10, 15, 20, 25, ...   b) 7, 10, 13, 16, 19, ...

3) How many crosses are in the nth pattern?

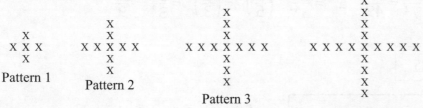

Pattern 1   Pattern 2   Pattern 3   Pattern 4

4) Simplify: a) $4^5 \times 4^{-2}$ b) $\dfrac{6^5}{6^2}$ c) $(3^3)^5$

5) Evaluate: a) $2^1 \times 1^{23} \times 9^0$ b) $(1\frac{2}{7})^2$ c) $27^{\frac{2}{3}}$

Worked Exam Question

To ease you into the exam questions on the next page, I've done one for you (aren't I kind?). Have a look at this worked exam question, and make sure you understand each step.

1   Simplify the following.

a) $a^5 \times a^{-3}$

It's a multiplication, so add the powers:
$$a^5 \times a^{-3} = a^{5 + -3} = a^{5 - 3} = a^2$$

.... a^2
[1 mark]

b) $x^7 \div x$

This time it's a division, so subtract the powers:
$$x^7 \div x = x^{7 - 1} = x^6 \qquad \text{Remember that } x = x^1$$

.... x^6
[1 mark]

c) $\dfrac{(d^9)^2}{d^4}$

On the numerator, you're raising a power to a power, so multiply...
$$\frac{(d^9)^2}{d^4} = \frac{d^{18}}{d^4}$$

... then subtract: $= d^{18 - 4} = d^{14}$

.... d^{14}
[2 marks]

Exam Questions

2 The first four terms in a sequence are 3, 8, 13, 18, …

a) Write down the next two terms in the sequence.

....
[1 mark]

b) Find the *n*th term of the sequence.

....
[2 marks]

c) What is the 30th term of the sequence?

....
[1 mark]

3 The first four terms of a sequence are 2, 3, 5, 9, …

 To find the next term in the sequence, you multiply the previous term by 2 and then subtract 1.

a) Find the fifth term.

....
[1 mark]

The first two terms in a different sequence are 1, 7, ...
The rule for finding the next term in this sequence is to multiply the previous term by 4 then add *a*.

b) Find the value of *a*.

....
[2 marks]

4 Find the value of *k* in each of the following expressions.

 a) $10^k = \frac{1}{100}$

$k =$ ....
[1 mark]

b) $9^k = \sqrt{9}$

$k =$ ....
[1 mark]

c) $3^k = (3^4)^2 \times \frac{3^5}{3^{11}}$

$k =$ ....
[2 marks]

Algebra Basics

Before you can really get your teeth into <u>algebra</u>, there are some basics you need to get your head around.

Negative Numbers

Negative numbers crop up everywhere so you need to learn these rules for dealing with them:

+	+	makes +
+	−	makes −
−	+	makes −
−	−	makes +

Use these rules when:
1) <u>Multiplying or dividing</u>.
   e.g. $-2 \times 3 = -6$, $-8 \div -2 = +4$, $-4p \times -2 = +8p$
2) <u>Two signs are together</u>.
   e.g. $5 - -4 = 5 + 4 = 9$, $x + -y - -z = x - y + z$

Letters *Multiplied* Together

Watch out for these combinations of letters in algebra that regularly catch people out:

1) abc means $a \times b \times c$. The ×'s are often left out to make it clearer.
2) gn^2 means $g \times n \times n$. Note that only the n is squared, not the g as well — e.g. πr^2 means $\pi \times r \times r$.
3) $(gn)^2$ means $g \times g \times n \times n$. The brackets mean that <u>BOTH</u> letters are squared.
4) $p(q - r)^3$ means $p \times (q - r) \times (q - r) \times (q - r)$. Only the brackets get cubed.
5) -3^2 is a bit ambiguous. It should either be written $(-3)^2 = 9$, or $-(3^2) = -9$ (you'd usually take -3^2 to be -9).

Terms

Before you can do anything else with algebra, you must understand what a term is:

> **A TERM is a collection of numbers, letters and brackets, all multiplied/divided together**

Terms are separated by <u>+ and – signs</u>. Every term has a + or – attached to the <u>front of it</u>.

If there's no sign in front of the first term, it means there's an invisible + sign.

$-4xy \quad +5x^2 \quad -2y \quad +6y^2 \quad +4$

'xy' term | 'x^2' term | 'y' term | 'y^2' term | 'number' term

Simplifying *or 'Collecting Like Terms'*

To <u>simplify</u> an algebraic expression, you combine '<u>like terms</u>' — terms that have the <u>same combination of letters</u> (e.g. all the x terms, all the y terms, all the number terms etc.).

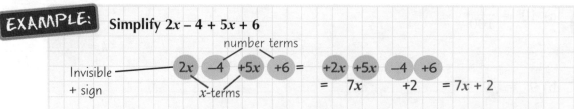

EXAMPLE: Simplify $2x - 4 + 5x + 6$

number terms

Invisible + sign | $2x \quad -4 \quad +5x \quad +6 =$ | $+2x \; +5x \quad -4 \; +6$
x-terms | | $= \quad 7x \quad +2 \quad = 7x + 2$

1) Put <u>bubbles</u> round each term — be sure you capture the <u>+/− sign</u> in front of each.
2) Then you can move the bubbles into the <u>best order</u> so that <u>like terms</u> are together.
3) <u>Combine like terms</u>.

These simple bits and bobs are the key to all algebra

Algebra gets people really fazed at first. If you don't get these basics in your head you will be really baffled in a few pages' time. So scribble this stuff over and over again until it's crystal clear.

Multiplying Out Brackets

You often find brackets in algebraic expressions. The first thing you need to be able to do is to expand them (multiply them out).

Single Brackets

There are a few <u>key things</u> to remember before you start multiplying out brackets:

1) The thing <u>outside</u> the brackets multiplies <u>each separate term</u> inside the brackets.
2) When letters are multiplied together, they are just written next to each other, e.g. pq.
3) Remember, $r \times r = r^2$, and xy^2 means $x \times y \times y$, but $(xy)^2$ means $x \times x \times y \times y$.
4) Remember, a minus outside the bracket <u>REVERSES ALL THE SIGNS</u> when you multiply.

EXAMPLE: **Expand the following:**

a) $3(2x + 5)$

$= (3 \times 2x) + (3 \times 5)$
$= 6x + 15$

b) $4a(3b - 2c)$

$= (4a \times 3b) + (4a \times -2c)$
$= 12ab - 8ac$

c) $-4(3p^2 - 7q^3)$

$= (-4 \times 3p^2) + (-4 \times -7q^3)$
$= -12p^2 + 28q^3$

Note: both signs have been reversed — see point 4.

Double Brackets

<u>Double</u> brackets are a bit more tricky than single brackets — this time, you have to multiply <u>everything</u> in the <u>first bracket</u> by <u>everything</u> in the <u>second bracket</u>.

5) <u>DOUBLE BRACKETS</u> — you get <u>4 terms</u>, and usually 2 of them combine to leave <u>3 terms</u>.

There's a handy way to multiply out double brackets — it's called the <u>FOIL method</u> and works like this:

<u>F</u>irst — multiply the first term in each bracket together
<u>O</u>utside — multiply the outside terms (i.e. the first term in the first bracket by the second term in the second bracket)
<u>I</u>nside — multiply the inside terms (i.e. the second term in the first bracket by the first term in the second bracket)
<u>L</u>ast — multiply the second term in each bracket together

EXAMPLE: **Expand and simplify $(2p - 4)(3p + 1)$**

$(2p - 4)(3p + 1) = (2p \times 3p) + (2p \times 1) + (-4 \times 3p) + (-4 \times 1)$
$= 6p^2 + 2p - 12p - 4$
$= 6p^2 - 10p - 4$

The two p terms combine together.

6) <u>SQUARED BRACKETS</u> — always write these out as <u>TWO BRACKETS</u> (to avoid mistakes), then multiply out as above.

EXAMPLE: **Expand and simplify $(3x + 5)^2$**

$(3x + 5)^2 = (3x + 5)(3x + 5)$
Using the FOIL method $= 9x^2 + 15x + 15x + 25 = 9x^2 + 30x + 25$

Don't make the mistake of thinking that $(3x + 5)^2 = 9x^2 + 25$ (this is wrong wrong wrong).

Use the FOIL method to make sure you don't miss out any terms

When multiplying squared brackets, remember that you should get four terms (2 of which will combine). As long as you write it out in full and do it like any other double brackets then you won't go wrong.

Factorising

Putting brackets into an expression is known as <u>factorising</u>.

Factorising — Putting Brackets In

This is the <u>exact reverse</u> of multiplying out brackets. Here's the method to follow:

1) Take out the <u>biggest number</u> that goes into all the terms.
2) <u>For each letter in turn</u>, take out the <u>highest power</u> (e.g. x, x^2 etc.) that will go into EVERY term.
3) Open the brackets and fill in all the bits needed to <u>reproduce each term</u>.
4) <u>Check</u> your answer by <u>multiplying out</u> the brackets and making sure it matches the original expression.

EXAMPLES:

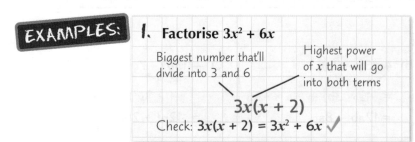

1. Factorise $3x^2 + 6x$

Biggest number that'll divide into 3 and 6

Highest power of x that will go into both terms

$$3x(x + 2)$$

Check: $3x(x + 2) = 3x^2 + 6x$ ✓

2. Factorise $8x^2y + 2xy^2$

Biggest number that'll divide into 8 and 2

Highest powers of x and y that will go into both terms

$$2xy(4x + y)$$

Check: $2xy(4x + y) = 8x^2y + 2xy^2$ ✓

<u>REMEMBER</u>: The bits <u>taken out</u> and put at the front are the <u>common factors</u>. The bits <u>inside the brackets</u> are what's needed to get back to the <u>original terms</u> if you multiply the brackets out again.

D.O.T.S. — The Difference Of Two Squares

The 'difference of two squares' (D.O.T.S. for short) is where you have 'one thing squared' <u>take away</u> 'another thing squared'. There's a quick and easy way to factorise it — just use the rule below:

$$a^2 - b^2 = (a + b)(a - b)$$

EXAMPLE:

Factorise: a) $x^2 - 1$ **Answer:** $x^2 - 1 = (x + 1)(x - 1)$
Don't forget that 1 is a square number (it's 1^2).

b) $9p^2 - 16q^2$ **Answer:** $9p^2 - 16q^2 = (3p + 4q)(3p - 4q)$
Here you had to spot that 9 and 16 are square numbers.

c) $3x^2 - 75y^2$ **Answer:** $3x^2 - 75y^2 = 3(x^2 - 25y^2) = 3(x + 5y)(x - 5y)$
This time, you had to take out a factor of 3 first.

Watch out — the difference of two squares can creep into other algebra questions. A popular <u>exam question</u> is to put a difference of two squares on the top or bottom of a <u>fraction</u> and ask you to simplify it. There's more on algebraic fractions on p61-62.

EXAMPLE:

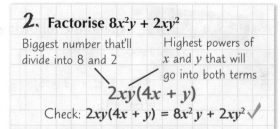

Simplify $\dfrac{x^2 - 36}{5x + 30}$

The numerator is a difference of two squares.

$$\frac{x^2 - 36}{5x + 30} = \frac{(x + 6)(x - 6)}{5(x + 6)} = \frac{x - 6}{5}$$

Factorise the denominator.

D.O.T.S. is straightforward as long as you recognise the pattern

Once you've seen one D.O.T.S. question, you've seen them all — they all follow the same basic pattern. If it doesn't look like a D.O.T.S. because there's a factor in it, taking out the factor makes it look d.o.t. ier.

Manipulating Surds

Surds are expressions with irrational square roots in them (remember from p4 that irrational numbers are ones which can't be written as fractions, such as most square roots, most cube roots and π).

Manipulating Surds — 6 Rules to Learn

There are 6 rules you need to learn for dealing with surds...

1 $\boxed{\sqrt{a} \times \sqrt{b} = \sqrt{a \times b}}$ e.g. $\sqrt{2} \times \sqrt{3} = \sqrt{2 \times 3} = \sqrt{6}$ — also $(\sqrt{b})^2 = \sqrt{b} \times \sqrt{b} = b$, fairly obviously

2 $\boxed{\dfrac{\sqrt{a}}{\sqrt{b}} = \sqrt{\dfrac{a}{b}}}$ e.g. $\dfrac{\sqrt{8}}{\sqrt{2}} = \sqrt{\dfrac{8}{2}} = \sqrt{4} = 2$

3 $\boxed{\sqrt{a} + \sqrt{b} - \underline{\text{DO NOTHING}}}$ — in other words it is definitely NOT $\sqrt{a+b}$

4 $\boxed{(a + \sqrt{b})^2 = (a + \sqrt{b})(a + \sqrt{b}) = a^2 + 2a\sqrt{b} + b}$ — NOT just $a^2 + (\sqrt{b})^2$ (see p43)

5 $\boxed{(a + \sqrt{b})(a - \sqrt{b}) = a^2 + a\sqrt{b} - a\sqrt{b} - (\sqrt{b})^2 = a^2 - b}$ (see p44)

6 $\boxed{\dfrac{a}{\sqrt{b}} = \dfrac{a}{\sqrt{b}} \times \dfrac{\sqrt{b}}{\sqrt{b}} = \dfrac{a\sqrt{b}}{b}}$ This is known as 'RATIONALISING the denominator' — it's where you get rid of the $\sqrt{}$ on the bottom of the fraction. You do this by multiplying the top and bottom of the fraction by the square root in the denominator ($\sqrt{b}$).

EXAMPLE: Write $\dfrac{3}{\sqrt{5}}$ in the form $\dfrac{a\sqrt{5}}{b}$, where a and b are whole numbers.

You have to rationalise the denominator — so multiply top and bottom by $\sqrt{5}$:

$$\frac{3\sqrt{5}}{\sqrt{5}\sqrt{5}} = \frac{3\sqrt{5}}{5} \text{ — so } a = 3 \text{ and } b = 5$$

Leave Surds and π in Exact Answers

π is an irrational number that comes up in calculations like finding the area of a circle. Most of the time you can use the π button on your calculator, but if you're asked to give an exact answer, just leave the π symbol in your answer. The same goes for surds — if you're asked for an exact answer, leave the surds in.

EXAMPLE: Find the exact area of a circle with radius 4 cm.

Area $= \pi r^2 = \pi \times 4^2 = 16\pi$ cm^2

If you're asked for an exact answer, it's usually a clue that you're going to need to use surds or π.

EXAMPLE: A rectangle has area 32 cm^2. It has length x cm and width $4x$ cm. Find the exact value of x, giving your answer in its simplest form.

Area of rectangle = length × width = $x \times 4x = 4x^2$

So $4x^2 = 32$
$x^2 = 8$
$x = \pm\sqrt{8}$

You can ignore the negative square root (see p49) as length must be positive.

Now get $\sqrt{8}$ into its simplest form:
$\sqrt{8} = \sqrt{4 \times 2} = \sqrt{4}\sqrt{2}$ (using rule 1)
$= 2\sqrt{2}$ So $x = 2\sqrt{2}$

Once you get used to them, surds are quite easy

They do seem a bit fiddly with all those square roots everywhere, but with a bit of practice, surds can become your best friend. Just learn these six rules, then practise, practise and practise some more.

Warm-up and Worked Exam Questions

Take a deep breath and go through these warm-up questions one by one. Then you'll be ready for the really exciting bit (well, slightly more exciting anyway) — the exam questions.

Warm-up Questions

1) Simplify: a) $4a + c - 2a - 6c$ b) $3r^2 - 2r + 4r^2 - 1 - 3r$.
2) Multiply out:
   a) $4(2p + 7)$ b) $(4x - 2)(2x + 1)$ c) $a(5a - 3)$.
3) Factorise:
   a) $6p - 12q + 4$ b) $4cd^2 - 2cd + 10c^2d^3$.
4) Factorise $x^2 - 4y^2$.
5) Work out $\sqrt{5} \times \sqrt{6}$, leaving your answer as a surd.
6) Work out $\sqrt{12} \times \sqrt{3}$, giving your answer as a normal number.

Worked Exam Questions

Don't skip over these worked exam questions just because they already have the answers written in. Work through them yourself so you know what's going on, then have a go at the next page.

1   Factorise the following expressions fully. **(B)**

   a) $x^2 - 16$

This is a difference of two squares:
$$x^2 - 16 = x^2 - 4^2$$
$$= (x + 4)(x - 4)$$

$(x + 4)(x - 4)$
[1 mark]

b) $9n^2 - 4m^2$

Here you have to spot that 9 and 4 are square numbers.

$$9n^2 - 4m^2 = (3n)^2 - (2m)^2$$
$$= (3n + 2m)(3n - 2m)$$

$(3n + 2m)(3n - 2m)$
[2 marks]

2   Show that $\dfrac{(\sqrt{2} - 4)^2}{\sqrt{2}}$ simplifies to $9\sqrt{2} - 8$. **(A*)**

$$(\sqrt{2} - 4)^2 = 2 - 4\sqrt{2} - 4\sqrt{2} + 16 = 18 - 8\sqrt{2}$$

So $\dfrac{(\sqrt{2} - 4)^2}{\sqrt{2}} = \dfrac{18 - 8\sqrt{2}}{\sqrt{2}} = \dfrac{\sqrt{2}(18 - 8\sqrt{2})}{2} = \dfrac{18\sqrt{2} - 16}{2} = 9\sqrt{2} - 8$

Multiply top and bottom by $\sqrt{2}$ to get rid of the square root on the denominator.

[3 marks]

Exam Questions

3 The diagram below shows a rectangle with sides that are $2x + 3$ cm and $5y - 8$ cm long.

The perimeter of the rectangle is $7y - 2x$ cm.

Show that $6x + 3y = 10$.

$5y - 8$ cm

$2x + 3$ cm

Diagram not
accurately drawn

[3 marks]

4 Expand the brackets in the following expressions.
Simplify your answers as much as possible.

 a) $(2t - 5)(3t + 4)$

....
[2 marks]

b) $(x + 3)^2$

....
[2 marks]

5 Factorise the following expressions fully.

 a) $6x + 3$

....
[1 mark]

b) $7y - 21y^2$

....
[2 marks]

c) $2v^3w + 8v^2w^2$

....
[2 marks]

6 Write $(2 + \sqrt{3})(5 - \sqrt{3})$ in the form $a + b\sqrt{3}$, where a and b are integers.

....
[2 marks]

Solving Equations

The basic idea of <u>solving equations</u> is very simple — keep <u>rearranging</u> until you end up with x = number. The two most common methods for <u>rearranging</u> equations are: 1) '<u>same to both sides</u>' and 2) do the <u>opposite</u> when you cross the '='. We'll use the 'same to both sides' method on these pages.

Rearrange Until You Have x = Number

The easiest ones to solve are where you just have a <u>mixture</u> of x's and numbers.

1) First, <u>rearrange</u> the equation so that all the <u>x's</u> are on one side and the <u>numbers</u> are on the other. <u>Combine</u> terms where you can.

2) Then <u>divide</u> both sides by the <u>number multiplying x</u> to find the value of x.

EXAMPLE: Solve $5x + 4 = 8x - 5$

This means 'add 5 to both sides'.

$(+5)$ $5x + 4 + 5 = 8x - 5 + 5$
$5x + 9 = 8x$
$(-5x)$ $5x + 9 - 5x = 8x - 5x$ Numbers on left, x's on right.
$9 = 3x$
$(÷3)$ $9 ÷ 3 = 3x ÷ 3$ Divide by number multiplying x.
$3 = x$

Once you're happy with the method, you don't have to write everything out in full — your working might be:
$5x + 9 = 8x$
$9 = 3x$
$3 = x$

Multiply Out Brackets First

If your equation has <u>brackets</u> in it...

1) <u>Multiply</u> them out <u>before rearranging</u>.

2) <u>Solve it</u> in the same way as above.

EXAMPLE: Solve $3(3x - 2) = 5x + 10$

$9x - 6 = 5x + 10$
$(-5x)$ $9x - 6 - 5x = 5x + 10 - 5x$
$4x - 6 = 10$
$(+6)$ $4x - 6 + 6 = 10 + 6$
$4x = 16$
$(÷4)$ $4x ÷ 4 = 16 ÷ 4$
$x = 4$

Get Rid of Fractions

1) <u>Fractions</u> make everything more complicated — so you need to get rid of them <u>before doing anything else</u> (yep, even before multiplying out brackets).

2) To get rid of fractions, multiply <u>every term</u> of the equation by whatever's on the <u>bottom</u> of the fraction. If there are <u>two</u> fractions, you'll need to multiply by <u>both</u> denominators.

EXAMPLES:

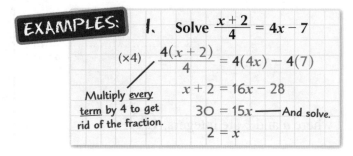

1. Solve $\dfrac{x + 2}{4} = 4x - 7$

$(×4)$ $\dfrac{4(x + 2)}{4} = 4(4x) - 4(7)$

Multiply <u>every</u> term by 4 to get rid of the fraction.

$x + 2 = 16x - 28$
$30 = 15x$ — And solve.
$2 = x$

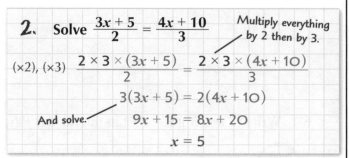

2. Solve $\dfrac{3x + 5}{2} = \dfrac{4x + 10}{3}$

Multiply everything by 2 then by 3.

$(×2), (×3)$ $\dfrac{2 × 3 × (3x + 5)}{2} = \dfrac{2 × 3 × (4x + 10)}{3}$

$3(3x + 5) = 2(4x + 10)$
And solve.
$9x + 15 = 8x + 20$
$x = 5$

Remember that you're trying to get x on its own

You can always check your answer by putting your value of x back into both sides of the original equation — you should get the same number on each side. If you don't, you've made a mistake somewhere.

Solving Equations

Now you know the basics of solving equations, it's time to put it all together into a step-by-step method.

Solving Equations Using the 6-Step Method

Here's the method to follow (just ignore any steps that don't apply to your equation):

1) Get rid of any <u>fractions</u>.
2) <u>Multiply out</u> any brackets.
3) Collect all the <u>x-terms</u> on one side and all <u>number terms</u> on the other.
4) Reduce it to the form '<u>$Ax = B$</u>' (by <u>combining like terms</u>).
5) Finally <u>divide both sides by A</u> to give '$x = \quad$', and that's your answer.
6) If you had '$x^2 = \quad$' instead, <u>square root</u> both sides to end up with '$x = \pm \quad$'.

EXAMPLE: Solve $\dfrac{3x + 4}{5} + \dfrac{4x - 1}{3} = 14$

Multiply everything by 5 then by 3.

1) Get rid of any <u>fractions</u>. $(\times 5), (\times 3)$

$$\frac{5 \times 3 \times (3x + 4)}{5} + \frac{5 \times 3 \times (4x - 1)}{3} = 5 \times 3 \times 14$$

$$3(3x + 4) + 5(4x - 1) = 210$$

2) <u>Multiply out</u> any brackets. $\quad 9x + 12 + 20x - 5 = 210$

3) Collect all the <u>x-terms</u> on one side and all <u>number terms</u> on the other.

$(-12), (+5) \quad 9x + 20x = 210 - 12 + 5$

4) Reduce it to the form '<u>$Ax = B$</u>' (by <u>combining like terms</u>).

$$29x = 203$$

5) Finally <u>divide both sides by A</u> to give '$x = \quad$', and that's your answer.

$(\div 29) \qquad x = 7 \qquad$ (You're left with '$x = \quad$' so you can ignore step 6.)

Dealing With Squares

If you're unlucky, you might get an $\underline{x^2}$ in an equation. If this happens, you'll end up with '$x^2 = ...$' at step 5, and then step 6 is to take <u>square roots</u>. There's one very important thing to remember: whenever you take the square root of a number, the answer can be <u>positive</u> or <u>negative</u>...

EXAMPLE: Solve $3x^2 = 75$.

$(\div 3) \qquad x^2 = 25$

$(\sqrt{\ }) \qquad x = \pm 5$

You always get a +ve and -ve version of the same number (your calculator only gives the +ve answer). This shows why:
$5^2 = 5 \times 5 = 25$ but also
$(-5)^2 = (-5) \times (-5) = 25$.

Learn the 6-step method for solving equations

You might not need to use all 6 steps to solve your equation — ignore any that you don't need and move onto the next step. Make sure you do them in the right order though — otherwise you'll get it wrong.

Rearranging Formulas

Rearranging formulas means making one letter the subject, e.g. getting '$y =$' from '$2x + z = 3(y + 2p)$' — you have to get the subject on its own.

Use the **Solving Equations** Method to **Rearrange Formulas**

Rearranging formulas is remarkably similar to solving equations. The method below is identical to the method for solving equations, except that I've added an extra step at the start.

1) Get rid of any square root signs by squaring both sides.
2) Get rid of any fractions.
3) Multiply out any brackets.
4) Collect all the subject terms on one side and all non-subject terms on the other.
5) Reduce it to the form '$Ax = B$' (by combining like terms). You might have to do some factorising here too.
6) Divide both sides by A to give '$x =$ '.
7) If you're left with '$x^2 =$ ', square root both sides to get '$x = \pm$ ' (don't forget the ±).

x is the subject term here. A and B could be numbers or letters (or a mix of both).

What To Do If...

...the **Subject** Appears in a **Fraction**

You won't always need to use all 7 steps in the method above — just ignore the ones that don't apply.

EXAMPLE: Make b the subject of the formula $a = \dfrac{5b + 3}{4}$.

There aren't any square roots, so ignore step 1.

2) Get rid of any fractions.	(by multiplying every term by 4, the denominator)

(×4) $\quad 4a = \dfrac{4(5b + 3)}{4}$

$4a = 5b + 3$

There aren't any brackets so ignore step 3.

4) Collect all the subject terms on one side and all non-subject terms on the other.

(remember that you're trying to make b the subject)   (−3) $\quad 5b = 4a - 3$

5) It's now in the form $Ax = B$.	(where A = 5 and B = 4a − 3)

6) Divide both sides by 5 to give '$b =$ '.

(÷5) $\quad b = \dfrac{4a - 3}{5}$

b isn't squared, so you don't need step 7.

The subject is the letter on its own

Remember that rearranging formulas is exactly the same as solving equations, except that instead of ending up with '$x =$ number' (e.g. $x = 3$), you'll end up with '$x =$ expression' (e.g. $x = 2y + 4$).

Rearranging Formulas

Carrying straight on from the previous page, now it's time for what to do if...

...there's a *Square* or *Square Root* Involved

If the subject appears as a <u>square</u> or in a <u>square root</u>, you'll have to use steps 1 and 7 (not necessarily both).

EXAMPLE: Make v the subject of the formula $u = 4v^2 + 5w$.

There aren't any square roots, fractions or brackets so ignore steps 1-3 (this is pretty easy so far).

4) Collect all the <u>subject terms</u> on one side and all <u>non-subject terms</u> on the other.

$(-5w)$ $4v^2 = u - 5w$

5) It's now in the form $\underline{Ax^2 = B}$ (where A = 4 and B = $u - 5w$)

6) <u>Divide both sides by 4</u> to give '$v^2 =$ '. $(\div 4)$ $v^2 = \dfrac{u - 5w}{4}$

7) <u>Square root</u> both sides to get '$v = \pm$ '. $(\sqrt{\ })$ $v = \pm\sqrt{\dfrac{u - 5w}{4}}$ Don't forget the ±!

EXAMPLE: Make n the subject of the formula $m = \sqrt{n + 5}$.

1) Get rid of any <u>square roots</u> by <u>squaring</u> both sides. $m^2 = n + 5$ $\sqrt{a}$ means the positive square root, so you don't need a ±.

There aren't any fractions so ignore step 2.
There aren't any brackets so ignore step 3.

4) Collect all the <u>subject terms</u> on one side and all <u>non-subject terms</u> on the other.

(-5) $n = m^2 - 5$ This is in the form '$n =$ ' so you don't need to do steps 5-7.

...the Subject Appears *Twice*

Go home and cry. No, not really — you'll just have to do some <u>factorising</u>, usually in step 5.

EXAMPLE: Make p the subject of the formula $q = \dfrac{p + 1}{p - 1}$.

There aren't any square roots so ignore step 1.

2) Get rid of any <u>fractions</u>. $q(p - 1) = p + 1$ 3) <u>Multiply out</u> any brackets. $pq - q = p + 1$

4) Collect all the <u>subject terms</u> on one side and all <u>non-subject terms</u> on the other.

$pq - p = q + 1$

This is where you factorise — p was in both terms on the LHS so it comes out as a common factor.

5) <u>Combine like terms</u> on each side of the equation. $p(q - 1) = q + 1$

6) <u>Divide both sides by $(q - 1)$</u> to give '$p =$ '. $p = \dfrac{q + 1}{q - 1}$ (p isn't squared, so you don't need step 7.)

Remember — you square first and square root last

Rearranging formulas is a bit harder if the subject appears twice. But if this happens, don't panic — just follow the 7-step method and be prepared to do some factorising (see page 44 if you need a reminder).

52

Warm-up and Worked Exam Questions

It's easy to think you've learnt everything in the section until you try the warm-up questions. Don't panic if there are bits you've forgotten. Just go back over them until they're firmly fixed in your brain.

Warm-up Questions

1) Solve these equations to find the value of x:
   a) $8x - 5 = 19$
   b) $3(2x + 7) = 3$
   c) $4x - 9 = x + 6$.

2) What is the subject of these formulas?
   a) $p = \sqrt{\dfrac{ml^2}{h}}$
   b) $t = px - y^3$.

3) Make q the subject of the formula $p = \dfrac{q}{7} + 2r$

4) Make z the subject of the formula $x = \dfrac{y + 2z}{3}$

Worked Exam Questions

Here are a couple of exam questions that I've done for you. You won't get any help for the questions on the next page though — so make the most of it while you can.

---

1 Solve the equation $\dfrac{5}{4}(2c - 1) = 3c - 2$ **C**

Get rid of the fraction...
...multiply out the brackets...
...and solve.

$$\dfrac{5}{4}(2c - 1) = 3c - 2$$
$(\times 4)$ $5(2c - 1) = 4(3c - 2)$
$10c - 5 = 12c - 8$
$(-10c)$ $-5 = 2c - 8$
$(+8)$ $3 = 2c$
$(\div 2)$ $1.5 = c$

$c = \underline{\quad 1.5 \quad}$
[3 marks]

---

2 Rearrange the formula $s = \dfrac{1}{2}gt^2$ to make t the subject.

Follow the 7-step method to get t on its own:

$$s = \dfrac{1}{2}gt^2$$
$(\times 2)$ $2s = gt^2$
$(\div g)$ $\dfrac{2s}{g} = t^2$
$(\sqrt{})$ $\pm\sqrt{\dfrac{2s}{g}} = t$

Don't forget the $\pm$ when you square root

$t = \pm\sqrt{\dfrac{2s}{g}}$
[3 marks]

SECTION TWO — ALGEBRA

Exam Questions

3 The quadrilateral below has a perimeter of 58 cm.

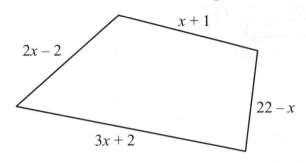

Diagram NOT
drawn to scale

All of the lengths on this diagram are in cm. Find the value of x.

$x = $ ....
[3 marks]

4 The formula for finding the volume of a pyramid is $V = \frac{1}{3}Ah$, where A
is the base area of the pyramid, and h is the height of the pyramid.

a) Rearrange the formula to make h the subject.

....
[2 marks]

b) Find the height of a pyramid which has volume 18 cm³ and base area 12 cm².

.... cm
[2 marks]

5 Solve this equation.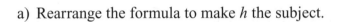

 $\dfrac{8 - 2x}{3} + \dfrac{2x + 4}{9} = 12$

$x = $ ....
[4 marks]

6 Rearrange the formula below to make n the subject.

$$x = \sqrt{\frac{(1 + n)}{(1 - n)}}$$

....
[5 marks]

Factorising Quadratics

There are several ways of solving a quadratic equation as detailed on the following pages.
You need to know all the methods as they sometimes ask for specific ones in the exam.

Factorising a Quadratic

1) 'Factorising a quadratic' means 'putting it into 2 brackets'.

2) The standard format for quadratic equations is: $\underline{ax^2 + bx + c = 0}$.

3) Most exam questions have $\underline{a = 1}$, making them much easier (e.g. $x^2 + 3x + 2 = 0$). *See next page for when 'a' is not 1.*

4) As well as factorising a quadratic, you might be asked to solve it.
This just means finding the values of x that make each bracket $\underline{0}$ (see example below).

Factorising Method when a = 1

1) ALWAYS rearrange into the STANDARD FORMAT: $ax^2 + bx + c = 0$.

2) Write down the TWO BRACKETS with the x's in: $(x\ \ \ )(x\ \ \ ) = 0$.

3) Then find 2 numbers that MULTIPLY to give 'c' (the end number) but also ADD/SUBTRACT to give 'b' (the coefficient of x). *Ignore any minus signs at this stage.*

4) Fill in the +/– signs and make sure they work out properly.

5) As an ESSENTIAL CHECK, expand the brackets to make sure they give the original equation.

6) Finally, SOLVE THE EQUATION by setting each bracket equal to 0.

You only need to do step 6) if the question asks you to solve the quadratic
— if it just tells you to factorise, you can stop at step 5).

EXAMPLE: Solve $x^2 - x = 12$.

1) $x^2 - x - 12 = 0$ 1) Rearrange into the standard format.

2) $(x\ \ \ )(x\ \ \ ) = 0$ 2) Write down the initial brackets.

3)
1×12	Add/subtract to give:	13 or 11
2×6	Add/subtract to give:	8 or 4
3×4	Add/subtract to give:	7 or ①

3) Find the right pairs of numbers that multiply to give c (= 12), and add or subtract to give b (= 1) (remember, we're ignoring the +/– signs for now).

$(x\ \ \ 3)(x\ \ \ 4) = 0$ *This is what we want.*

4) $(x + 3)(x - 4) = 0$

4) Now fill in the +/– signs so that 3 and 4 add/subtract to give –1 (= b).

5) Check:
$(x + 3)(x - 4) = x^2 - 4x + 3x - 12$
$= x^2 - x - 12$ ✓

5) ESSENTIAL check — EXPAND the brackets to make sure they give the original equation.

But we're not finished yet — we've only factorised it, we still need to...

6) $(x + 3) = 0 \Rightarrow x = -3$
$(x - 4) = 0 \Rightarrow x = 4$

6) SOLVE THE EQUATION by setting each bracket equal to 0.

Factorising quadratics is not easy — but it is important

To help you work out which signs you need, look at c. If c is positive, the signs will be the same (both positive or both negative), but if c is negative the signs will be different (one positive and one negative).

Factorising Quadratics

It gets a bit more complicated when 'a' isn't 1, but don't panic — just follow the method on this page.

When 'a' is Not 1

The basic method is still the same but it's <u>a bit messier</u> — the initial brackets are <u>different</u> as the first terms in each bracket have to multiply to give 'a'. This means finding the <u>other</u> numbers to go in the brackets is harder as there are more <u>combinations</u> to try. The best way to get to grips with it is to have a look at an <u>example</u>.

EXAMPLE: Solve $3x^2 + 7x - 6 = 0$.

1) $3x^2 + 7x - 6 = 0$

2) $(3x \quad)(x \quad) = 0$

3) Number pairs: 1×6 and 2×3

$(3x \quad 1)(x \quad 6)$ <u>multiplies</u> to give $\underline{18x}$ and $\underline{1x}$ which <u>add/subtract</u> to give $\underline{17x}$ or $\underline{19x}$

$(3x \quad 6)(x \quad 1)$ <u>multiplies</u> to give $\underline{3x}$ and $\underline{6x}$ which <u>add/subtract</u> to give $\underline{9x}$ or $\underline{3x}$

$(3x \quad 3)(x \quad 2)$ <u>multiplies</u> to give $\underline{6x}$ and $\underline{3x}$ which <u>add/subtract</u> to give $\underline{9x}$ or $\underline{3x}$

$(3x \quad 2)(x \quad 3)$ <u>multiplies</u> to give $\underline{9x}$ and $\underline{2x}$ which <u>add/subtract</u> to give $\underline{11x}$ or $\underline{7x}$ ✓

$(3x \quad 2)(x \quad 3)$

4) $(3x - 2)(x + 3)$

5) $(3x - 2)(x + 3) = 3x^2 + 9x - 2x - 6$
$= 3x^2 + 7x - 6$ ✓

6) $(3x - 2) = 0 \Rightarrow x = \dfrac{2}{3}$
$(x + 3) = 0 \Rightarrow x = -3$

1) <u>Rearrange</u> into the standard format.

2) Write down the <u>initial brackets</u> — this time, one of the brackets will have a $3x$ in it.

3) The <u>tricky part</u>: first, find <u>pairs of numbers</u> that <u>multiply to give c</u> (= 6), ignoring the minus sign for now.

Then, <u>try out</u> the number pairs you just found in the brackets until you find one that gives $7x$. But remember, each pair of numbers has to be tried in <u>2 positions</u> (as the brackets are different — one has $3x$ in it).

4) <u>Now fill in the +/– signs</u> so that 9 and 2 add/subtract to give $+7$ (= b).

5) <u>ESSENTIAL check</u> — <u>EXPAND the brackets</u>.

6) <u>SOLVE THE EQUATION</u> by setting each bracket <u>equal to 0</u> (if a isn't 1, one of your answers will be a <u>fraction</u>).

EXAMPLE: Solve $2x^2 - 9x = 5$.

1) Put in standard form: $2x^2 - 9x - 5 = 0$

2) Initial brackets: $(2x \quad)(x \quad) = 0$

3) Number pairs: 1×5

$(2x \quad 5)(x \quad 1)$ <u>multiplies</u> to give $\underline{2x}$ and $\underline{5x}$ which <u>add/subtract</u> to give $\underline{3x}$ or $\underline{7x}$

$(2x \quad 1)(x \quad 5)$ <u>multiplies</u> to give $\underline{1x}$ and $\underline{10x}$ which <u>add/subtract</u> to give $\underline{9x}$ or $\underline{11x}$

$(2x \quad 1)(x \quad 5)$ ✓

4) Put in the signs: $(2x + 1)(x - 5)$

5) Check:
$(2x + 1)(x - 5) = 2x^2 - 10x + x - 5$
$= 2x^2 - 9x - 5$ ✓

6) Solve:
$(2x + 1) = 0 \Rightarrow x = -\dfrac{1}{2}$
$(x - 5) = 0 \Rightarrow x = 5$

Factorising quadratics when a is not 1 is quite a bit harder

The problem is that it's a lot harder to work out the right combination of numbers to go in the brackets. Don't get stressed out, just take your time and work through the possibilities one at a time.

The Quadratic Formula

The solutions to ANY quadratic equation $ax^2 + bx + c = 0$ are given by this formula:

$$x = \frac{-b \pm \sqrt{b^2 - 4ac}}{2a}$$

<u>LEARN THIS FORMULA</u> — and <u>how to use it</u>. It's usually given in the exam, but if you don't learn it, you won't know how to use it. Using it isn't that hard, but there are a few pitfalls — so <u>TAKE HEED of these crucial details</u>:

Quadratic Formula — Five Crucial Details

1) Take it nice and slowly — always write it down in stages as you go.

2) **WHENEVER YOU GET A MINUS SIGN, <u>THE ALARM BELLS SHOULD ALWAYS RING!</u>**

3) Remember it's <u>2a</u> on the bottom line, not just a — and you <u>divide ALL of the top line by 2a</u>.

4) The ± sign means you end up with <u>two solutions</u> (by replacing it in the final step with '+' and '−').

5) If you get a <u>negative</u> number inside your square root, go back and <u>check your working</u>. Some quadratics do have a negative value in the square root, but they won't come up at GCSE.

If either 'a' or 'c' is negative, the -4ac effectively becomes +4ac, so watch out. Also, be careful if b is negative, as -b will be positive.

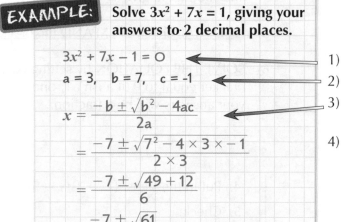

EXAMPLE: Solve $3x^2 + 7x = 1$, giving your answers to 2 decimal places.

$3x^2 + 7x - 1 = 0$

$a = 3, \quad b = 7, \quad c = -1$

$x = \dfrac{-b \pm \sqrt{b^2 - 4ac}}{2a}$

$= \dfrac{-7 \pm \sqrt{7^2 - 4 \times 3 \times -1}}{2 \times 3}$

$= \dfrac{-7 \pm \sqrt{49 + 12}}{6}$

$= \dfrac{-7 \pm \sqrt{61}}{6}$

$= \dfrac{-7 + 7.81...}{6}$ or $\dfrac{-7 - 7.81...}{6}$

$= 0.1350...$ or $-2.468...$

So to 2 d.p. the solutions are:
$x = 0.14$ or -2.47

Notice that you do two calculations at the final stage — one + and one −.

1) First get it into the form $\underline{ax^2 + bx + c = 0}$.

2) Then carefully identify a, b and c.

3) Put these values into the quadratic formula and <u>write down each stage</u>.

4) Finally, <u>as a check</u> put your values back into the <u>original equation</u>:
E.g. for $x = 0.1350$: $3 \times 0.135^2 + 7 \times 0.135$
$= 0.999675$, which is 1, as near as...

When to use the quadratic formula:
- If you have a quadratic that <u>won't</u> easily <u>factorise</u>.
- If the question mentions <u>decimal places</u> or <u>significant figures</u>.
- If the question asks for <u>surds</u> (though this could be completing the square instead — see next page).

Looks nightmarish — but you'll soon be chanting it in your sleep

This formula looks difficult to use and learn, but after you've said "minus b plus or minus the square root of b squared minus four a c all over 2 a" a few times, you'll wonder what all the fuss was about.

Completing the Square

There's just one more method to learn for solving quadratics — and it's a bit of a nasty one.
It's called 'completing the square', and takes a bit to get your head round it.

Solving Quadratics by *'Completing the Square'*

To 'complete the square' you have to:

    1) Write down a <u>SQUARED</u> bracket, and then   2) Stick a number on the end to '<u>COMPLETE</u>' it.

$$x^2 + 12x - 5 = (x + 6)^2 - 41$$

The SQUARE...   ...COMPLETED

It's not that bad if you learn all the steps — some of them aren't all that obvious.

1) As always, <u>REARRANGE THE QUADRATIC INTO THE STANDARD FORMAT</u>: $\mathbf{a}x^2 + \mathbf{b}x + \mathbf{c}$
(the rest of this method is for a = 1, as that's what you'll almost certainly be given).

2) <u>WRITE OUT THE INITIAL BRACKET</u>: $(x + \frac{b}{2})^2$ — just divide the value of b by 2.

3) <u>MULTIPLY OUT THE BRACKETS</u> and <u>COMPARE TO THE ORIGINAL</u>
to find what you need to add or subtract to complete the square.

4) Add or subtract the <u>ADJUSTING NUMBER</u> to make it
<u>MATCH THE ORIGINAL</u>.

> If a isn't 1, you have to divide through by 'a' or take out a factor of 'a' before you start.

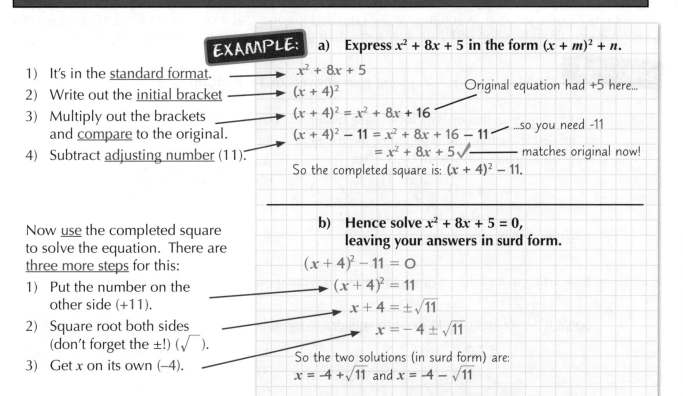

EXAMPLE: **a)**   **Express $x^2 + 8x + 5$ in the form $(x + m)^2 + n$.**

1) It's in the <u>standard format</u>. $x^2 + 8x + 5$

2) Write out the <u>initial bracket</u> $(x + 4)^2$ Original equation had +5 here...

3) Multiply out the brackets
and <u>compare</u> to the original. $(x + 4)^2 = x^2 + 8x + 16$
$(x + 4)^2 - 11 = x^2 + 8x + 16 - 11$ ...so you need –11

4) Subtract <u>adjusting number</u> (11). $= x^2 + 8x + 5$ ✓   matches original now!

So the completed square is: $(x + 4)^2 - 11$.

Now <u>use</u> the completed square
to solve the equation. There are
<u>three more steps</u> for this:

b)   **Hence solve $x^2 + 8x + 5 = 0$,**
leaving your answers in surd form.

1) Put the number on the
other side (+11). $(x + 4)^2 - 11 = 0$
$(x + 4)^2 = 11$

2) Square root both sides
(don't forget the ±!) ($\sqrt{}$). $x + 4 = \pm\sqrt{11}$

3) Get x on its own (–4). $x = -4 \pm \sqrt{11}$

So the two solutions (in surd form) are:
$x = -4 + \sqrt{11}$ and $x = -4 - \sqrt{11}$

> If you really don't like steps 3-4, just remember that the
value you need to add or subtract is <u>always</u> $c - \left(\frac{b}{2}\right)^2$.

Make a SQUARE (bracket) and COMPLETE it (add or take away)

Completing the square basically means working out a squared bracket which is almost the same as your
quadratic and then working out what has to be added or subtracted to make it the same as the original.

58

Quadratic Equations — Tricky Ones

Now it's time to have a go at some tricky 'hidden quadratic' questions that sometimes pop up in the exam.

Shape Questions Involving *Quadratics*

Sometimes examiners like to <u>disguise</u> quadratic equations by hiding them in <u>shape</u> questions — it might look like an <u>area</u> or <u>volume</u> question where you have to find the <u>length</u> of a side. Don't be fooled though.

EXAMPLE: **The rectangle on the right has sides of length x cm and $(2x + 1)$ cm. The area of the rectangle is 15 cm². Find the value of x.**

You're told the <u>side lengths</u> and the <u>area</u>, and you know the <u>formula</u> for the area of a rectangle ($A = l \times w$), so this gives you:

$x \times (2x + 1) = 15$
$2x^2 + x = 15$

x cm

$(2x + 1)$ cm

This is a <u>quadratic</u>, so just <u>rearrange</u> into the <u>standard format</u> and solve (see p54-55):

$2x^2 + x - 15 = 0$

$(2x - 5)(x + 3) = 0$ so $x = \frac{5}{2}$ or $x = -3$.

You couldn't have a shape with sides of length -3 cm and -5 cm.

However, you're looking for a <u>length</u>, which means x <u>can't be negative</u> — so $x = \frac{5}{2}$

Quadratics Hidden as *Fractions*

This is a nasty exam question — you're given an <u>equation</u> to solve that looks like it's an <u>algebraic fractions</u> question (more about these on p61), but after some <u>rearranging</u>, it turns out you've got a <u>quadratic</u>.

EXAMPLE: **Solve $x - \dfrac{5}{x-1} = 2$, giving your answers to 3 significant figures.**

At first glance, this doesn't look like a quadratic, but wait and see...

The first thing to do is to <u>get rid of the fraction</u> (by multiplying every term by $(x - 1)$):

$x(x-1) - \dfrac{5(x-1)}{x-1} = 2(x-1)$

$\Rightarrow x(x-1) - 5 = 2(x-1)$

This is using the method for solving equations from p49.

Next, <u>multiply out the brackets</u>:

$x^2 - x - 5 = 2x - 2$

It's starting to look like a <u>quadratic</u> now, so write it out in the <u>standard format</u>:

$x^2 - 3x - 3 = 0$

<u>Solve it</u> — you're going to need the <u>quadratic formula</u> (see p56):

$a = 1, b = -3, c = -3$

The mention of significant figures in the question is a hint that you're going to need to use the quadratic formula.

$x = \dfrac{-b \pm \sqrt{b^2 - 4ac}}{2a} = \dfrac{-(-3) \pm \sqrt{(-3)^2 - (4 \times 1 \times -3)}}{2 \times 1}$

$= \dfrac{3 \pm \sqrt{9 - (-12)}}{2} = \dfrac{3 \pm \sqrt{21}}{2}$

$x = \dfrac{3 + \sqrt{21}}{2} = 3.7912... = 3.79 \text{ (3 s.f.)}$ or $x = \dfrac{3 - \sqrt{21}}{2} = -0.7912... = -0.791 \text{ (3 s.f.)}$

Watch out for hidden quadratics

Once you've found your quadratic, just use any of the methods from the last 4 pages to solve them — factorising is probably the easiest method, but if it won't factorise, you might have to use the formula.

Section Two — Algebra

Warm-up and Worked Exam Questions

This quadratic stuff isn't everyone's cup of tea. But once you get the knack of it, through lots of practice, you'll find a lot of the questions are really similar. Which is nice.

Warm-up Questions

1) Factorise:
   a) $x^2 + 11x + 28$ b) $x^2 + 16x + 28$ c) $x^2 + 12x - 28$.

2) Solve by factorisation:
   a) $x^2 + 8x + 15 = 0$ b) $x^2 + 5x - 14 = 0$ c) $x^2 - 7x + 7 = -5$.

3) Factorise $3x^2 + 32x + 20$.

4) Solve $5x^2 - 13x = 6$.

5) Solve $3x^2 - 3x = 2$, giving your answers to 2 decimal places.

6) Complete the square for the expression $x^2 + 8x + 20$.

7) Express $x^2 - 10x + 9$ as a completed square, and hence solve $x^2 - 10x + 9 = 0$.

Worked Exam Questions

Now, the exam questions — the good news is, if you've got the hang of the warm-up questions, you'll find that the exam questions are pretty much the same.

1   Fully factorise the expression $x^2 + 9x + 18$.

$(x \quad\quad)(x \quad\quad)$

     1×18 Add/subtract to give: 19 or 17
     2×9 Add/subtract to give: 11 or 7
     3×6 Add/subtract to give: ⑨ or 3 ✓

$(x \quad 3)(x \quad 6)$

     c (= 18) is positive, so the signs will be the same.
     b is also positive, so both signs will be +.

$(x + 3)(x + 6)$

     Check your final answer by expanding the brackets — you should get the original expression.

$\underline{(x + 3)(x + 6)}$

[2 marks]

2   Solve the quadratic equation $x^2 + 5x + 3 = 0$, giving your answers to 2 decimal places.

2 d.p. suggests you should use the quadratic formula:

a = 1, b = 5 and c = 3

$$x = \frac{-b \pm \sqrt{b^2 - 4ac}}{2a} = \frac{-5 \pm \sqrt{5^2 - 4 \times 1 \times 3}}{2 \times 1} = \frac{-5 \pm \sqrt{13}}{2} = -0.697... \text{ or } -4.302...$$

$x = \underline{-0.70}$ or $x = \underline{-4.30}$

     You need to include the O on the end as it's to 2 d.p.

[3 marks]

Exam Questions

3   The equation $2x^2 + x - 28 = 0$ is an example of a quadratic equation.

   a) Fully factorise the expression $2x^2 + x - 28$.

....
[2 marks]

b) Use your answer to part a) to solve the equation $2x^2 + x - 28 = (2x - 7)^2$.

$x =$ .... or $x =$ ....
[4 marks]

4   Solve the equation $x^2 + 6x - 3 = 0$. Give your answers correct to 2 decimal places.

The quadratic formula will
be on your formula sheet.

$x =$ .... or $x =$ ....
[3 marks]

5   Jiao is solving an equation of the form $ax^2 + bx + c = 0$. She correctly substitutes
the values of a, b and c into the quadratic formula. Her working is shown below.

$$x = \frac{6 \pm \sqrt{(36 - 24)}}{4}$$

Find the values of a, b and c.

$a =$ ...., $b =$ ...., $c =$ ....
[3 marks]

6   Write the expression $x^2 - 6x + 3$ in the form $(x + a)^2 + b$.

....
[3 marks]

7   Given that $x^2 + ax + b = (x + 2)^2 - 9$, work out the values of a and b.

$a =$ .... and $b =$ ....
[2 marks]

Algebraic Fractions

Unfortunately, fractions aren't limited to numbers — you can get <u>algebraic fractions</u> too.
Fortunately, everything you learnt about fractions on p10-12 can be applied to algebraic fractions as well.

Simplifying Algebraic Fractions

You can <u>simplify</u> algebraic fractions by <u>cancelling</u> terms on the top and bottom — just deal with each <u>letter</u> individually and cancel as much as you can. You might have to <u>factorise</u> first (see pages 44 and 54-55).

EXAMPLES:

1. Simplify $\dfrac{21x^3y^2}{14xy^3}$

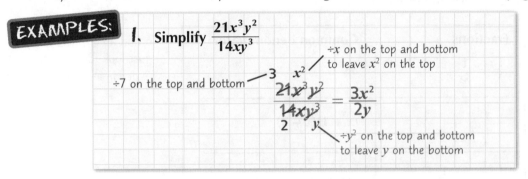

$\div x$ on the top and bottom to leave x^2 on the top

$\div 7$ on the top and bottom

$$\frac{21x^3y^2}{14xy^3} = \frac{3x^2}{2y}$$

$\div y^2$ on the top and bottom to leave y on the bottom

2. Simplify $\dfrac{x^2 - 16}{x^2 + 2x - 8}$

Factorise the top using D.O.T.S.

Factorise the quadratic on the bottom

$$\frac{(x+4)(x-4)}{(x-2)(x+4)} = \frac{x-4}{x-2}$$

Then cancel the common factor of $(x + 4)$

Multiplying/Dividing Algebraic Fractions

1) To <u>multiply</u> two fractions, just multiply tops and bottoms <u>separately</u>.

EXAMPLE: Simplify $\dfrac{x^2}{4} \times \dfrac{2}{x+1}$

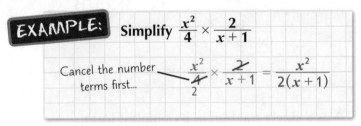

Cancel the number terms first...

$$\frac{x^2}{4} \times \frac{2}{x+1} = \frac{x^2}{2(x+1)}$$

2) To <u>divide</u>, turn the second fraction <u>upside down</u> then <u>multiply</u>.

EXAMPLE: Simplify $\dfrac{2}{x} \div \dfrac{x^3}{5}$

$$\frac{2}{x} \div \frac{x^3}{5} = \frac{2}{x} \times \frac{5}{x^3} = \frac{10}{x^4}$$

It's exactly the same as normal fractions

This stuff should be second nature by now because the rules are the same as those for normal fractions.
OK, it might look a bit harder with all those letters instead of numbers, but that's algebra for you.

Algebraic Fractions

Adding and subtracting algebraic fractions is a bit more difficult than multiplying and dividing them — you have to put them over a common denominator before you can do anything with them.

Adding/Subtracting Algebraic Fractions

Here's the method for <u>adding</u> and <u>subtracting</u> algebraic fractions:

1) Work out the <u>common denominator</u> (see p11).

Fractions	Common denominator
$\dfrac{1}{x} + \dfrac{1}{3x}$	$3x$
$\dfrac{1}{x+1} + \dfrac{1}{x-2}$	$(x+1)(x-2)$
$\dfrac{1}{x} + \dfrac{1}{x(x+1)}$	$x(x+1)$

To find a common denominator, just look for something both denominators divide into.

2) Multiply <u>top and bottom</u> of each fraction by whatever gives you the common denominator.

3) Add or subtract the <u>numerators</u> only.

EXAMPLE: Write $\dfrac{3}{(x+3)} + \dfrac{1}{(x-2)}$ as a single fraction.

1st fraction: multiply top and bottom by $(x-2)$

2nd fraction: multiply top and bottom by $(x+3)$

$$\frac{3}{(x+3)} + \frac{1}{(x-2)} = \frac{3(x-2)}{(x+3)(x-2)} + \frac{(x+3)}{(x+3)(x-2)}$$

Common denominator will be $(x+3)(x-2)$

$$= \frac{3x-6}{(x+3)(x-2)} + \frac{x+3}{(x+3)(x-2)}$$

Add the numerators

$$= \frac{4x-3}{(x+3)(x-2)}$$

EXAMPLE: Write $\dfrac{6}{x(2-x)} - \dfrac{3}{x}$ as a single fraction in its simplest form.

You don't need to do anything to the first fraction as it's already over the common denominator

2nd fraction: multiply top and bottom by $(2-x)$

$$\frac{6}{x(2-x)} - \frac{3}{x} = \frac{6}{x(2-x)} - \frac{3(2-x)}{x(2-x)} = \frac{6}{x(2-x)} - \frac{6-3x}{x(2-x)}$$

Common denominator will be $x(2-x)$

$$= \frac{6-6+3x}{x(2-x)} = \frac{3x}{x(2-x)} = \frac{3}{(2-x)}$$

The x's will cancel

Put fractions over a common denominator

One more thing — never do this: $\dfrac{x}{x+y} = \dfrac{1}{y}$ ✗. It's wrong wrong WRONG and will lose you marks.

Inequalities

Before you can really get going with <u>inequalities</u>, you need to know what the <u>symbols</u> mean.
Once you've got your head round them, you can move on to <u>algebra</u> with inequalities.

The **Inequality Symbols**

> means '<u>Greater than</u>'

< means '<u>Less than</u>'

≥ means '<u>Greater than or equal to</u>'

≤ means '<u>Less than or equal to</u>'

<u>REMEMBER</u> — the one at the <u>BIG</u> end is <u>BIGGEST</u> —
so $x > 4$ and $4 < x$ both say: '<u>x is greater than 4</u>'.

You Can Show Inequalities on **Number Lines**

Drawing inequalities on a <u>number line</u> is dead easy — all you have to remember is that you use
an <u>open circle</u> (O) for > or < and a <u>coloured-in circle</u> (●) for ≥ or ≤.

EXAMPLE: **Show the inequality $x > -3$ on a number line.**

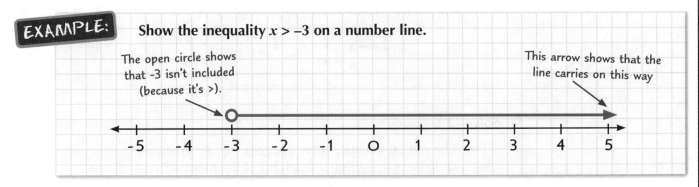

EXAMPLE: **Show the inequality $-5 < x \le 4$ on a number line.**

Just treat each part of the inequality separately — you have $x > -5$
and $x \le 4$, so draw each end of the line and join in the middle.

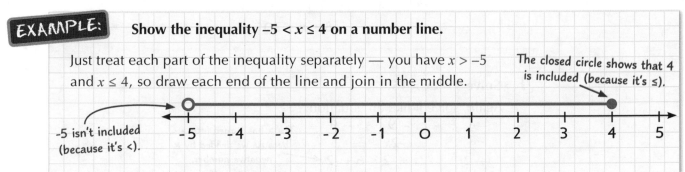

Make sure you know what the inequality symbols mean

Nothing too tricky on this page — as long as you remember which circle goes with which inequality,
you've netted yourself easy marks. And for no more effort than drawing a line and one or two circles.

Inequalities

Algebra with inequalities isn't as bad as it looks. Once you've learned the tricks involved, most of the algebra is identical to ordinary equations (have a look back at p48-49 if you need a reminder).

Algebra With Inequalities

The key thing about inequalities — solve them just like regular equations but WITH ONE BIG EXCEPTION:

Whenever you MULTIPLY OR DIVIDE by a NEGATIVE NUMBER, you must FLIP THE INEQUALITY SIGN.

EXAMPLES:

1. x **is an integer such that** $-4 < x \le 3$. **Write down all the possible values of** x.

Work out what each bit of the inequality is telling you:
$-4 < x$ means 'x is greater than -4',
$x \le 3$ means 'x is less than or equal to 3'.

Now just write down all the values that x can take.
(Remember, integers are just positive or negative whole numbers)

–4 isn't included because of the < but 3 is included because of the ≤.

$$-3, -2, -1, 0, 1, 2, 3$$

2. Solve $2x + 7 > x + 11$.

Just solve it like an equation:
$(-7) \quad 2x + 7 - 7 > x + 11 - 7$
$\qquad\qquad 2x > x + 4$
$(-x) \quad 2x - x > x + 4 - x$
$\qquad\qquad x > 4$

3. Solve $-2 \le \dfrac{x}{4} \le 5$.

Don't be put off because there are two inequality signs — just do the same thing to each bit of the inequality:
$(\times 4) \quad 4 \times -2 \le \dfrac{4 \times x}{4} \le 4 \times 5$
$\qquad\qquad -8 \le x \le 20$

4. Solve $9 - 2x > 15$.

Again, solve it like an equation:
$(-9) \quad 9 - 2x - 9 > 15 - 9$
$\qquad\qquad -2x > 6$
$(\div -2) \quad -2x \div -2 < 6 \div -2$
$\qquad\qquad x < -3$

The > has turned into a <, because we divided by a negative number.

Treat inequalities like equations — but remember the exception

The good news is, if you know how to solve equations, you also know how to solve inequalities. The bad news is, if you forget to flip the inequality sign when dividing by a negative number, you'll lose marks.

Graphical Inequalities

These questions always involve <u>shading a region on a graph</u>. The method sounds
very complicated, but once you've seen it in action with an example, you'll see that it's OK...

Showing *Inequalities* on a *Graph*

Here's the method to follow:

1) <u>CONVERT each INEQUALITY to an EQUATION</u>
   by simply putting an '=' in place of the inequality sign.

2) <u>DRAW THE GRAPH FOR EACH EQUATION</u> — if the inequality sign is < or >
   draw a <u>dotted line</u>, but if it's ≥ or ≤ draw a <u>solid line</u>.

3) <u>Work out WHICH SIDE of each line you want</u> — put a point (usually the origin, (0, 0))
   into the inequality to see if it's on the correct side of the line.

4) <u>SHADE THE REGION this gives you</u>.

> If using the origin doesn't work (e.g. if the origin lies on a line), just pick another point with easy coordinates and use that instead.

EXAMPLE: Shade the region that satisfies all three of the following inequalities:
$x + y < 5$ $y \le x + 2$ $y > 1$.

1) CONVERT EACH INEQUALITY TO AN EQUATION:
   $x + y = 5$, $y = x + 2$ and $y = 1$

2) DRAW THE GRAPH FOR EACH EQUATION (see p80)
   You'll need a <u>dotted</u> line for $x + y = 5$ and $y = 1$ and a <u>solid</u> line for $y = x + 2$.

3) WORK OUT WHICH SIDE OF EACH LINE YOU WANT
   This is the fiddly bit. Put $x = 0$ and $y = 0$ (the origin) into
   each inequality and see if this makes the inequality <u>true</u> or <u>false</u>.

   <u>$x + y < 5$:</u>
   $x = 0$, $y = 0$ gives $0 < 5$ which is <u>true</u>.
   This means the <u>origin</u> is on the <u>correct</u> side of the line.

   <u>$y \le x + 2$:</u>
   $x = 0$, $y = 0$ gives $0 \le 2$ which is <u>true</u>.
   So the origin is on the <u>correct</u> side of this line.

   <u>$y > 1$:</u>
   $x = 0$, $y = 0$ gives $0 > 1$ which is <u>false</u>.
   So the origin is on the <u>wrong side</u> of this line.

4) SHADE THE REGION
   You want the region that satisfies all of these:
   — below $x + y = 5$ (because the origin <u>is</u> on this side)
   — right of $y = x + 2$ (because the origin <u>is</u> on this side)
   — above $y = 1$ (because the origin <u>isn't</u> on this side).

Dotted lines mean the region <u>doesn't</u> include the points on the line.

A <u>solid</u> line means the region <u>does</u> include the points on the line

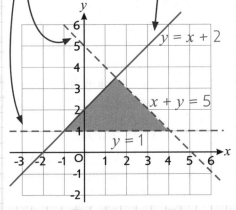

Make sure you read the question <u>carefully</u> — you might be asked to <u>label</u> the region instead of shade it,
or just <u>mark on points</u> that satisfy all three inequalities. No point throwing away marks because you didn't
read the question properly.

Just draw the graphs and shade the region

Don't panic if you're not quite sure how to sketch the graphs — you'll find out how on p80.
Then you just have to make sure you shade the right region — pick a point (usually (0, 0)) and try it.

Trial and Improvement

<u>Trial and improvement</u> is a way of finding an <u>approximate</u> solution to an equation that's too hard to be solved using normal methods. You'll always be told <u>WHEN</u> to use trial and improvement.

*Keep Trying **Different Values** in the Equation*

The basic idea of trial and improvement is to keep trying <u>different values</u> of x that are getting <u>closer</u> and <u>closer</u> to the solution. Here's the <u>method</u> to follow:

1) **<u>SUBSTITUTE TWO INITIAL VALUES</u> into the equation that give <u>OPPOSITE CASES</u>.**
   These are usually suggested in the question. 'Opposite cases' means <u>one answer too big, one too small</u>.

2) **Now CHOOSE YOUR NEXT VALUE <u>IN BETWEEN</u> THE PREVIOUS TWO, and <u>SUBSTITUTE</u> it into the equation.**
   <u>Continue this process</u>, always choosing a new value <u>between the two closest opposite cases</u> (and preferably nearer to the one that was closer to the answer).

3) **<u>AFTER ONLY 3 OR 4 STEPS</u> you should have <u>2 numbers</u> which are to the <u>right degree of accuracy but DIFFER BY 1 IN THE LAST DIGIT</u>.** You'll be asked for a certain level of accuracy (often 1 d.p.) in the question.
   For example, if you had to get your answer to 1 d.p. then you'd eventually end up with say 5.4 and 5.5, with these giving OPPOSITE results of course.

4) **<u>At this point</u> you ALWAYS take the <u>exact middle value</u> to decide which is the answer you want.**
   E.g. for 5.4 and 5.5 you'd try 5.45 to see if the real answer was between <u>5.4 and 5.45</u> (so 5.4 to 1 d.p.) or between <u>5.45 and 5.5</u> (so 5.5 to 1 d.p.).

It's a good idea to keep track of your working in a <u>table</u> — see example below.

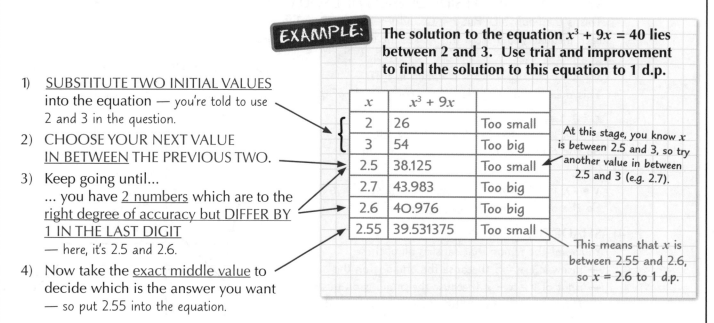

EXAMPLE: The solution to the equation $x^3 + 9x = 40$ lies between 2 and 3. Use trial and improvement to find the solution to this equation to 1 d.p.

1) <u>SUBSTITUTE TWO INITIAL VALUES</u> into the equation — you're told to use 2 and 3 in the question.

2) CHOOSE YOUR NEXT VALUE <u>IN BETWEEN</u> THE PREVIOUS TWO.

3) Keep going until...
   ... you have <u>2 numbers</u> which are to the <u>right degree of accuracy but DIFFER BY 1 IN THE LAST DIGIT</u>
   — here, it's 2.5 and 2.6.

4) Now take the <u>exact middle value</u> to decide which is the answer you want
   — so put 2.55 into the equation.

x	$x^3 + 9x$	
2	26	Too small
3	54	Too big
2.5	38.125	Too small
2.7	43.983	Too big
2.6	40.976	Too big
2.55	39.531375	Too small

At this stage, you know x is between 2.5 and 3, so try another value in between 2.5 and 3 (e.g. 2.7).

This means that x is between 2.55 and 2.6, so $x = 2.6$ to 1 d.p.

Make sure you show <u>all your working</u> — otherwise the examiner won't be able to tell what method you've used and you'll lose marks.

It's like playing a game of higher and lower

You need to learn this method. Luckily it's simple — like a guessing game where you guess a number too high, then too low and get gradually closer until you get to the right answer. That's all this method does.

Warm-up and Worked Exam Questions

OK, the three topics in this mini-section don't have much in common — but for all of them, it's just a case of learning the methods and practising lots of questions...

Warm-up Questions

1) Express as single fractions:

   a) $\frac{x}{2} + \frac{3x}{5}$ b) $\frac{abc}{d} \div \frac{b^2}{dc}$

2) List all integer values for x where $12 < x < 17$.

3) Find all integer values of n if $-3 \leq n \leq 3$.

4) Find all integer values of x such that $8 < 4x < 20$.

5) Solve the inequality $2q + 2 \leq 12$.

6) Solve the inequality $4p + 12 > 30$.

7) a) Using the same axes, draw the graphs of $y = 0$, $y = 2x$, $y = 6 - x$.

   b) R is the region defined by the inequalities $y \leq 2x$, $y \leq 6 - x$, $y \geq 0$.
   Shade this region and label it R.

8) $x^3 + 6x = 69$ has a solution between 3 and 4.
   Use trial and improvement to find this solution to 1 d.p.

9) $x^3 - 12x = 100$ has a solution between 5 and 6.
   Use trial and improvement to find this solution to 1 d.p.

Worked Exam Questions

I'll show you how to do two exam questions, then you're on your own for the questions on the next page. Enjoy.

1   Write down the inequality that is shown on the number line below. **C**

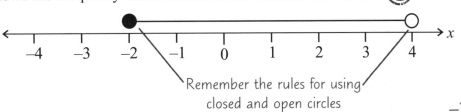

Remember the rules for using closed and open circles

$-2 \leq x < 4$

[1 mark]

2   Write $\frac{2}{3} + \frac{m - 2n}{m + 3n}$ as a single fraction.

Finding the common denominator is the tricky bit — you often just need to multiply the denominators together

$$\frac{2}{3} + \frac{m - 2n}{m + 3n} = \frac{2 \times (m + 3n)}{3 \times (m + 3n)} + \frac{3 \times (m - 2n)}{3 \times (m + 3n)}$$

$$= \frac{2m + 6n}{3(m + 3n)} + \frac{3m - 6n}{3(m + 3n)}$$

$$= \frac{5m}{3(m + 3n)}$$

$\dfrac{5m}{3(m + 3n)}$

[3 marks]

Exam Questions

3 Use trial and improvement to find a solution to the equation $x^2(x + 1) = 64$.

Give your solution to 1 decimal place and show your working.

$x =$ ....
[4 marks]

4 Solve the following inequalities.

 a) $4q - 5 < 23$

....
[2 marks]

b) $\dfrac{2x}{5} \leq 3$

....
[2 marks]

c) $4x + 1 > x - 5$

....
[2 marks]

5 Look at the grid on the right.

On the grid, shade the region that represents the inequalities
$y \geq 2$, $x + y < 8$, $y \leq x$.

[4 marks]

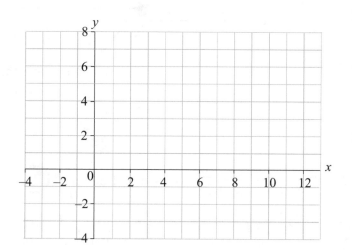

6 Solve $\dfrac{16}{2x + 5} - \dfrac{1}{x} = 6$

....
[5 marks]

Simultaneous Equations and Graphs

You can use <u>graphs</u> to solve <u>simultaneous equations</u> — just plot the graph of each equation, and the solutions are the points where the graphs <u>cross</u> (you can usually just read off the coordinates from the graph).

Plot **Both Graphs** and See Where They **Cross**

EXAMPLE: **Draw the graphs of $y = 2x + 3$ and $y = 6 - 4x$ and use the diagram to solve the equations simultaneously.**

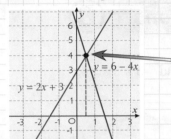

1) <u>DRAW BOTH GRAPHS.</u>

There's more on sketching straight-line graphs on p80.

2) <u>LOOK FOR WHERE THE GRAPHS CROSS.</u>
The straight lines cross at <u>one point</u>.
Reading the <u>x- and y-values</u> of this point gives the solution $x = \frac{1}{2}$ and $y = 4$.

If you were asked for the point where the graphs cross, give your answer in coordinate form — i.e. (x, y).

The point at which the two graphs cross is actually the <u>solution</u> you'd find if you set the two equations <u>equal to each other</u> (so in the first example, you're actually solving $2x + 3 = 6 - 4x$).
This fact comes in handy for the next (trickier) example.

EXAMPLE: **The equation $y = x^2 - 4x + 3$ is shown on the graph below.**
By drawing a suitable straight line, solve the equation $x^2 - 5x + 3 = 0$.

1) <u>WORK OUT WHICH STRAIGHT LINE YOU NEED.</u>

This is a bit nasty — the trick is to rearrange the given equation $x^2 - 5x + 3 = 0$ so that you have $x^2 - 4x + 3$ (the graph) on one side.

$x^2 - 5x + 3 = 0$

Adding x to both sides:

$x^2 - 4x + 3 = x$ ◀——

So the line needed is $y = x$.

The sides of this equation represent the two graphs $y = x^2 - 4x + 3$ and $y = x$.

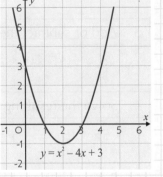

2) <u>DRAW IN THE LINE AND READ OFF THE SOLUTIONS.</u>

Once you have two graphs, read off the x-values where they cross.

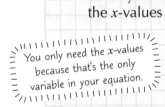
You only need the x-values because that's the only variable in your equation.

The graphs cross at <u>two points</u>.
Reading the <u>x-values</u> of these points gives the solutions $x = 0.7$ and $x = 4.3$.

The actual solutions are 0.69722... and 4.30277...
I don't know about you, but I can't read a graph that accurately, so if you're near enough you'll get the marks.

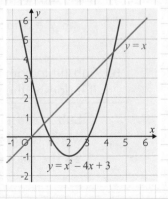

A point which satisfies two graphs is the point where they cross

This is pretty obvious, but it's the key to these questions. When you are solving two simultaneous equations, you're finding a point which satisfies both graphs. So draw them and see where they cross.

Simultaneous Equations

You've seen the easy way to solve simultaneous equations using graphs. Now it's time to learn the less fun algebra methods. The rules are really quite simple, but you must follow ALL the steps, in the right order, and treat them as a strict method.

There are two types of simultaneous equations you could get
— EASY ONES (where both equations are linear) and TRICKY ONES (where one's quadratic).

1 $2x = 6 - 4y$ and $-3 - 3y = 4x$ **2** $7x + y = 1$ and $2x^2 - y = 3$

1 Six Steps for *Easy Simultaneous Equations* **B**

EXAMPLE: Solve the simultaneous equations $2x = 6 - 4y$ and $-3 - 3y = 4x$

1. Rearrange both equations into the form $\underline{ax + by = c}$, and label the two equations ① and ②.

   a, b and c are numbers (which can be negative)

   $2x + 4y = 6$ — ①
   $-4x - 3y = 3$ — ②

2. Match up the numbers in front (the 'coefficients') of either the x's or y's in both equations. You may need to multiply one or both equations by a suitable number. Relabel them ③ and ④.

   ① × 2: $4x + 8y = 12$ — ③
   $-4x - 3y = 3$ — ④

3. Add or subtract the two equations to eliminate the terms with the same coefficient.

   ③ + ④ $0x + 5y = 15$

   If the coefficients have the same sign (both +ve or both −ve) then subtract. If the coefficients have opposite signs (one +ve and one −ve) then add.

4. Solve the resulting equation.

   $5y = 15 \Rightarrow \underline{y = 3}$

5. Substitute the value you've found back into equation ① and solve it.

   Sub $y = 3$ into ①: $2x + (4 \times 3) = 6 \Rightarrow 2x + 12 = 6 \Rightarrow 2x = -6 \Rightarrow \underline{x = -3}$

6. Substitute both these values into equation ② to make sure it works. If it doesn't then you've done something wrong and you'll have to do it all again.

   Sub x and y into ②: $(-4 \times -3) - (3 \times 3) = 12 - 9 = 3$, which is right, so it's worked.
   So the solutions are: $x = -3$, $y = 3$

And these are the easy simultaneous equations

It might just be me, but I think simultaneous equations are quite fun... well, maybe not fun... but quite satisfying. Anyway, it doesn't matter whether you like them or not — you have to learn how to do them.

Simultaneous Equations

2 Seven Steps for *TRICKY Simultaneous Equations*

EXAMPLE: Solve these two equations simultaneously:

$$7x + y = 1 \quad \text{and} \quad 2x^2 - y = 3$$

1. Rearrange the quadratic equation so that you have the non-quadratic unknown on its own. Label the two equations ① and ②.

   $7x + y = 1 \quad — \quad ①$

   $y = 2x^2 - 3 \quad — \quad ②$

2. Substitute the quadratic expression into the other equation. You'll get another equation — label it ③.

   $7x + y = 1 \quad — ①$

   $y = \boxed{2x^2 - 3} \quad — ②$

   $\Rightarrow 7x + (2x^2 - 3) = 1 \quad — ③$

   In this example you just shove the expression for y into equation ① in place of y.

3. Rearrange to get a quadratic equation. And guess what... You've got to solve it.

   $2x^2 + 7x - 4 = 0$

   $(2x - 1)(x + 4) = 0$

   So $2x - 1 = 0 \quad$ OR $\quad x + 4 = 0$

   $x = 0.5 \quad$ OR $\quad x = -4$

   Remember — if it won't factorise, you can either use the formula or complete the square. Have a look at p56-57 for more details.

4. Stick the first value back in one of the original equations (pick the easy one).

   ① $7x + y = 1$

   Substitute in $x = 0.5$: $3.5 + y = 1$, so $y = 1 - 3.5 = -2.5$

5. Stick the second value back in the same original equation (the easy one again).

   ① $7x + y = 1$

   Substitute in $x = -4$: $-28 + y = 1$, so $y = 1 + 28 = 29$

6. Substitute both pairs of answers back into the other original equation to check they work.

   ② $y = 2x^2 - 3$

   Substitute in $x = 0.5$: $y = (2 \times 0.25) - 3 = -2.5$ — jolly good.

   Substitute in $x = -4$: $y = (2 \times 16) - 3 = 29$ — smashing.

7. Write the pairs of answers out again, clearly, at the bottom of your working.

   The two pairs of solutions are: $x = 0.5, y = -2.5$ and $x = -4, y = 29$

Remember to write the two pairs out clearly

You are basically combining the two equations to make one quadratic equation. Solve that equation and stick the solutions back in to get the other two corresponding answers. What could be easier?*

*Inventive answers on a postcard to "Entertain the editor", CGP, Cumbria.
Examples of inventive answers do not include "falling off a log" or "pie".

Direct and Inverse Proportion

Proportion questions involve two variables (often x and y) which are <u>linked</u> in some way. You'll have to figure out the <u>relationship</u> between them, and use this to find <u>values</u> of x or y, given one value.

Simple Proportions

$\propto$ means 'is proportional to'.

The easiest types of proportions you might get are <u>direct proportion</u> ($y \propto x$) and <u>inverse proportion</u> ($y \propto \frac{1}{x}$).

Direct Proportion

<u>BOTH INCREASE TOGETHER</u>

The graph is a <u>straight line</u> <u>through the origin</u>: $y = kx$

If it doesn't go through the origin, it's not a direct proportion.

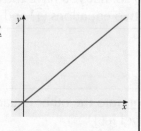

Inverse Proportion

One <u>INCREASES</u>, one <u>DECREASES</u>

The graph is $y = \frac{k}{x}$:

See p88 for more on these graphs.

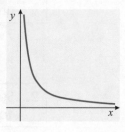

Handling Questions on Proportion

More complex proportions involve y varying <u>proportionally</u> or <u>inversely</u> to some <u>function</u> of x, e.g. x^2, x^3, $\sqrt{x}$ etc. You can always turn a <u>proportion statement</u> into an <u>equation</u> by replacing '$\propto$' with '$= k$' like this:

	Proportionality	Equation
'y is proportional to the square of x'	$y \propto x^2$	$y = kx^2$
't is proportional to the square root of h'	$t \propto \sqrt{h}$	$t = k\sqrt{h}$
'D varies with the cube of t'	$D \propto t^3$	$D = kt^3$
'V is inversely proportional to r cubed'	$V \propto \frac{1}{r^3}$	$V = \frac{k}{r^3}$

k is just some constant (unknown number).

Here's the method for handling proportion questions:

1) <u>Convert</u> the sentence into a proportionality.
2) <u>Replace</u> '$\propto$' with '$= k$' to make an <u>equation</u> (as above).
3) Find a <u>pair of values</u> of x and y somewhere in the question, and <u>substitute</u> them into the equation with the sole purpose of <u>finding k</u>.
4) Put <u>the value of k</u> into the equation and it's now ready to use, e.g. $y = 3x^2$.
5) Inevitably, they'll ask you to <u>find y</u>, having given you a value for x (or vice versa).

Once you've got it in the form of an equation with k, the rest is easy.

EXAMPLE: **G is inversely proportional to the square root of H. When G = 2, H = 16. Find an equation for G in terms of H, and use it to work out the value of G when H = 36.**

1) <u>Convert</u> to a <u>proportionality</u>. $G \propto \dfrac{1}{\sqrt{H}}$

2) <u>Replace</u> $\propto$ with '$= k$' to form an <u>equation</u>. $G = \dfrac{k}{\sqrt{H}}$

3) Use the values of G and H (2 and 16) to <u>find k</u>. $2 = \dfrac{k}{\sqrt{16}} = \dfrac{k}{4} \Rightarrow k = 8$

4) Put the <u>value of k</u> back into the equation. $G = \dfrac{8}{\sqrt{H}}$ ← *This is the equation for G in terms of H.*

5) Use your equation to <u>find the value</u> of G.

$G = \dfrac{8}{\sqrt{H}} = \dfrac{8}{\sqrt{36}}$

$= \dfrac{8}{6}$

$= \dfrac{4}{3}$

Direct proportion means x and y increase together

But with inverse proportion, one increases and the other decreases. Don't get them muddled up.

Proof

I'm not going to lie — <u>proof questions</u> can be a bit terrifying. They're usually not as bad as they seem though — you often just have to do a bit of <u>rearranging</u> to show that one thing is <u>equal</u> to another.

Use *Algebra* to *Show* That Two Things are *Equal*

Before you get started, there are a few things you need to know — they'll come in very handy when you're trying to prove things.

> This can be extended to multiples of other numbers too — e.g. to prove that something is a multiple of 5, show that it can be written as 5 × something.

- Any <u>even number</u> can be written as <u>$2n$</u> — i.e. 2 × something.
- Any <u>odd number</u> can be written as <u>$2n + 1$</u> — i.e. 2 × something + 1.
- <u>Consecutive numbers</u> can be written as <u>n</u>, <u>$n + 1$</u>, <u>$n + 2$</u> etc. — you can apply this to e.g. consecutive even numbers too (they'd be written as 2n, 2n + 2, 2n + 4).

In all of these statements, *n* is just any <u>integer</u>.

Armed with these facts, you can tackle just about any proof question the examiners might throw at you.

EXAMPLE: **Prove that the sum of any three odd numbers is odd.**

> So what you're trying to do here is show that the sum of three odd numbers can be written as (2 × something) + 1.

Take three odd numbers:
2a + 1, 2b + 1 and 2c + 1
(they don't have to be consecutive)

Add them together:

> You'll see why I've written 3 as 2 + 1 in a second.

2a + 1 + 2b + 1 + 2c + 1 = 2a + 2b + 2c + 2 + 1
$\qquad\qquad\qquad\quad$ = 2(a + b + c + 1) + 1
$\qquad\qquad\qquad\quad$ = 2n + 1 (where n = a + b + c + 1)

So the sum of any three odd numbers is odd.

EXAMPLE: **Prove that $(n + 3)^2 - (n - 2)^2 \equiv 5(2n + 1)$.**

Take one side of the equation and play about with it until you get the other side:

$\quad$ LHS: $(n + 3)^2 - (n - 2)^2 \equiv n^2 + 6n + 9 - (n^2 - 4n + 4)$
$\qquad\qquad\qquad\qquad\qquad\quad \equiv n^2 + 6n + 9 - n^2 + 4n - 4$
$\qquad\qquad\qquad\qquad\qquad\quad \equiv 10n + 5$
$\qquad\qquad\qquad\qquad\qquad\quad \equiv 5(2n + 1) =$ RHS ✓

> $\equiv$ is the identity symbol, and means that two things are identically equal to each other. So a + b $\equiv$ b + a is true for all values of a and b (unlike an equation, which is only true for certain values).

Disprove Things by Finding an *Example* That *Doesn't Work*

If you're asked to prove a statement <u>isn't</u> true, all you have to do is find <u>one example</u> that the statement doesn't work for — this is known as <u>disproof by counter example</u>.

EXAMPLE: **Ross says "the difference between any two consecutive square numbers is always a prime number". Prove that Ross is wrong.**

Just keep trying pairs of consecutive square numbers (i.e. 1^2 and 2^2) until you find one that doesn't work:

1 and 4 — difference = 3 (a prime number)
4 and 9 — difference = 5 (a prime number)
9 and 16 — difference = 7 (a prime number)
16 and 25 — difference = 9 (NOT a prime number) so Ross is wrong.

> You don't have to go through loads of examples if you can spot one that's wrong straightaway — you could go straight to 16 and 25.

Proof questions aren't as bad as they look.

If you're asked to prove that two things are equal, a bit of rearranging should do the trick. If you're asked to prove something is wrong, just find a counter example. And <u>always</u> keep in mind what you're aiming for.

Warm-up and Worked Exam Questions

There was a lot of maths to take in over the last few pages — but you can breathe a sigh of relief as you've made it to the end of the algebra section. Just a few of pages of questions to go.

Warm-up Questions

1) The graphs of $2y = 3x - 6$, $y = 0.5x + 3$ and $y + 2x = 8$ are shown.

   Use the graphs to solve the following pairs of simultaneous equations.
   a) $2y = 3x - 6$; $y = 0.5x + 3$.
   b) $y + 0.5x = 5$; $y = 0.5x + 3$.
   c) $2y = 3x - 6$; $y + 0.5x = 5$.

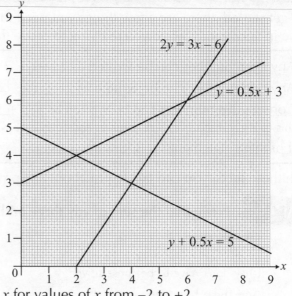

2) Draw the graphs of $y = 4 - 2x^2$ and $y = 1 - x$ for values of x from -2 to $+2$. Use the graphs to solve the equation $2x^2 = x + 3$.

3) Assume the graph of $y = x^2 - 3x + 2$ has been drawn. What other graph needs to be drawn to find the solution of the equation $x^2 - 2x - 3 = 0$?

4) Solve, by elimination, the simultaneous equations $2x + 3y = 19$ and $2x + y = 9$.

5) Solve simultaneously by elimination: $3x + 2y = 20$ and $x - 2y = -4$.

6) Write each of the following as an equation:
   a) A is proportional to the square of r b) $D \propto \dfrac{1}{R}$

   c) H is inversely proportional to the cube of D d) $V \propto S^3$

Worked Exam Question

There's only room for me to do one exam question for you here — sorry.
However, there are lots for you to have a go at for yourself on the next page.

---

1   The value of p is directly proportional to the cube root of q. When $p = 15$, $q = 27$.

     Find the value of q when $p = 20$.

$$p \propto \sqrt[3]{q}$$ — Write as a proportionality statement...
$$p = k\sqrt[3]{q}$$ — ...then turn into an equation

$p = 15$ when $q = 27$ gives:
$$15 = k\sqrt[3]{27}$$
$$15 = 3k \Rightarrow k = 5$$
So $p = 5\sqrt[3]{q}$ — This is the equation for p

Now $p = 20$ gives:
$$20 = 5\sqrt[3]{q}$$
$$4 = \sqrt[3]{q}$$
$$q = 4^3 = 64$$

$q = $ ......**64**......
[4 marks]

Exam Questions

2 Solve this pair of simultaneous equations.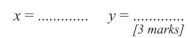

$$x + 3y = 11$$
$$3x + y = 9$$

$x =$ .... $y =$ ....
[3 marks]

3 c is inversely proportional to d^2. When $c = 2$, $d = 3$.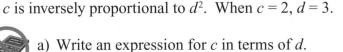

a) Write an expression for c in terms of d.

....
[3 marks]

b) Find the values of d when $c = 0.5$.

....
[2 marks]

4 Solve the following pair of simultaneous equations.

$$x^2 + y = 4$$
$$y = 4x - 1$$

$x =$ .... , $y =$ ....

and $x =$ .... , $y =$ ....
[5 marks]

*5 Prove that the difference between the squares of two consecutive even numbers is always a multiple of 4.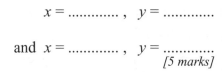

The little * means that you're tested on your quality of written communication — so make sure you explain things clearly

[3 marks]

6 The diagram to the right shows part of the graph of $y = 4x - x^2$.

 Use the graph to solve these simultaneous equations.

$$y = 5x - 2$$
$$y = 4x - x^2$$

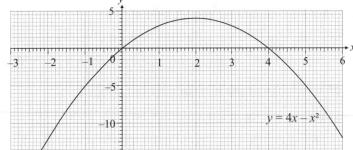

$x =$ .... , $y =$ ....

and $x =$ .... , $y =$ ....
[3 marks]

Revision Questions for Section Two

There's no denying, Section Two is nasty, grisly algebra — so check now how much you've learned.

- Try these questions and <u>tick off each one</u> when you <u>get it right</u>.
- When you've done <u>all the questions</u> for a topic and are <u>completely happy</u> with it, tick off the topic.

Sequences, Powers and Roots (p37-39) ☑

1) Find the expressions for the *n*th terms of the following sequences: a) 7, 9, 11, 13   b) 11, 8, 5, 2 ☑

2) The *n*th term of a sequence is given by $n^2 + 7$. Is 32 a term in this sequence? ☑

3) Simplify the following: a) $x^3 \times x^6$ b) $y^7 \div y^5$ c) $(z^3)^4$ ☑

Algebra (p42-45) ☑

4) Simplify by collecting like terms: $3x + 2y - 5 - 6y + 2x$ ☑

5) Multiply out these brackets: a) $3(2x + 1)$ b) $(x + 2)(x - 3)$ ☑

6) Factorise: a) $x^2 - 16y^2$ b) $49 - 81p^2q^2$ c) $12x^2 - 48y^2$ ☑

7) Simplify the following: a) $\sqrt{27}$ b) $\sqrt{125} \div \sqrt{5}$ ☑

Solving Equations and Rearranging Formulas (p48-51) ☑

8) Solve these equations: a) $5(x + 2) = 8 + 4(5 - x)$ b) $x^2 - 21 = 3(5 - x^2)$ ☑

9) Make p the subject of these: a) $\dfrac{p}{p + y} = 4$ b) $\dfrac{1}{p} = \dfrac{1}{q} + \dfrac{1}{r}$ ☑

Quadratics (p54-58) ☑

10) Solve the following by factorising them first: a) $x^2 + 9x + 18 = 0$ b) $5x^2 - 17x - 12 = 0$ ☑

11) Write down the quadratic formula. ☑

12) Find the solutions of these equations (to 2 d.p.) using the quadratic formula:
    a) $x^2 + x - 4 = 0$ b) $5x^2 + 6x = 2$ c) $(2x + 3)^2 = 15$ ☑

13) Find the exact solutions of these equations by completing the square:
    a) $x^2 + 12x + 15 = 0$ b) $x^2 - 6x = 2$ ☑

Algebraic Fractions and Inequalities (p61-65) ☑

14) Write $\dfrac{2}{x + 3} + \dfrac{1}{x - 1}$ as a single fraction. ☑

15) Solve this inequality: $4x + 3 \leq 6x + 7$ ☑

16) Show on a graph the region described by these conditions: $x + y \leq 6$, $y > 0.5$, $y \leq 2x - 2$ ☑

Trial and Improvement (p66) ☑

17) Given that $x^3 + 8x = 103$ has a solution between 4 and 5, find this solution to 1 d.p. ☑

Simultaneous Equations (p69-71) ☑

18) How can you find the solutions to a pair of simultaneous equations using their graphs? ☑

19) Solve these simultaneous equations: $y = 3x + 4$ and $x^2 + 2y = 0$ ☑

Direct and Inverse Proportion (p72) ☑

20) Write the following statement as an equation: "y is proportional to the square of x". ☑

21) p is proportional to the cube of q. When $p = 9$, $q = 3$. Find the value of p when $q = 6$. ☑

Proof (p73) ☑

22) Prove that the product of an odd number and an even number is even. ☑

X, Y and Z Coordinates

To start off with, here's some basic stuff about coordinates.
Get stuck into it — it'll get you off to a running start.

The Four Quadrants

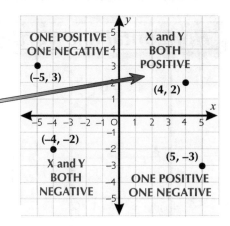

1) A graph has <u>four different quadrants</u> (regions). The top-right region is the easiest because here <u>all the coordinates in it are positive</u>.

2) You have to be careful in the <u>other regions</u> though, because the x- and y- coordinates could be <u>negative</u>, and that makes life much more difficult.

3) Coordinates are always written in brackets like this: (x, y) — remember x is <u>across</u>, and y is <u>up</u>.

Finding the Midpoint of a Line Segment

This regularly comes up in exams and is dead easy...

A line segment is part of a line. Lines continue forever in both directions, but line segments have two end points. Things that are actually line segments are often referred to as lines though.

> 1) **Find the average of the two x-coordinates, then do the same for the y-coordinates.**
>
> 2) **These will be the coordinates of the midpoint.**

EXAMPLE:

Point P has coordinates (8, 3) and point Q has coordinates (–4, 8). Find the midpoint of the line PQ.

See p142 for finding the length of a line segment.

① Average of x-coordinates $= \dfrac{8 + (-4)}{2} = \underline{2}$

Average of y-coordinates $= \dfrac{3 + 8}{2} = \underline{5.5}$

② So, coordinates of midpoint = (2, 5.5)

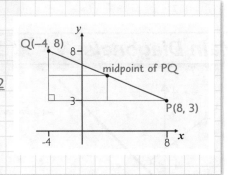

Q(–4, 8)

midpoint of PQ

P(8, 3)

Z Coordinates are for 3D Space

All z-coordinates do is extend the normal x-y coordinates into a third direction, z, so that <u>all positions</u> then have <u>3 coordinates</u>: (x, y, z)

EXAMPLE: **The diagram shows a cuboid. Write down the coordinates of vertices B and F.**

Decide how many units along the x, y and z-axes the vertices lie and write these distances as an (x, y, z) coordinate. B(7, 4, 0) F(7, 4, 2)

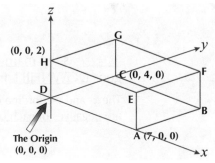

(0, 0, 2)

C (0, 4, 0)

The Origin (0, 0, 0)

A (7, 0, 0)

Midpoint of a line — just two averages

Learn how to use coordinates in all four quadrants and how to find the midpoint of a line segment. It'll get your head in gear for the rest of the section. Then make sure you understand x, y and z coordinates.

Straight-Line Graphs

You ought to know these simple graphs straight off with no hesitation:

Horizontal and *Vertical* lines: '*x = a*' and '*y = a*'

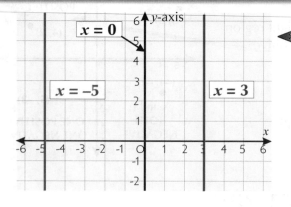

$x = a$ is a <u>vertical line</u> through '*a*' on the *x*-axis.

A common error is to mix up $x = 3$ and $y = 3$, etc. Remember — all the points on $x = 3$ have an *x*-coordinate of 3, and all the points on $y = 3$ have a *y*-coordinate of 3.

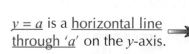

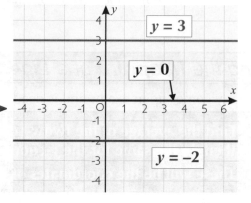

$y = a$ is a <u>horizontal line</u> through '*a*' on the *y*-axis.

The *Main Diagonals*: '*y = x*' and '*y = –x*'

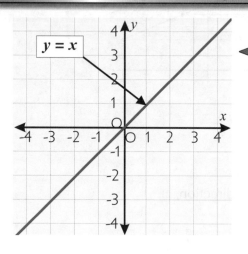

'$y = x$' is the <u>main diagonal</u> that goes <u>UPHILL</u> from left to right.

The *x*- and *y*-coordinates of each point are <u>the same</u>.

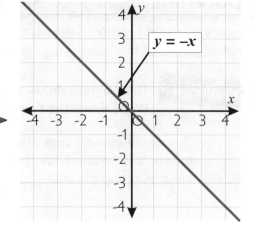

'$y = -x$' is the <u>main diagonal</u> that goes <u>DOWNHILL</u> from left to right.

The *x*- and *y*-coordinates of each point are <u>negatives of each other</u>, e.g. (–4, 4).

Simple lines you have to learn — it'll only take a second

Vertical line: $x = a$, horizontal line: $y = a$, main diagonals: $y = x$ and $y = -x$.
Say no more...

Straight-Line Graphs

Here are some more of the basic straight-line graphs that you really need to know:

Other **Sloping Lines** Through the Origin: '$y = ax$' and '$y = -ax$'

> $y = ax$ and $y = -ax$ are the equations for
> **A SLOPING LINE THROUGH THE ORIGIN.**

The value of 'a' (known as the <u>gradient</u>) tells you the steepness of the line.
The bigger 'a' is, the steeper the slope.
A <u>MINUS SIGN</u> tells you it slopes <u>DOWNHILL</u>.

See p81 for how to find a gradient.

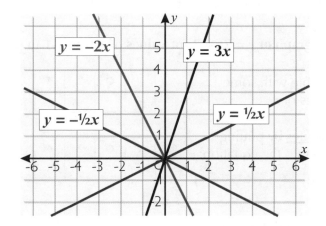

Learn to **Spot Straight Lines** from their **Equations**

All straight-line equations just contain '<u>something x, something y and a number</u>'.

EXAMPLE: **Decide whether each of the following are equations of straight lines.**

$$2y - 4x = 7 \qquad y = x^2 + 3 \qquad xy + 3 = 0$$

$$6y - 8 = x \qquad \frac{2}{y} - \frac{1}{x} = 7$$

Straight lines: $2y - 4x = 7$
                 $6y - 8 = x$

These equations only have <u>something x, something y</u> and <u>a number</u>. These 'terms' can be added or subtracted in any order.

Not straight lines: $y = x^2 + 3$
                     $xy + 3 = 0$
                     $\frac{2}{y} - \frac{1}{x} = 7$

'x^2', 'xy', '$2/y$' and '$1/x$' mean that these <u>aren't</u> straight-line equations.

Get it straight — which lines are straight (and which aren't)

The graphs $y = ax$ and $y = -ax$ are sloping lines just like $y = x$ and $y = -x$ on the last page.
The main thing to remember is that the "a" represents the gradient of the line.

Plotting Straight-Line Graphs

Drawing straight-line graphs is very likely to come up in the exam. We'll cover two methods on this page:

The 'Table of 3 Values' Method

You can easily draw the graph of
any equation using this easy method:

> 1) **Choose 3 values of x and draw up a table,**
> 2) **Work out the corresponding y-values,**
> 3) **Plot the coordinates, and draw the line.**

*Don't forget to use a ruler to draw your line
— you can lose exam marks if you don't.*

If it's a straight-line equation, the 3 points will be in a dead straight line with each other.
If they aren't, you need to go back and CHECK YOUR WORKING.

EXAMPLE: **Draw the graph of $y = 2x - 3$ for values of x from –1 to 4.**

1) Draw up a table with some
   suitable values of x.

x	0	2	4
y			

2) Find the y-values by putting
   each x-value into the equation:

   When $x = 4$, $y = 2x - 3$
   $= 2 \times 4 - 3 = \underline{5}$

x	0	2	4
y	–3	1	5

3) Plot the points and draw the line.

   The table gives the points (0, –3), (2, 1) and (4, 5)

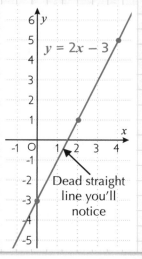

$y = 2x - 3$

Dead straight
line you'll
notice

The 'x = 0, y = 0' Method Ⓒ

> 1) **Set x = 0 in the equation, and find y** — this is where it **crosses the y-axis.**
> 2) **Set y = 0 in the equation and find x** — this is where it **crosses the x-axis.**
> 3) **Plot these two points and join them up with a straight line** — and just hope it
>   should be a straight line, since with only 2 points you can't really tell, can you!

EXAMPLE: **Draw the graph of $3x + 5y = 15$ between $x = -1$ and $x = 6$.**

*Only doing 2 points is risky
unless you're sure the equation
is definitely a straight line —
but then that's the big thrill of
living life on the edge...*

Putting $x = 0$ gives "$5y = 15$" $\Rightarrow y = 3$
Putting $y = 0$ gives "$3x = 15$" $\Rightarrow x = 5$

So plot (0, 3) and (5, 0) on the graph
and join them up with a straight line.

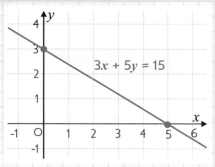

$3x + 5y = 15$

Plotting straight-line graphs is straightforward with these simple methods

This page gives you two simple methods for drawing straight-line graphs. It's a very popular topic
with examiners. If you learn the methods it'll be very popular with you too.

Finding the Gradient

Time to hit the slopes. Well, find them anyway...

Finding the *Gradient* Ⓒ

The <u>gradient</u> of a line is a measure of its <u>slope</u>. The <u>bigger</u> the number, the <u>steeper</u> the line.

 EXAMPLE: **Find the gradient of the straight line shown.**

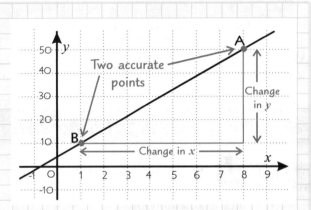

1) Find <u>two accurate points</u> and complete the triangle.

Both points should be in the upper right quadrant if possible (to keep all the numbers positive).

Two points that can be read accurately are:

Point A: (8, 50)   Point B: (1, 10)

2) Find the <u>change in y</u> and the <u>change in x</u>.

Change in y = 50 − 10 = <u>40</u>
Change in x = 8 − 1 = <u>7</u>

> Make sure you subtract the x-coordinates the <u>same way round</u> as you do the y-coordinates. E.g. y-coord. of pt A − y-coord. of pt B and x-coord. of pt A − x-coord. of pt B

3) <u>LEARN</u> this formula, and use it:

$$\text{GRADIENT} = \frac{\text{CHANGE IN Y}}{\text{CHANGE IN X}}$$

Gradient = $\frac{40}{7}$ = 5.71 (2 d.p.)

4) Check the <u>sign's</u> right.

If it slopes <u>uphill</u> left → right (⟋) then it's <u>positive</u>.
If it slopes <u>downhill</u> left → right (⟍) then it's <u>negative</u>.

As the graph goes uphill, the gradient is <u>positive</u>.
So the gradient is 5.71 (not −5.71)

> If you subtracted the coordinates the <u>right way round</u>, the sign should be correct. If it's not, go back and <u>check</u> your working.

<u>Step 4</u> catches a lot of folks out in exams. It's easy to divide, get a nice positive number and breathe a sigh of relief. You've <u>got</u> to check that sign.

Gradients are incredibly useful

It might seem unlikely but gradients are one of maths' most useful tools. The more maths you do, the more you come across. But even if you plan to do no maths after GCSE, you need them for the exam.

"y = mx + c"

Using '$y = mx + c$' is perhaps the 'proper' way of dealing with straight-line equations, and it's a nice trick if you can do it. The first thing you have to do though is <u>rearrange</u> the equation into the standard format like this:

Straight line:		Rearranged into '$y = mx + c$'	
$y = 2 + 3x$	$\rightarrow$	$y = 3x + 2$	(m = 3, c = 2)
$x - y = 0$	$\rightarrow$	$y = x + 0$	(m = 1, c = 0)
$4x - 3 = 5y$	$\rightarrow$	$y = 0.8x - 0.6$	(m = 0.8, c = -0.6)

<u>REMEMBER</u>:
'm' = gradient of the line
'c' = 'y-intercept' (where it hits the y-axis)

<u>WATCH OUT</u>: people mix up 'm' and 'c' when they get something like $y = 5 + 2x$. Remember, 'm' is the number <u>in front of the 'x'</u> and 'c' is the number <u>on its own</u>.

Sketching a **Straight Line** using y = mx + c

EXAMPLE: **Draw the graph of $y - 2x = 1$.**

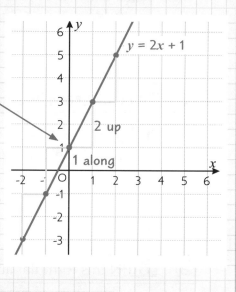

1) Get the equation into the form $y = mx + c$.

$y - 2x = 1 \rightarrow y = 2x + 1$

2) Put a dot on the <u>y-axis</u> at the <u>value of c</u>.

'c' = 1, so put a dot here.

3) Go <u>along 1 unit</u> and <u>up or down</u> by <u>m</u>. Make another dot, then repeat this step a few times in both directions.

Go <u>1 along</u> and <u>2 up</u> because 'm' = +2.

If 'm' was –2, you'd go down.

4) When you have 4 or 5 dots, draw a <u>straight line</u> through them.

5) Finally check that the <u>gradient</u> looks right.

A gradient of <u>+2</u> should be <u>quite steep</u> and <u>uphill</u> left to right — which it is, so it looks OK.

Finding the **Equation** of a Straight-Line **Graph**

This is the reverse process and is <u>easier</u>.

EXAMPLE: **Find the equation of the line on the graph in the form $y = mx + c$.**

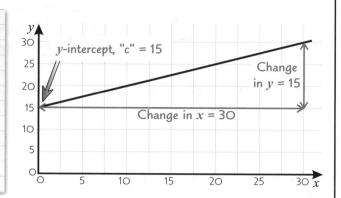

1) Find '<u>m</u>' (gradient) and '<u>c</u>' (y-intercept).

$$'m' = \frac{\text{change in } y}{\text{change in } x} = \frac{15}{30} = \frac{1}{2}$$

'c' = 15

2) Use these to write the equation in the form $y = mx + c$.

$$y = \frac{1}{2}x + 15$$

---

m is the gradient and c is the y-intercept

The key thing to remember is that m is the number in front of the x, and c is the number on its own. If you remember that, then $y = mx + c$ is a very easy way of sketching or identifying straight lines.

Parallel and Perpendicular Lines

You've just seen how to write the <u>equation of a straight line</u>. Well, you also have to be able to write the equation of a line that's <u>parallel</u> or <u>perpendicular</u> to the straight line you're given. The fun just never ends.

Parallel Lines Have the *Same Gradient* (B)

Parallel lines all have the <u>same gradient</u>, which means their $y = mx + c$ equations all have the same values of <u>m</u>.

So the lines: $y = 2x + 3$, $y = 2x$ and $y = 2x - 4$ are all parallel.

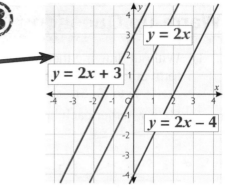

EXAMPLE: **Line J has a gradient of -0.25. Find the equation of Line K, which is parallel to Line J and passes through point (2, 3).**

1) Lines J and K are <u>parallel</u> so their <u>gradients</u> are the same $\Rightarrow$ m = −O.25

2) $y = -O.25x + c$

3) $x = 2$, $y = 3$
$3 = (-O.25 \times 2) + c \Rightarrow 3 = -O.5 + c$
$c = 3 + O.5 = 3.5$

4) $y = -O.25x + 3.5$

1) First find the '<u>m</u>' value for Line K.

2) Substitute the value for 'm' into <u>$y = mx + c$</u> to give you the 'equation so far'.

3) Substitute the <u>x and y values</u> for the given point on Line K and solve for '<u>c</u>'.

4) Write out the <u>full equation</u>.

Perpendicular Line Gradients (A)

<u>Perpendicular</u> lines are at <u>right angles</u> to each other. The product of their <u>gradients</u> is –1. So, if the gradient of the first line is <u>m</u>, the gradient of the other line will be $-\frac{1}{m}$, because $m \times -\frac{1}{m} = -1$.

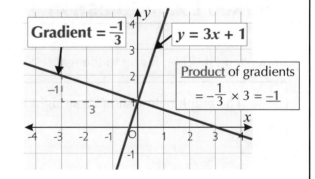

EXAMPLE: **Lines A and B are perpendicular and intersect at (3, 5). If Line A has the equation $3y - x = 6$, what is the equation of Line B?**

1) Find '<u>m</u>' (the gradient) for Line A.
$3y - x = 6 \Rightarrow 3y = x + 6$
$\Rightarrow y = \frac{1}{3}x + 2$, so $m_A = \frac{1}{3}$

2) Find the 'm' value for the <u>perpendicular</u> line (Line B).
$m_B = -\frac{1}{m_A} = -1 \div \frac{1}{3} = -3$

3) Put this into <u>$y = mx + c$</u> to give the 'equation so far'.
$y = -3x + c$

4) Put in the <u>x and y values</u> of the point and solve for '<u>c</u>'.
$x = 3$, $y = 5$ gives:
$5 = (-3 \times 3) + c$
$\Rightarrow 5 = -9 + c \Rightarrow c = 14$

5) Write out the full equation.
$y = -3x + 14$

Parallel lines have the same gradient

Perpendicular lines can be a little more tricky, so it's important that you remember that their gradients multiply together to give –1. Make sure the equation of your first line is in the form $y = mx + c$ before you try to find –1/m. You should practise finding 'c' using 'm' and a point on the line too.

Warm-up and Worked Exam Questions

On the day of the exam you'll have to know straight-line graphs like the back of your hand. If you struggle with any of the warm-up questions, go back over the section again before you go any further.

Warm-up Questions

1) Without drawing them, state whether the lines passing through the following points form a horizontal line, a vertical line, the line $y = x$ or the line $y = -x$.
   a) (1, 1) to (5, 5)   b) (0, 4) to (–3, 4)   c) (–1, 3) to (–1, 7)   d) (4, –4) to (–3, 3).

2) State whether each line below has a positive gradient, a negative gradient or no gradient.

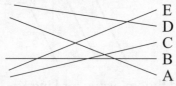

3) a) Plot the line $y = 3x - 4$.
   b) Describe the position of the line with equation $y = 3x + 2$ in relation to $y = 3x - 4$.

4) The equation of line S is $y = 2x - 3$.
   a) Find the equation of the line which is parallel to line S and passes through the point (0, 4).
   b) Find the gradient of a line which is perpendicular to S.

Worked Exam Question

You know the routine by now — work carefully through this example and make sure you understand it. Then it's on to the real test of doing some exam questions for yourself.

1   The graph below shows a straight line which passes through the points (2, 1) and (5, 7).

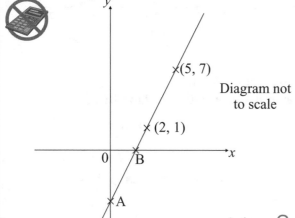

Diagram not to scale

a) Find the coordinates of A and B. **C**

First, find the equation of the line using $y = mx + c$:

$$m = \frac{7-1}{5-2} = 2$$

Using the point (2, 1):
$1 = (2 \times 2) + c$, so $c = -3$

Use the coordinates of a point you know to find c.

The equation of the line is $y = 2x - 3$

At A, $x = 0$:   At B, $y = 0$:
$y = 2(0) - 3$ $0 = 2x - 3$
$y = -3$ $x = 1.5$

A (........0........, ...–3........)   B (........1.5........, ...0........)

[4 marks]

b) Write down the equation of the line which is parallel to the line above and passes through the point (2, 10).   **B**

A line which is parallel to the line above will have the same gradient.

$m = 2$, so $y = 2x + c$

Then substitute in the x and y values of the point to find c.

$10 = (2 \times 2) + c$

$c = 10 - 4 = 6$

So $y = 2x + 6$

........$y = 2x + 6$........

[3 marks]

Exam Questions

2 The diagram below shows a straight line.

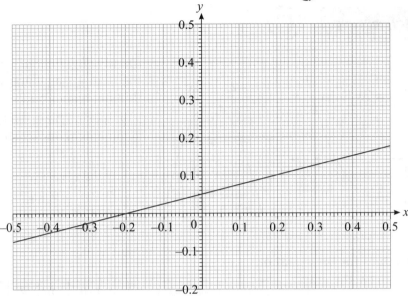

Find the equation of the line.

....
[3 marks]

3 Draw the graph $2y + x = 7$ on the axes below,
for values of x in the range $-2 \leq x \leq 10$.

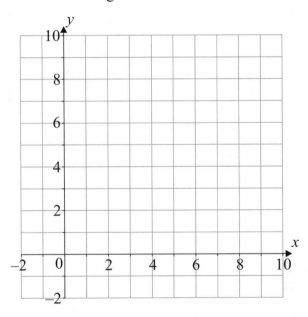

[3 marks]

4 The lines $y = 3x + 4$ and $y = 2x + 6$ intersect at the point M.
Line N goes through point M and is perpendicular to the line $y = 2x + 6$.
Find the equation of line N.

....
[5 marks]

Quadratic Graphs

As well as plotting straight line graphs (p80) you have to be able to plot quadratic graphs — and you need to know how to use them to solve quadratic equations too.

Plotting and Solving *Quadratics* Ⓒ

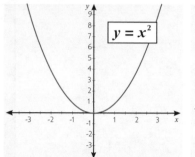

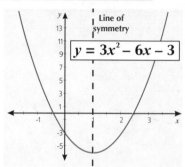

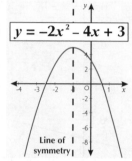

Quadratic functions are of the form $y = $ anything with x^2 (but not higher powers of x).

x^2 graphs all have the same symmetrical bucket shape.

If the x^2 bit has a '–' in front of it then the bucket is upside down.

EXAMPLE: **Complete the table of values for the equation $y = x^2 + 2x - 3$ and then draw the graph.**

x	–5	–4	–3	–2	–1	0	1	2	3
y	12	5	0	–3	–4	–3	0	5	12

1) Work out each *y*-value by substituting the corresponding *x*-value into the equation.

$$y = (-5)^2 + (2 \times -5) - 3$$
$$= 25 - 10 - 3 = 12$$

$$y = (2)^2 + (2 \times 2) - 3$$
$$= 4 + 4 - 3 = 5$$

To check you're doing it right, make sure you can reproduce the y-values they've already given you.

2) Plot the points and join them with a <u>completely smooth curve</u>. Definitely <u>DON'T</u> use a ruler.

<u>NEVER EVER</u> let one point drag your line off in some ridiculous direction. When a graph is generated from an equation, you never get spikes or lumps — only <u>MISTAKES</u>.

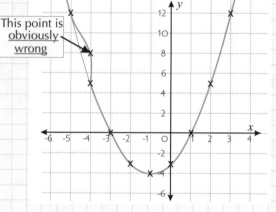

This point is <u>obviously wrong</u>

Solving Quadratic Equations Ⓑ

EXAMPLE: **Use the graph of $y = x^2 + 2x - 3$ to solve the equation $x^2 + 2x - 3 = 0$.**

The equation $x^2 + 2x - 3 = 0$ is what you get when you put $\underline{y = 0}$ into the graph's equation, $y = x^2 + 2x - 3$.

So to <u>solve</u> the equation, all you do is <u>read the *x*-values</u> where $y = 0$, i.e. where it crosses the *x*-axis.

So the solutions are $x = -3$ and $x = 1$.

Quadratic equations usually have 2 solutions.

Tables of values, plotting — easy marks, as long as you're accurate

Filling in tables of values and plotting graphs are easy questions, but too many people rush them and make silly errors. Take your time and get them right — if your curve isn't smooth, check the points in your table.

Harder Graphs

Graphs come in all sorts of shapes, sizes and wiggles — here's the first of four more types you need to know:

x^3 Graphs: $y = ax^3 + bx^2 + cx + d$ (b, c and/or d can be zero)

All x^3 graphs have a <u>wiggle</u> in the middle — sometimes it's a flat wiggle, sometimes it's more pronounced. $-x^3$ graphs always go down from <u>top left</u>, $+x^3$ ones go up from <u>bottom left</u>.

Note that x^3 must be the highest power and there must be no other bits like $1/x$ etc.

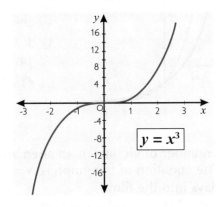

$y = x^3$

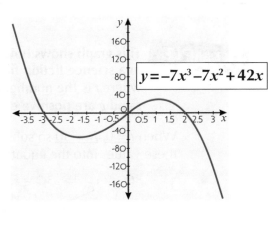

$y = -7x^3 - 7x^2 + 42x$

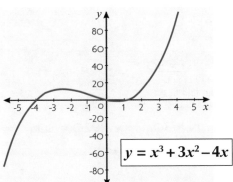

$y = x^3 + 3x^2 - 4x$

EXAMPLE: **Draw the graph of $y = x^3 + 4x^2$ for values of x between -5 and $+2$.**

1 Start by making a <u>table of values</u>.

x	-5	-4	-3	-2	-1	0	1	2
$y = x^3 + 4x^2$	-25	0	9	8	3	0	5	24

2 Plot the points and join them with a lovely <u>smooth curve</u>. <u>DON'T</u> use your ruler — that would be a trifle daft.

A wiggle tells you it's an x^3 graph

The good news about the graphs over the next couple of pages is that they all have distinct shapes (like the x^3 wiggle) — so it should be pretty easy to work out which is which.

Harder Graphs

k^x Graphs: $y = k^x$ or $y = k^{-x}$ (k is some positive number)

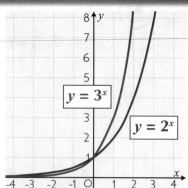

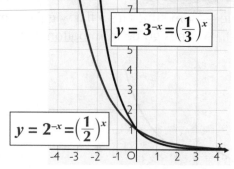

1) These 'exponential' graphs are always above the x-axis, and always go through the point (0, 1).

2) If $k > 1$ and the power is +ve, the graph curves upwards.

3) If k is between 0 and 1 OR the power is negative, then the graph is flipped horizontally.

EXAMPLE: This graph shows how the number of victims of an alien virus (N) increases in a science fiction film. The equation of the graph is $N = fg^t$, where t is the number of days into the film. f and g are positive constants. Find the values of f and g.

When $t = 0$, $N = 30$ so substitute these values into the equation:

$$30 = fg^0 \Rightarrow 30 = f \times 1 \Rightarrow \underline{f = 30}$$

$g^0 = 1$, so you can find f.

Substitute in $t = 3$, $N = 1920$: $N = 30g^t \Rightarrow 1920 = 30g^3 \Rightarrow g = \sqrt[3]{64} \Rightarrow \underline{g = 4}$

(3, 1920)

30

1/x (Reciprocal) Graphs: $y = A/x$ or $xy = A$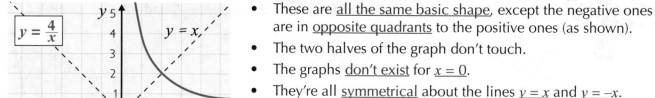

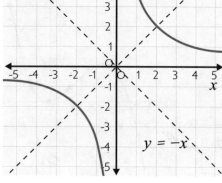

$y = \dfrac{4}{x}$

$y = x$

$y = -x$

- These are all the same basic shape, except the negative ones are in opposite quadrants to the positive ones (as shown).
- The two halves of the graph don't touch.
- The graphs don't exist for $x = 0$.
- They're all symmetrical about the lines $y = x$ and $y = -x$.

(You get this type of graph with inverse proportion — see p72)

$y = -\dfrac{4}{x}$

$y = x$

$y = -x$

---

k^x graphs always pass through (0, 1)

You need to be able to recognise the basic shape of each graph. Then learn the key facts about each type. Remember — graphs of $y = A/x$ don't exist when $x = 0$ (because you can't divide by 0).

Harder Graphs

Here's the final graph type you need to be able to sketch (well, there are actually two different graphs on this page, but they're pretty much the same shape — once you know the shape of one, you know the shape of the other). These are both trig graphs — there's more on trigonometry in Section Five.

Sine 'Waves' and Cos 'Buckets'

1) The underlying shape of the sin and cos graphs is <u>identical</u> — they both wiggle between <u>y-limits of exactly +1 and –1</u>.

2) The only difference is that the <u>sin graph</u> is <u>shifted right by 90°</u> compared to the cos graph.

3) <u>For 0° – 360°</u>, the shapes you get are a <u>Sine 'Wave'</u> (one peak, one trough) and a <u>Cos 'Bucket'</u> (starts at the top, dips, and finishes at the top).

4) The key to drawing the extended graphs is to first draw the 0° – 360° cycle of either the <u>Sine 'WAVE'</u> or the <u>Cos 'BUCKET'</u> and then <u>repeat it</u> as shown. You can also repeat it for values of x <u>greater than 360°</u> or <u>less than –360°</u>.

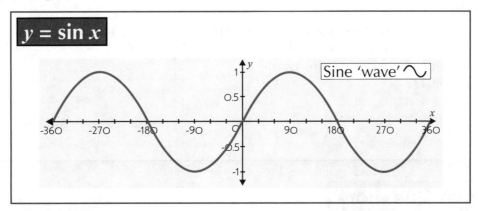

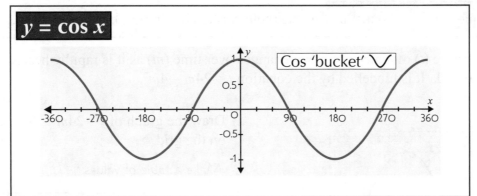

5) You might have to <u>read off</u> solutions from a sin or cos graph — you do this in exactly the same way as you would for any other graph, but you'll usually end up with <u>more than one</u> value.

6) You'll be given a <u>range</u> over which to find your solutions (e.g. $0° \leq x \leq 360°$) — otherwise you'd end up with an <u>infinite</u> number of solutions because the pattern keeps <u>repeating</u>.

7) So if you were asked to solve $\cos x = 0.5$ in the range $0° \leq x \leq 360°$, you'd draw the <u>horizontal line</u> $y = 0.5$ and read off the x-values where it crosses the curve $y = \cos x$. The solutions in the <u>given range</u> are $x = 60°$ and $x = 300°$ (try it for yourself on the graph above to see how it works).

Be careful with the range — if you'd been asked to find the solutions in the range $-360° \leq x \leq 360°$, you'd end up with 4 solutions (–300°, –60°, 60° and 300°).

Four different graph shapes — do a quick sketch of each to be sure

All the graphs over the last three pages look quite different — so you should be able to recognise the general shapes as easy as pie (though quite how easy pie is, I have no idea).

Warm-up and Worked Exam Questions

The warm-up questions run quickly over the basic facts you'll need in the exam. The exam questions come later — but unless you've learnt the facts first you'll find the exams tougher than stale bread.

Warm-up Questions

1) a) Complete the table of values for $y = x^2 - 2x - 1$.

x	–2	–1	0	1	2	3	4	5
y								

   b) Plot the x and y values from the table and join the points up to form a smooth curve.
   c) Use your curve to find the value of y when $x = 3.5$.
   d) Find the two values of x when $y = 5$.

2) Draw the graph of $y = x^2 - 3x$ for values of x from –2 to 5.
   Use your graph to solve the following equations.
   a) $x^2 - 3x = 0$.
   b) $x^2 - 3x = 3$.

3) To the right is the graph of $y = \cos x$ for $0° \leq x \leq 360°$
   As shown on the graph, $\cos 50° = 0.643$.
   Give another value of x, found on this graph,
   where $\cos x = 0.643$.

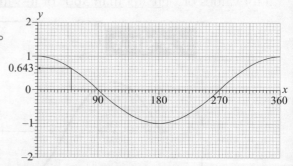

Worked Exam Question

Wow, an exam question — with the answers helpfully written in. It must be your birthday.

1 The temperature (t) of a piece of metal changes over time (m) as it is rapidly heated and then cooled. It is modelled by the equation $t = 24m - 4m^2$.

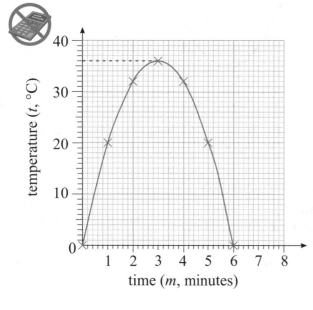

a) Draw the graph of $t = 24m - 4m^2$ **C** on the grid.

   Make a table of values:

m	0	1	2	3	4	5	6
t	0	20	32	36	32	20	0

   Plot these points on the graph and draw a smooth curve through them.

   [2 marks]

b) Using the graph, estimate the maximum **B** temperature of the piece of metal.

   Read across to the temperature from the highest point on the graph.

   ....36.................. °C
   [1 mark]

Exam Questions

2 This question is about the function $y = x^3 - 4x^2 + 4$. Ⓑ

a) Complete the table below.

x	−1	−0.5	0	0.5	1	1.5	2	2.5	3	3.5	4
y	−1	2.875	4	3.125	1	−1.625	−4				

[2 marks]

b) Use your table to draw the graph of $y = x^3 - 4x^2 + 4$ on the grid, for values of x in the range $-1 \leq x \leq 4$.

[2 marks]

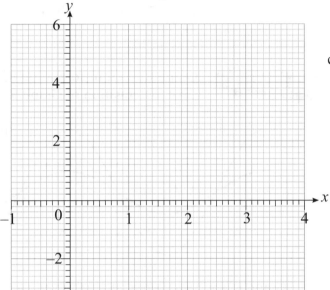

c) Estimate the solutions of the equation $x^3 - 4x^2 + 4 = 0$.

....
[1 mark]

Don't use a ruler to join up the dots in curved graphs.

3 Sketches of different graphs are shown below. Ⓐ

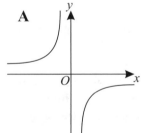

A

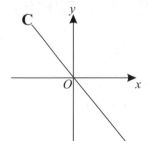

B

C

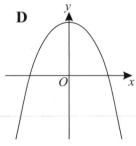

D

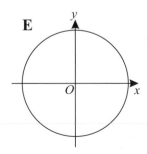

E

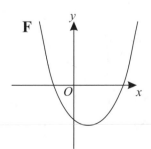

F

Match each equation below to one of the graphs above.

a) $y = 3x^2 - 6x - 3$ ....

b) $y = -\dfrac{4}{x}$ ....

c) $y = x^3 - 6x + 13$ ....

[3 marks]

Graph Transformations

Don't be put off by <u>function notation</u> involving f(x). It doesn't mean anything complicated, it's just a fancy way of saying "an equation in x". In other words "y = f(x)" just means "y = some totally mundane equation in x, which we won't tell you, we'll just call it f(x) instead to see how many of you get in a flap about it".

Learn These **Five Types** of **Graph Transformation**

In a question on transforming graphs they will either use <u>function notation</u> or they'll use a <u>known function</u> instead. There aren't many different types of graph transformations so just learn them and be done with it.

1) *y-Stretch*: $y = k \times f(x)$

This is where the original graph is <u>stretched parallel to the y-axis</u> by multiplying the whole function by a number, i.e. $y = f(x)$ becomes $y = kf(x)$ (where $k = 2$ or 5 etc.).
If k is less than 1, then the graph is <u>squashed down</u> in the y-direction instead:

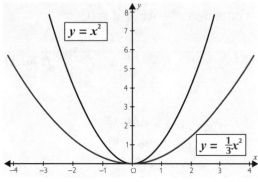

This graph shows $y = f(x)$ and $y = \frac{1}{3}f(x)$
($y = x^2$ and $y = \frac{1}{3}x^2$)

EXAMPLE: **Graph R is a transformation of $y = \sin(x)$. Give the equation of Graph R.**

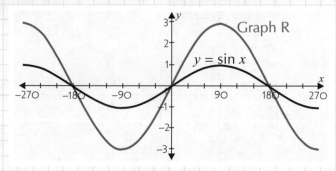

Graph R is $y = \sin x$ <u>stretched in the vertical direction</u>. $y = \sin x$ 'wiggles' between 1 and –1 on the y-axis and Graph R 'wiggles' between 3 and –3, so the stretch has a <u>scale factor of 3</u>.

So the equation of Graph R is $y = 3 \sin x$

2) *y-Shift*: $y = f(x) + a$

This is where the whole graph is <u>slid up or down</u> the y-axis <u>with no distortion</u>, and is achieved by simply <u>adding a number</u> onto the <u>end</u> of the equation: $y = f(x) + a$.

This shows $y = f(x)$ and $y = f(x) - 3$
i.e. $y = \sin x$ and $y = (\sin x) - 3$

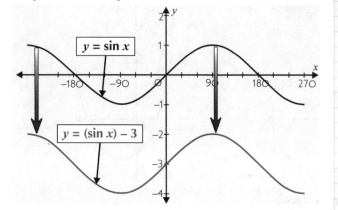

EXAMPLE: **Below is the graph of $y = f(x)$.**
Write down the coordinates of the minimum point of the graph with equation $y = f(x) + 5$.

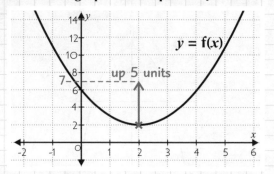

The minimum point of $y = f(x)$ has coordinates (2, 2). $y = f(x) + 5$ is the same shape graph, <u>slid 5 units up</u>. So the minimum point of $y = f(x) + 5$ is at **(2, 7)**.

Graph Transformations

Keep going, this is the last page on graph transformations. Promise.

3) *x-Shift*: *y = f(x − a)*

This is where the whole graph <u>slides to the left or right</u> and it only happens when you replace '<u>x</u>' everywhere in the equation <u>with '$x - a$'</u>. These are tricky because they go '<u>the wrong way</u>'. If you want to go from $y = f(x)$ to $y = f(x - a)$ you must move the whole graph a distance 'a' in the <u>positive</u> x-direction → (and vice versa).

EXAMPLE: **The graph $y = f(x)$ is shown. Give the coordinates of the points where the graph $y = f(x + 5)$ will cross the x-axis.**

$y = f(x + 5)$ is $y = f(x)$ shifted in the <u>negative</u> x direction.

$y = f(x)$ crosses the x-axis at:

(-2, O), (O, O) and (2, O).

So $y = f(x + 5)$ will cross at:

(-7, O), (-5, O) and (-3, O).

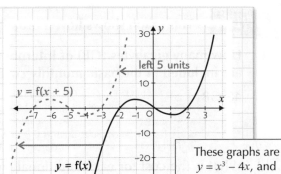

These graphs are $y = x^3 - 4x$, and $y = (x+5)^3 - 4(x+5)$. Notice that <u>both</u> x's are replaced by $x + 5$.

4) *x-Stretch*: *y = f(kx)*

These go '<u>the wrong way</u>' too — when k is a '<u>multiplier</u>' it <u>scrunches the graph up</u>, whereas when it's a '<u>divider</u>', it <u>stretches the graph out</u>. (The opposite of the y-stretch.)

EXAMPLE: **Sketch the graph $y = \sin 4x$ for $0° \leq x \leq 360°$. The graph of $y = \sin x$ is shown.**

$y = \sin 4x$ has a <u>multiplier of 4</u>, so its graph will be <u>4 times as squashed up</u> as $y = \sin x$.

There is <u>one</u> cycle of up and down on the $y = \sin x$ graph, so you can fit <u>four</u> cycles of the $y = \sin 4x$ graph in the same space.

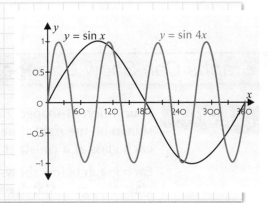

Remember, if k is a <u>divider</u>, then the graph <u>spreads out</u>. So if the squashed-up graph was the original, $y = f(x)$, then the more spread out one would be $y = f(\frac{x}{4})$.

5) *Reflections*: *y = −f(x) and y = f(−x)*

$y = -f(x)$ is the <u>reflection</u> in the <u>x-axis</u> of $y = f(x)$.

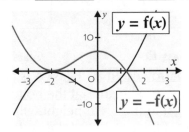

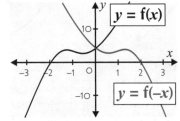

$y = f(-x)$ is the <u>reflection</u> in the <u>y-axis</u> of $y = f(x)$.

Remember f(x) just means an equation in x

Graphs can be stretched or squashed along the y-axis by multiplying the whole function by a number, and stretched or squashed along the x-axis when x is replaced with kx. They can slide up or down by adding a number to the whole function, and slide left or right when x is replaced with $x - a$.

Real-Life Graphs

Now and then, graphs mean something more interesting than just $y = x^3 + 4x^2 - 6x + 4$...

Graphs Can Show **Billing Structures**

Many bills are made up of two charges — a <u>fixed charge</u> and a <u>cost per unit</u>. E.g. You might pay £11 each month for your phone line, and then be charged 3p for each minute of calls you make. This type of thing is <u>perfect exam question fodder</u>.

EXAMPLE: This graph shows how a broadband bill is calculated.

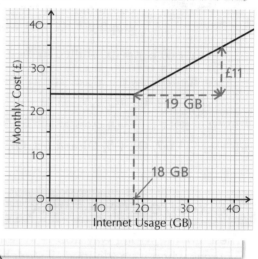

a) How many gigabytes (GB) of Internet usage are included in the basic monthly cost?

18 GB

The first section of the graph is <u>horizontal</u>. You're charged £24 even if you <u>don't</u> use the Internet during the month. It's only after you've used <u>18 GB</u> that the bill starts rising.

b) What is the cost for each additional gigabyte (to the nearest 1p)?

Gradient of sloped section = cost per GB

$$\frac{\text{vertical change}}{\text{horizontal change}} = \frac{11}{19} = £0.5789... \text{ per GB}$$

To the nearest 1p this is £0.58

No matter what the graph, the gradient is always the y-axis unit per the x-axis unit.

Graphs Can Show **Changes with Time** Ⓑ

EXAMPLE: Four different-shaped glasses containing juice are shown on the right. The juice is siphoned out of each glass at a constant rate.

Each graph below shows how the height of juice in one glass changes. Match each graph to the correct glass.

 A steeper slope means that the juice height is changing faster.

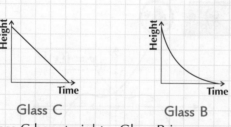

Glass C — **Glass C** has <u>straight sides</u>, so the juice height falls steadily.

Glass B — **Glass B** is <u>narrowest at the top</u>, so the juice height falls <u>fastest at first</u>.

Glass D — **Glass D** is <u>narrowest in the middle</u>, so the height will fall <u>fastest</u> in the <u>middle part</u> of the graph.

Glass A — **Glass A** is <u>narrowest at the bottom</u>, so the height will fall <u>fastest</u> at the end of the graph.

Always think carefully about what the gradient means

Distance-time graphs and unit conversion graphs are real-life graphs too — see p128 and p130.

Warm-up and Worked Exam Questions

Warm-up Questions

1) Graphs are drawn showing the functions $y = f(x)$ and $y = f(x) + 2$.
   Describe how the shape and position of the two graphs are related.

2) Each of the vessels below is filled with water at a constant rate.

1	2	3	4

Each of these graphs show the depth of water within a vessel in relation to time.

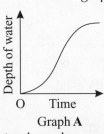 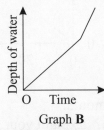 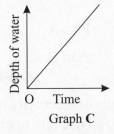 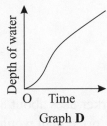

Graph **A**	Graph **B**	Graph **C**	Graph **D**

Match each vessel with the correct graph.

Worked Exam Question

Exam questions don't tend to vary that wildly, the basic format is almost always the same.
So you'd be mad not to spend a bit of time learning how to answer a common question wouldn't you...

1 The graph of $y = \sin x$ for $0° \leq x \leq 360°$ is shown on the grids below. (**A***)

a) On this grid sketch the graph of $y = \sin \dfrac{x}{2}$

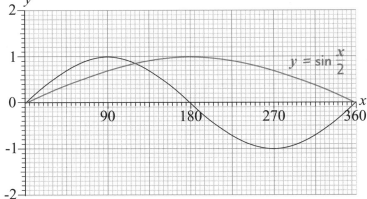

Since x has been replace by $\dfrac{x}{2}$, the new graph will be twice as stretched out as the original one.

[1 mark]

b) On this grid sketch the graph of $y = 2 \sin x$

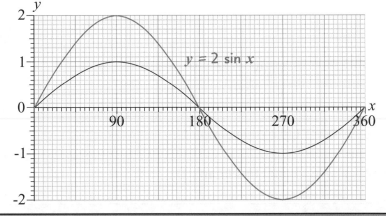

Here, the graph is stretched vertically by a factor of 2, so instead of 'wiggling' between 1 and −1 on the y-axis, it 'wiggles' between 2 and −2.

[1 mark]

Exam Questions

2 An electricity company offers its customers two different price plans.

Plan **A:**
Monthly tariff of £18,
plus 10p for each unit used.

Plan **B:**
No monthly tariff, just pay
40p for each unit used.

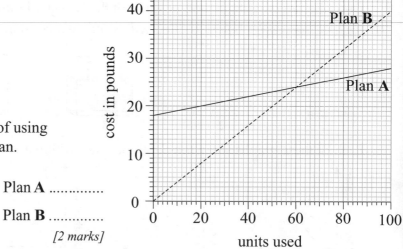

a) Use the graph to find the cost of using
   70 units in a month for each plan.

Plan **A** ....

Plan **B** ....

[2 marks]

*b) Mr Barker uses about 85 units of electricity each month.
    Which price plan would you advise him to choose? Explain your answer.

....

....
[2 marks]

3 The diagram below shows a sketch of $y = f(x)$. Ⓐ*
   Graph **B** is a translation of $y = f(x)$.

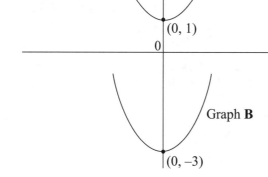

a) Write down the equation of
   Graph **B** in terms of $f(x)$.

$y =$ ....
[1 mark]

b) Find the minimum point of the graph of $y = f(x + 2)$.

(................. , ...)
[2 marks]

c) Find the minimum point of the graph of $y = f(x - 4) + 1$.

(................. , ...)
[2 marks]

d) Sketch $y = f(x) - 2$ on the axes above. Label this Graph **C**.
[1 mark]

e) Sketch $y = f(x + 3)$ on the axes above. Label this Graph **D**.
[1 mark]

Revision Questions for Section Three

Well, that wraps up <u>Section Three</u> — time to put yourself to the test and find out <u>how much you really know</u>.
* Try these questions and <u>tick off each one</u> when you <u>get it right</u>.
* When you've done <u>all the questions</u> for a topic and are <u>completely happy</u> with it, tick off the topic.

<u>X, Y and Z Coordinates (p77)</u> ☑

1) Find the midpoint of a line segment with end points (–2, 3) and (7, –4).

2) Give the coordinates of point A and point B on the diagram on the right.

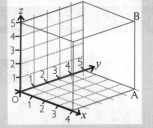

<u>Straight-Line Graphs and their Gradients (p78-81)</u> ☑

3) Sketch the lines a) $y = -x$, b) $y = -4$, c) $x = 2$

4) What does a straight-line equation look like?

5) Use the 'table of three values' method to draw the graph $y = x + \frac{1}{10}x$

6) Use the '$x = 0$, $y = 0$' method to draw the graph $y = 3x + 5$.

7) What does a line with a negative gradient look like?

8) Find the gradient of the line on the right.

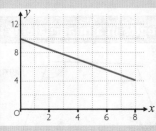

<u>y = mx + c and Parallel and Perpendicular Lines (p82-83)</u> ☑

9) What do 'm' and 'c' represent in $y = mx + c$?

10) Draw the graph of $5x = 2 + y$ using the '$y = mx + c$' method.

11) Find the equation of the graph on the right.

12) How are the gradients of perpendicular lines related?
    And how are the gradients of parallel lines related?

13) Find the equation of the line passing through (4, 2)
    which is perpendicular to $y = 2x - 1$.

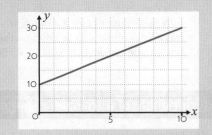

<u>Other Graphs (p86-89)</u> ☑

14) Describe the shapes of the graphs $y = x^2 + 2x - 8$ and $y = -x^2 + 2x - 8$.

15) Plot the graph $y = x^2 + 2x - 8$ and use it to estimate the solutions to $-2 = x^2 + 2x - 8$ (to 1 d.p).

16) Describe in words and with a sketch the forms of these graphs:
    a) $y = ax^3 + bx^2 + cx + d$ $(a > 0)$;   b) $xy = a$ $(a > 0)$;   c) $y = k^x$ $(k > 0)$.

17) The graph of $y = bc^x$ goes through (2, 16) and (3, 128).
    Given that b and c are positive constants, find their values.

<u>Graph Transformations (p92-93)</u> ☑

18) What are the five types of graph transformation you need to learn and how does
    the equation $y = f(x)$ change for each of them?

19) Describe how each of the following graphs differs from the graph of $y = x^3 + 1$
    a) $y = (-x)^3 + 1$,   b) $y = (x + 2)^3 + 1$,   c) $y = (3x)^3 + 1$,   d) $y = x^3 - 1$

<u>Real-Life Graphs (p94)</u> ☑

20) Sweets'R'Yum sells chocolate drops. They charge 90p per 100 g for the first kg,
    then 60p per 100 g after that. Sketch a graph to show the cost of buying up to
    3 kg of chocolate drops.

Geometry

If you know <u>all</u> these rules <u>thoroughly</u>, you'll at least have a fighting chance of working out problems with lines and angles. If you don't — you've no chance. Sorry to break it to you like that.

6 Simple Rules — *that's all*

1) Angles in a <u>triangle</u> add up to 180°

$a + b + c = 180°$

2) Angles on a <u>straight line</u> add up to 180°

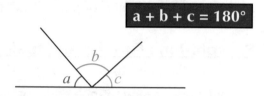

$a + b + c = 180°$

3) Angles in a <u>quadrilateral</u> add up to 360°

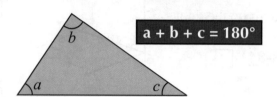

Remember that a quadrilateral is a 4-sided shape.

$a + b + c + d = 360°$

You can <u>see why</u> this is if you split the quadrilateral into <u>two triangles</u> along a <u>diagonal</u>. Each triangle has angles adding up to 180°, so the two together have angles adding up to 180° + 180° = 360°.

4) Angles <u>round a point</u> add up to 360°

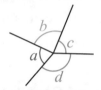

$a + b + c + d = 360°$

5) <u>Exterior angle</u> of a triangle = <u>sum</u> of <u>opposite interior angles</u>

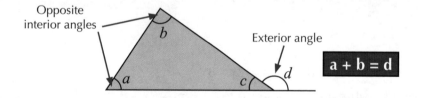

Opposite interior angles

Exterior angle

$a + b = d$

There's a nice easy proof of this:
$a + b + c = 180°$ (angles in a triangle) and
$c + d = 180°$ (angles on a straight line),
so $a + b = d$.

6) <u>Isosceles triangles</u> have <u>2 sides</u> the same and <u>2 angles</u> the same

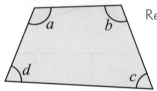

These dashes indicate two sides the <u>same length</u>.

These angles are the <u>same</u>.

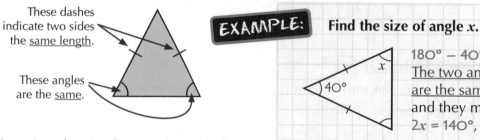

EXAMPLE: **Find the size of angle *x*.**

$180° - 40° = 140°$
<u>The two angles on the right are the same</u> (they're both *x*)
and they must add up to 140°, so
$2x = 140°$, which means $x = 70°$.

In an isosceles triangle, you only need to know one angle to be able to find the other two.

Six simple rules, make sure you LEARN THEM...

Scribble them down again and again until they're ingrained in your brain (or desk).
The basic facts are pretty easy really, but examiners like to combine them in questions to confuse you — if you've learnt them all you've got a much better chance of spotting which ones you need.

Parallel Lines

Parallel lines are quite straightforward really. (They're also quite straight. And parallel.)
There are a few rules you need to learn — make sure you don't get them mixed up.

Angles Around **Parallel Lines**

When a line crosses two parallel lines, it forms special sets of angles.

1) The two bunches of angles formed at the points of
    intersection are the same.

2) There are only actually two different angles involved
    (labelled a and b here), and they add up to 180°
    (from rule 2 on the previous page).

3) Vertically opposite angles (ones opposite each other) are equal
    (in the diagram, a and a are vertically opposite, as are b and b).

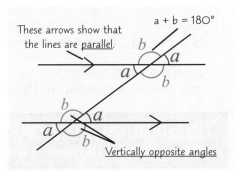

These arrows show that the lines are parallel.

$a + b = 180°$

Vertically opposite angles

Alternate, Interior and Corresponding Angles

The diagram above has some characteristic shapes to look out for — and each shape contains a
specific pair of angles. The angle pairs are known as alternate, interior and corresponding angles.

You need to spot the characteristic Z, C, U and F shapes:

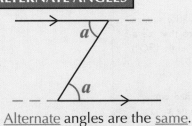

ALTERNATE ANGLES

Alternate angles are the same.
They are found in a Z-shape.

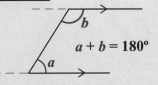
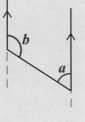

INTERIOR ANGLES

$a + b = 180°$

Interior angles add up to 180°.
They are found in a C- or U-shape.

Interior angles are sometimes
called allied angles

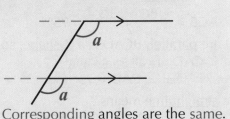

CORRESPONDING ANGLES

Corresponding angles are the same.
They are found in an F-shape.

EXAMPLE: **Find the size of angle x.**

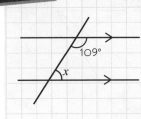

109°

x

This diagram shows interior
angles (look out for the
characteristic C-shape).

Interior angles add up to 180°,
so $x + 109° = 180°$,
which means $x = 71°$

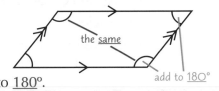

the same

add to 180°

Parallelograms are quadrilaterals made from two sets of parallel lines.
You can use the properties above to show that opposite angles in a
parallelogram are equal, and each pair of neighbouring angles add up to 180°.

Parallel lines are key things to look out for in geometry

Watch out for parallel lines and Z, C, U and F shapes — extending the lines can make spotting them easier.
Learn the proper names (alternate, interior and corresponding angles) as you have to use them in the exam.

Geometry Problems

Once you've learnt <u>all</u> of the <u>geometry rules</u> on the last two pages you can have a go at using them:

Try Out *All The Rules* One By One

1) <u>Don't</u> concentrate too much on the angle you have been asked to find. The best method is to find <u>ALL</u> the angles in <u>whatever order</u> they become obvious.

2) <u>Don't</u> sit there waiting for inspiration to hit you. It's all too easy to find yourself staring at a geometry problem and <u>getting nowhere</u>. The method is this:

> **<u>GO THROUGH ALL THE RULES OF GEOMETRY</u> (including <u>PARALLEL LINES</u>), <u>ONE BY ONE</u>, and apply each of them in turn <u>in as many ways as possible</u> — one of them is bound to work.**

3) Before we get going, there's one bit of <u>notation</u> you need to be familiar with — <u>three-letter angle notation</u>. It's not hard — if you get an angle written as ∠ABC (or just ABC), it's the angle formed at letter <u>B</u> (it's always the middle letter).

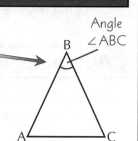

EXAMPLE: **Find the size of angles *x* and *y*.**

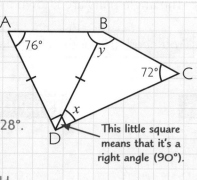

Write down everything you know (or can work out) about the shape:

Triangle ABD is <u>isosceles</u>, so ∠BAD = ∠ABD = 76°.
That means ∠ADB = 180° − 76° − 76° = 28°.
∠ADC is a right angle (= 90°), so angle *x* = 90° − 28° = 62°

ABCD is a <u>quadrilateral</u>, so all the angles <u>add up to 360°</u>. 76° + 90° + *y* + 72° = 360°, so *y* = 360° − 76° − 90° − 72° = 122°

This little square means that it's a right angle (90°).

You could have worked out angle y before angle x.

EXAMPLE: **Find all the missing angles in the diagram below.**

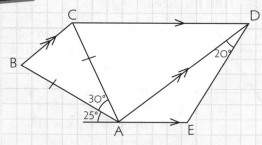

1) Triangle ABC is <u>isosceles</u>, so...
    $$\angle ABC = \angle ACB = \frac{(180° - 30°)}{2} = 75°$$

2) BC and AD are <u>parallel</u>, BCAD is a <u>Z-shape</u>, so... ∠ACB and ∠CAD are <u>alternate angles</u>. As ∠ACB = 75° then ∠CAD = 75° too.

3) Angles on a <u>straight line</u> means... ∠EAD = 180° − 25° − 30° − 75° = 50°

4) AE and CD are <u>parallel</u> so ∠ADC = ∠EAD = 50°

5) Angles in triangle ACD add up to <u>180°</u> so ∠ACD = 180° − 75° − 50° = 55°

6) Angles in triangle ADE add up to <u>180°</u> so ∠AED = 180° − 50° − 20° = 110°

The most important rule of all — don't panic

Geometry problems often look a lot worse than they are — don't panic, just write down everything you can work out. You'll need all the rules from the last two pages so make sure they're clear in your head. Watch out for parallel lines and isosceles triangles too — they can help you work out angles.

Polygons

A <u>polygon</u> is a <u>many-sided shape</u>, and can be regular or irregular. A <u>regular</u> polygon is one where all the sides and angles are the <u>same</u> (in an <u>irregular</u> polygon, the sides and angles are <u>different</u>).

Regular Polygons

You need to be familiar with the first few <u>regular polygons</u> — ones with up to <u>10 sides</u>. You need to know their <u>names</u> and how many <u>sides</u> they have (remember that all the <u>sides</u> and <u>angles</u> in a regular polygon are the <u>same</u>).

EQUILATERAL TRIANGLE
3 sides

SQUARE (regular quadrilateral)
4 sides

PENTAGON
5 sides

HEXAGON
6 sides

HEPTAGON
7 sides

OCTAGON
8 sides

NONAGON
9 sides

DECAGON
10 sides

Interior and *Exterior* Angles Ⓓ

Questions on <u>interior</u> and <u>exterior angles</u> often come up in exams — so you need to know <u>what</u> they are and <u>how to find them</u>. There are a couple of <u>formulas</u> you need to learn as well.

For <u>ANY POLYGON</u> (regular or irregular):

Exterior angle

Interior angle

SUM OF EXTERIOR ANGLES = 360°

SUM OF INTERIOR ANGLES = (n − 2) × 180°
(n is the number of sides)

This is because a polygon can be divided up into (n − 2) triangles, and the sum of angles in a triangle is 180°. Try it for yourself on the polygons above.

For <u>REGULAR POLYGONS</u> only:

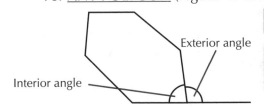 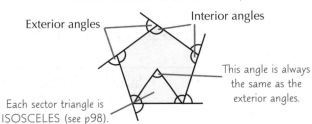

Exterior angles

Interior angles

This angle is always the same as the exterior angles.

Each sector triangle is ISOSCELES (see p98).

EXTERIOR ANGLE = $\frac{360°}{n}$

INTERIOR ANGLE = 180° − EXTERIOR ANGLE

EXAMPLE: The interior angle of a regular polygon is 165°. How many sides does the polygon have?

First, find the <u>exterior angle</u> of the shape: exterior angle = 180° − 165° = 15°

Use this value to find the <u>number of sides</u>: exterior angle = $\frac{360°}{n}$ so n = $\frac{360°}{\text{exterior angle}}$ = $\frac{360°}{15°}$ = 24 sides

Four very simple and very important formulas

There are all sorts of questions they can ask on angles in polygons, but you can answer them all with the four formulas here — check you've learnt them and you know which ones go with regular and irregular polygons.

Symmetry

This page is pretty straightforward, but you still need to <u>learn</u> it. So, there are <u>two types</u> of symmetry:

Symmetry

Line Symmetry

This is where you draw one or more <u>MIRROR LINES</u> across a shape and both sides will <u>fold exactly</u> together. A <u>regular polygon</u> (see previous page) has the same number of <u>lines of symmetry</u> as the number of <u>sides</u>.

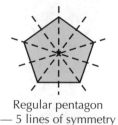
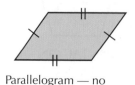
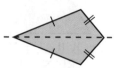

Regular pentagon — 5 lines of symmetry

Parallelogram — no lines of symmetry

Rhombus — 2 lines of symmetry

Kite — 1 line of symmetry

Rotational Symmetry

This is where you can <u>rotate</u> the shape into different positions that <u>look exactly the same</u>. Again, <u>regular polygons</u> have the same <u>order of rotational symmetry</u> as <u>number of sides</u>.

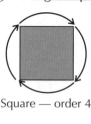

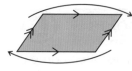
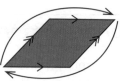

Square — order 4

Regular hexagon — order 6

Parallelogram — order 2

Rhombus — order 2

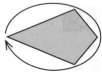

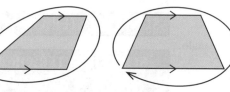

Kite — order 1

Trapezium — order 1

If a shape has only 1 position, you can either say 'order 1 symmetry' or 'no rotational symmetry'.

Symmetry of Triangles

<u>Triangles</u> crop up all the time in geometry questions, so it pays to learn <u>as much as you can</u> about them. Take note of the <u>symmetry</u> properties of the <u>different types</u> of triangle:

EQUILATERAL Triangle	RIGHT-ANGLED Triangle	ISOSCELES Triangle	SCALENE Triangle
		2 sides and 2 angles equal	No sides or angles equal
	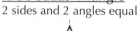		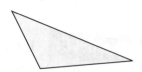
<u>3 lines</u> of symmetry. Rotational symmetry <u>order 3</u>.	<u>No lines</u> of symmetry (unless the angles are <u>45°</u> — then it's isosceles). Rotational symmetry <u>order 1</u>.	<u>1 line</u> of symmetry. Rotational symmetry <u>order 1</u>.	<u>No lines</u> of symmetry. Rotational symmetry <u>order 1</u>.

There are two types of symmetry to learn

This is a nice easy page — but make sure you learn the key facts. You need to get some practice too — for example, try drawing a shape with 5 lines of symmetry, or a shape with rotational symmetry of order 6.

Warm-up and Worked Exam Questions

Oh look at all those lovely big diagrams. But don't just look at them — you need to work through them one by one and make sure that you've remembered all those rules...

Warm-up Questions

1) Write down the sum of the angles in a triangle.

2) Find the missing angles *a-d* below. State any angle laws used.

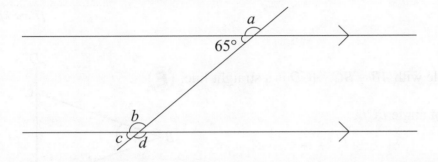

3) How many sides does a hexagon have?

4) Write down the name of this shape:

5) A regular polygon has an exterior angle of 24°. How many sides does it have?

Worked Exam Question

There'll probably be a question in the exam that asks you to find angles. That means you have to remember all the different angle rules and practise using them in the right places...

1 *DEF* and *BEC* are straight lines that cross at *E*. *AFB* and *AC* are perpendicular to each other.

a) Find angle *x*.
   Give a reason for each stage of your working.

   Angles on a straight line add up to 180°, so angle FEC = 180° − 14° = 166°

   Angles in a quadrilateral add up to 360°, so *x* = 360° − 90° − 62° − 166° = 42°

Angle *x* is in quadrilateral ACEF, so find the other missing angle in ACEF, then you can find *x*.

   x = ...42....°

   [2 marks]

b) Use your answer to a) to show that *y* = 48°.

   Angles in a triangle add up to 180°, so *y* = 180° − 90° − 42° = 48°

   Angle *y* and angle *x* are both in the triangle ACB.

   [2 marks]

Exam Questions

2   Below is an image of a cog.

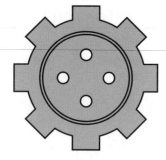

  a) Draw all the lines of symmetry for the cog.

[2 marks]

b) What order of rotational symmetry does the cog have?

....
[1 mark]

3 ABC is an isosceles triangle with $AB = BC$. ACD is a straight line.

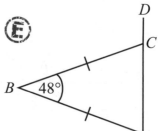

Work out the size of angle BCD.

Diagram not accurately drawn

...................................°
[3 marks]

4 $ABCD$ is a trapezium. Lines AB and DC are parallel to each other.

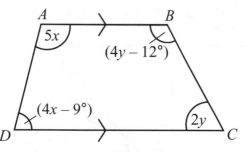

Find the values of x and y.   *If you extend the lines in the diagram, it might be easier to see how to solve the problem.*

Diagram not accurately drawn

$x =$ ....° $y =$ ....°
[4 marks]

5   The diagram shows a regular octagon. AB is a side of the octagon and O is its centre.

  a) Work out the size of the angle marked x.

$x =$ ....°
[2 marks]

b) Work out the size of the angle marked y.

Diagram not accurately drawn

$y =$ ....°
[2 marks]

Circle Geometry

Take a deep breath — it's time to plunge into the depths of mathematical peril with a 3-page extravaganza on <u>circle theorems</u>. There are nine rules for you to learn — four on this page and five on the next.

9 Rules to Learn

1) A <u>TANGENT</u> and a <u>RADIUS</u> meet at <u>90°</u>.

A <u>TANGENT</u> is a line that just touches a single point on the circumference of a circle. A tangent always makes an angle of <u>exactly 90°</u> with the <u>radius</u> it meets at this point.

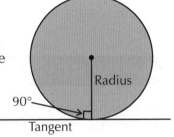

2) <u>TWO RADII</u> form an <u>ISOSCELES TRIANGLE</u>.

<u>Unlike other isosceles triangles</u> they <u>don't have the little tick marks on the sides</u> to remind you that they are the same — the fact that <u>they are both radii</u> is enough to make it an isosceles triangle.

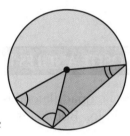

Radii is the plural of radius.

3) The <u>PERPENDICULAR BISECTOR</u> of a <u>CHORD</u> passes through the <u>CENTRE</u> of the circle.

A <u>CHORD</u> is any line <u>drawn across a circle</u>. And no matter where you draw a chord, the line that <u>cuts it exactly in half</u> (at 90°), will <u>go through the centre of the circle</u>.

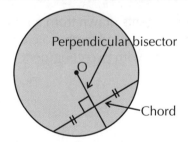

4) The <u>CENTRE</u> of a circle is <u>TWICE</u> the angle at the <u>CIRCUMFERENCE</u>.

The angle subtended at the <u>centre</u> of a circle is <u>EXACTLY DOUBLE</u> the angle subtended at the <u>circumference</u> of the circle from the <u>same two points</u> (two ends of the same <u>chord</u>).

<u>'Angle subtended at'</u> is just a posh way of saying '<u>angle made at</u>'.

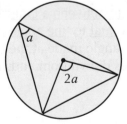

Four down, five to go...

There's a pile of words (like tangent, chord, bisector...) which make this stuff sound more complicated than it really is. Once you've got them in your head, it's just four simple rules to learn.

Circle Geometry

5) The <u>ANGLE</u> in a <u>SEMICIRCLE</u> is <u>90°</u>.

A triangle drawn from the <u>two ends of a diameter</u> will <u>ALWAYS</u> make an <u>angle of 90° where it hits</u> the circumference of the circle, no matter where it hits.

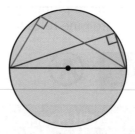

6) Angles in the <u>SAME SEGMENT</u> are <u>EQUAL</u>.

All triangles drawn from a chord will have <u>the same angle where they touch the circumference</u>. Also, the two angles on opposite sides of the chord <u>add up to 180°</u>.

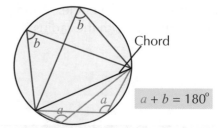

Chord

$$a + b = 180°$$

7) <u>OPPOSITE ANGLES</u> in a <u>CYCLIC QUADRILATERAL</u> add up to <u>180°</u>.

A <u>cyclic quadrilateral</u> is a <u>4-sided shape with every corner touching the circle</u>. Both pairs of opposite angles add up to 180°.

$$a + c = 180°$$
$$b + d = 180°$$

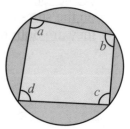

8) <u>TANGENTS</u> from the <u>SAME POINT</u> are the <u>SAME LENGTH</u>.

Two tangents drawn from an outside point are <u>always equal in length</u>, so creating an 'isosceles' situation, with <u>two congruent right-angled triangles</u>.

There's more about congruence on p113.

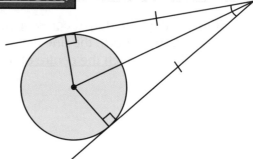

9) The <u>ALTERNATE SEGMENT THEOREM</u>.

This is probably the hardest rule, so take care.

The <u>angle between</u> a <u>tangent</u> and a <u>chord</u> is always <u>equal</u> to 'the angle in the opposite segment' (i.e. the angle made at the circumference by two lines drawn from ends of the chord).

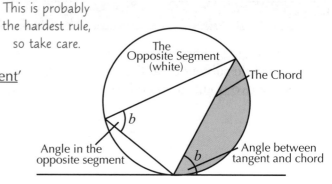

The Opposite Segment (white)

The Chord

Angle in the opposite segment

Angle between tangent and chord

...and that's your lot

This page is just more of the same: five more rules to cram into your overcrowded brain. But there's no way round learning this stuff, and once you've learnt all nine, circle geometry becomes child's play.

Circle Geometry

Now that you've seen the <u>circle theorems</u>, it's time to have a bash at <u>using</u> them. Good times.

Using the Circle Theorems

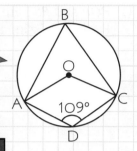

EXAMPLE: **A, B, C and D are points on the circumference of the circle, and O is the centre of the circle. Angle ADC = 109°. Work out the size of angles ABC and AOC.**

You'll probably have to use more than one rule to solve circle theorem questions — here, ABCD is a <u>cyclic quadrilateral</u> so use rule 7:

> **7) OPPOSITE ANGLES in a CYCLIC QUADRILATERAL add up to 180°.**

Angles ADC and ABC are <u>opposite</u>, so: angle ABC = 180° − 109° = 71°.

Remember three-letter angle notation from p100 — angle ADC is the angle formed at D (it's always the middle letter).

Now, angles ABC (which you've just found) and AOC both come from chord AC, so you can use rule 4:

> **4) The angle at the CENTRE of a circle is TWICE the angle at the CIRCUMFERENCE.**

So angle AOC is <u>double</u> angle ABC, which means: angle AOC = 71° × 2 = 142°.

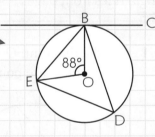

EXAMPLE: **Line ABC is a tangent to the circle with centre O, and points B, D and E are points on the circumference. Angle EOB = 88°. Work out the size of angles BEO and ABE.**

To find <u>angle BEO</u>, use rule 2:

> **2) TWO RADII form an ISOSCELES TRIANGLE.**

Triangle <u>EOB</u> is an <u>isosceles triangle</u> with an angle of 88°, so:
Angle BEO = (180° − 88°) ÷ 2 = 46°.

To find angle <u>ABE</u>, use rule 9:

> **9) The ALTERNATE SEGMENT THEOREM.**

So angle <u>ABE</u> is the <u>same</u> as angle <u>EDB</u>, which we can find using <u>rule 4</u> again:
Angle EDB = 88° ÷ 2 = 44°, so angle ABE = 44°.

Have you remembered those nine rules?

If you find this page isn't making much sense, you need to go back for another look at pages 105 and 106. Sometimes you'll find there's more than one way of finding the angle you want — in the second example on this page, you could have just used rule 1 to find angle ABE once you'd found angle BEO.

Warm-up and Worked Exam Questions

Time to have a go at using all those lovely circle theorems. The only way this stuff is going to sink in is if you practise answering questions — luckily you've got two pages of them here so you can do just that...

Warm-up Question

1) *PQR* and *RST* are tangents to the circle.
Find the missing angles *L*, *M* and *N*.

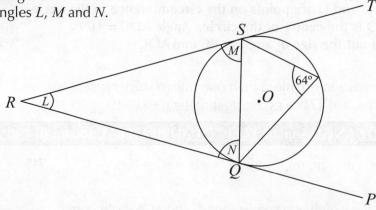

Worked Exam Question

Circle theorem questions can sometimes be a bit overwhelming, and it can be difficult to know where to start. The best approach is to begin by finding any angles you can using the circle theorems and the angle rules from pages 98 and 99, until you have enough information to find the angle you want.

1 In the diagram, *O* is the centre of the circle.
A, *B* and *C* are points on the circumference.

 (A*)

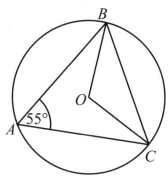

Not to scale

Work out the size of angle *OCB*.
Give reasons for each step in your working.

Angle BOC = 2 × 55° = 110° because the angle at the centre is twice the angle at the circumference.

Triangle OBC is isosceles as it's formed from two radii, so angle OCB = angle OBC.

Angles in a triangle add up to 180°,
so 180° = 110° + (2 × angle OCB)
    70° = 2 × angle OCB
    35° = angle OCB.

..........35.......... °

[4 marks]

Exam Questions

2 The diagram shows a circle, centre *O*. *A*, *B*, *C* and *D* are points on the circumference. (A*)

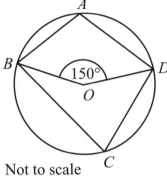

Not to scale

a) Work out the size of angle *BCD*. Give a reason for your answer.

....

....
[2 marks]

b) Explain why angle *BAD* = 105°.

....

....
[1 mark]

3 The diagram below shows a circle with centre *O*. *A*, *B*, *C* and *D* are (A*) points on the circumference of the circle and *AOC* is a straight line.

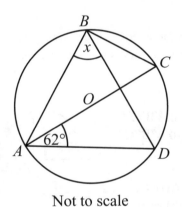

Not to scale

 Work out the size of the angle marked *x*.

x = ...°
[3 marks]

4 The diagram below shows a circle, centre *O*. *P*, *Q* and *R* are points on the (A*) circumference of the circle. *SPT* is a tangent to the circle. Angle *RPS* is 52°.

Not to scale

a) Work out the size of angle *QPT*.

.........................°
[2 marks]

b) Explain why angle *QRP* = 38°.

....

....
[1 mark]

The Four Transformations

There are four <u>transformations</u> you need to know — <u>translation</u>, <u>rotation</u>, <u>reflection</u> and <u>enlargement</u>.

1) Translations

In a <u>translation</u>, the <u>amount</u> the shape moves by is given as a <u>vector</u> (see page 151) written $\begin{pmatrix} x \\ y \end{pmatrix}$ — where x is the <u>horizontal movement</u> (i.e. to the <u>right</u>) and y is the <u>vertical movement</u> (i.e. <u>up</u>). If the shape moves <u>left and down</u>, x and y will be <u>negative</u>.

> **EXAMPLE:**
> **a) Describe the transformation that maps triangle ABC onto A′B′C′.**
> **b) Describe the transformation that maps triangle ABC onto A″B″C″.**
>
> a) To get from A to A′, you need to move <u>8 units left</u> and <u>6 units up</u>, so...
> The transformation from ABC to A′B′C′ is a translation by the vector $\begin{pmatrix} -8 \\ 6 \end{pmatrix}$.
>
> b) The transformation from ABC to A″B″C″ is a **translation by the vector** $\begin{pmatrix} 0 \\ 7 \end{pmatrix}$.

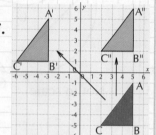

2) Rotations

To describe a <u>rotation</u>, you must give <u>3 details</u>:

1) The <u>angle of rotation</u> (usually 90° or 180°).
2) The <u>direction of rotation</u> (clockwise or anticlockwise). ← For a rotation of 180°, it doesn't matter whether you go clockwise or anticlockwise.
3) The <u>centre of rotation</u> (often, but not always, the origin).

> **EXAMPLE:**
> **a) Describe the transformation that maps triangle ABC onto A′B′C′.**
> **b) Describe the transformation that maps triangle ABC onto A″B″C″.**
>
> a) The transformation from ABC to A′B′C′ is a rotation of <u>90°</u> <u>anticlockwise</u> about the <u>origin</u>.
>
> b) The transformation from ABC to A″B″C″ is a rotation of <u>180°</u> clockwise (or anticlockwise) about the <u>origin</u>.
>
> If it helps, you can use tracing paper to help you find the centre of rotation.

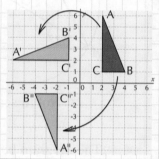

3) Reflections

For a <u>reflection</u>, you must give the <u>equation</u> of the <u>mirror line</u>.

> **EXAMPLE:**
> **a) Describe the transformation that maps shape A onto shape B.**
> **b) Describe the transformation that maps shape A onto shape C.**
>
> a) The transformation from A to B is a reflection in the y-axis.
>
> b) The transformation from A to C is a reflection in the line $y = x$.

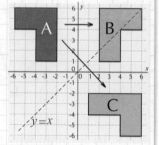

You must remember to give specific details

E.g. it's no use saying it's a translation if you don't give the vector it's translated by. Shapes are <u>congruent</u> under translation, reflection and rotation — their <u>size</u> and <u>shape</u> don't change (congruence is on p113).

The Four Transformations

One more transformation coming up — <u>enlargements</u>. They're the trickiest, but also the most fun (honest).

4) Enlargements

For an <u>enlargement</u>, you must specify:

1) The <u>scale factor</u>. ◄———————   scale factor = $\dfrac{\text{new length}}{\text{old length}}$
2) The <u>centre of enlargement</u>.

EXAMPLE:
   a) Describe the transformation that maps triangle A onto triangle B.
   b) Describe the transformation that maps triangle B onto triangle A.

a) Use the formula above to find the <u>scale factor</u> (just choose one side): scale factor = $\dfrac{6}{3} = 2$

For the <u>centre of enlargement</u>, draw <u>lines</u> that go through <u>corresponding vertices</u> of both shapes and see where they <u>cross</u>.

So the transformation from A to B is an enlargement of scale factor 2, centre (2, 6)

b) Using a similar method, scale factor = $\dfrac{3}{6} = \dfrac{1}{2}$ and the centre of enlargement is the same as before.

So the transformation from B to A is an enlargement of scale factor $\dfrac{1}{2}$, centre (2, 6)

If the scale factor is less than 1, the shape will get smaller (A is smaller than B). There's more on this below.

Scale Factors — Four Key Facts

1) If the scale factor is <u>bigger than 1</u> the <u>shape gets bigger</u>.

2) If the scale factor is <u>smaller than 1</u> (e.g. ½) it <u>gets smaller</u>.

3) If the scale factor is <u>negative</u> then the shape pops out the other side of the enlargement centre. If the scale factor is –1, it's exactly the same as a rotation of 180°.

4) The scale factor also tells you the <u>relative distance</u> of old points and new points from the <u>centre of enlargement</u> — this is very useful for <u>drawing an enlargement</u>, because you can use it to trace out the positions of the new points.

EXAMPLE: **Enlarge shape A below by a scale factor of –3, centre (1, 1). Label the transformed shape B.**

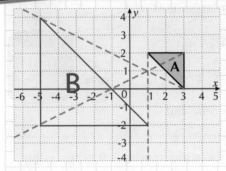

1) First, <u>draw lines</u> going through <u>(1, 1)</u> from each <u>vertex</u> of shape A.

2) Then, <u>multiply</u> the distance from each vertex to the centre of enlargement by <u>3</u>, and measure this distance coming out the <u>other side</u> of the centre of enlargement.
So on shape A, vertex (3, 2) is 2 right and 1 up from (1, 1) — so the corresponding point on shape B will be 6 left and 3 down from (1, 1). Do this for every point.

3) <u>Join</u> the points you've drawn to form shape B.

Remember the four types of transformation

Shapes are <u>similar</u> under enlargement — the <u>position</u> and the <u>size</u> change, but the <u>angles</u> and <u>ratios of the sides</u> don't (see p114). Make sure you learn the 4 key facts about scale factors.

More Transformation Stuff

Just one more page on transformations, and then you're done. With transformations anyway, not with maths.

Combinations of *Transformations*

If they're feeling really mean, the examiners might make you do <u>two transformations</u> to the <u>same shape</u>, then ask you to <u>describe</u> the <u>single transformation</u> that would get you to the <u>final shape</u>. It's not as bad as it looks.

EXAMPLE:

a) **Reflect shape A in the *x*-axis. Label this shape B.**
b) **Reflect shape B in the *y*-axis. Label this shape C.**
c) **Describe the single transformation that will map shape A onto shape C.**

For a) and b), just draw the reflections.

For c), you can ignore shape B and just work out how to get from A to C. You can see it's a <u>rotation</u>, but the tricky bit is working out the <u>centre of rotation</u>. Use <u>tracing paper</u> if you need to.

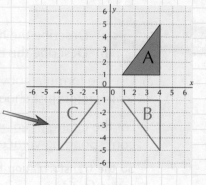

The transformation from A to C is a <u>rotation of 180°</u> clockwise (or anticlockwise) about the <u>origin</u>.

How *Enlargement* Affects *Area* and *Volume*

If a shape is enlarged by a <u>scale factor</u> (see previous page), its <u>area</u>, or surface area and <u>volume</u> (if it's a 3D shape), will change too. However, they <u>don't</u> change by the <u>same value</u> as the scale factor:

For a SCALE FACTOR *n*:		And:	
The <u>SIDES</u> are	*n* times bigger		
The <u>AREAS</u> are	n^2 times bigger	$n = \dfrac{\text{new length}}{\text{old length}}$	$n^2 = \dfrac{\text{new area}}{\text{old area}}$
The <u>VOLUMES</u> are	n^3 times bigger	$n^3 = \dfrac{\text{new volume}}{\text{old volume}}$	

So if the <u>scale factor</u> is <u>2</u>, the lengths are <u>twice as long</u>, the area is $2^2 = \underline{4 \text{ times}}$ as big, and the volume is $2^3 = \underline{8 \text{ times}}$ as big.

There's more on areas on p119-120 and volumes on p122-123.

EXAMPLE: **Cylinder A has surface area 6π cm², and cylinder B has surface area 54π cm². The volume of cylinder A is 2π cm³. Find the volume of cylinder B, given that B is an enlargement of A.**

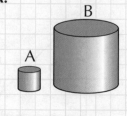

First, work out the <u>scale factor</u>, *n*: $n^2 = \dfrac{\text{Area B}}{\text{Area A}} = \dfrac{54\pi}{6\pi} = 9$, so $\underline{n = 3}$

Use this in the volume formula: $n^3 = \dfrac{\text{Volume B}}{\text{Volume A}} \Rightarrow 3^3 = \dfrac{\text{Volume B}}{2\pi}$

$\Rightarrow$ Volume of B $= 2\pi \times 27 = 54\pi$ cm³

This shows that if the scale factor is <u>3</u>, lengths are <u>3 times as long</u>, the surface area is <u>9 times as big</u> and the volume is <u>27 times as big</u>.

When you make lengths bigger, **areas get bigger and *volumes even bigger***

It's easy to make the mistake of thinking that length, area and volume all get bigger at the same rate — make sure you've got the rule on this page very clear in your mind to avoid a lot of confusion.

Congruent Shapes

Congruence is another ridiculous maths word which sounds really complicated when it's not. If two shapes are congruent, they are simply the same — the same size and the same shape. That's all it is. They can however be reflected or rotated.

CONGRUENT
— same size, same shape

Proving Triangles are Congruent

To prove that two triangles are congruent, you have to show that one of the conditions below holds true:

1) SSS   three sides are the same
2) AAS   two angles and a corresponding side match up
3) SAS   two sides and the angle between them match up
4) RHS   a right angle, the hypotenuse and one other side all match up

The hypotenuse is the longest side of a right-angled triangle — the one opposite the right angle.

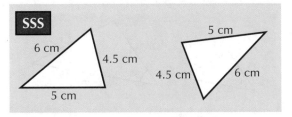

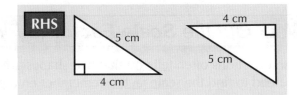

Make sure the sides match up — here, the side is opposite the 81° angle.

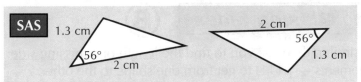

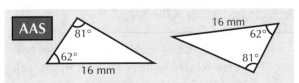

Work Out All the Sides and Angles You Can Find

The best approach to proving two triangles are congruent is to write down everything you can find out, then see which condition they fit. Watch out for things like parallel lines (p99) and circle theorems (p105-106).

EXAMPLE: **XY and YZ are tangents to the circle with centre O, and touch the circle at points X and Z respectively. Prove that the triangles OXY and OYZ are congruent.**

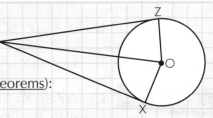

Write down what you know (you're going to have to use circle theorems):

- Sides OX and OZ are the same length (as they're both radii).
- Both triangles have a right angle (OXY and OZY) as a tangent meets a radius at 90°.
- OY is the hypotenuse of each triangle.

So the condition RHS holds, as there is a right angle, the hypotenuses are the same and one other side (OX and OZ) of each triangle are the same.

RHS holds, so OXY and OYZ are congruent triangles.

Congruent just means same size, same shape
Learn all 4 conditions and make sure you know how to use them to prove that triangles are congruent. Take your time and think about it carefully — make sure you're using the right sides and angles in each shape.

Similar Shapes

Similar shapes are <u>exactly the same shape</u>, but can be <u>different sizes</u> (they can also be <u>rotated</u> or <u>reflected</u>).

SIMILAR — same shape, <u>different size</u>

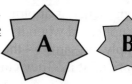

Similar Shapes Have the Same Angles 🅑

Generally, for two shapes to be <u>similar</u>, all the <u>angles</u> must match and the <u>sides</u> must be <u>proportional</u>. But for <u>triangles</u>, there are <u>three special conditions</u> — if any one of these is true, you know they're similar.

Two triangles are similar if:

1) All the <u>angles</u> match up
   i.e. the angles in one triangle are the same as the other.

2) All three <u>sides</u> are <u>proportional</u>
   i.e. if one side is twice as long as the corresponding side in the other triangle, all the sides are twice as long as the corresponding sides.

3) Any <u>two sides</u> are <u>proportional</u> and the <u>angle between them</u> is the <u>same</u>.

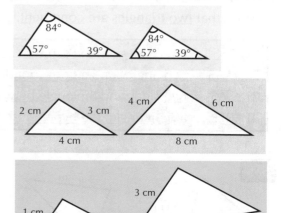

Watch out — if one of the triangles has been rotated or flipped over, it might look as if they're not similar, but don't be fooled.

Work Out the Scale Factor to Find Missing Sides 🅑

Exam questions often <u>tell you</u> that two shapes are similar, then ask you to find the <u>length</u> of a <u>missing side</u>. You need to find the <u>scale factor</u> (remember enlargements — p111) to get from one shape to the other.

EXAMPLE: **Triangles ABC and DEF are similar. Calculate the length of side EF.**

The first thing to do is to work out the <u>scale factor</u>: AB and DE are <u>corresponding sides</u>:

scale factor $= \dfrac{DE}{AB} = \dfrac{9}{6} = 1.5$.

Now <u>use</u> the scale factor to work out the length of EF:

$EF = BC \times 1.5 = 5 \times 1.5 = 7.5$ cm

EXAMPLE: **Quadrilaterals ABCD and EFGH are similar. Calculate the length of side CD.**

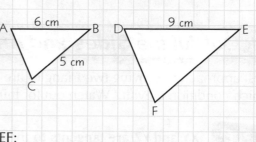

First, work out the <u>scale factor</u>: AB and EF are <u>corresponding sides</u>.

So the scale factor is $\dfrac{EF}{AB} = \dfrac{7}{4} = 1.75$.

Now <u>use</u> the scale factor to work out the length of CD (this time, instead of multiplying by the scale factor, you need to <u>divide</u> by it):

$CD = GH \div 1.75 = 10.5 \div 1.75 = 6$ cm

To get from the original shape to the new one you multiply by the scale factor — so to get from EFGH to ABCD you divide by the scale factor.

Similar means the same shape but a different size

Make sure you really know the difference between congruent and similar shapes — to help you remember, think '<u>similar siblings</u>, <u>congruent clones</u>' — siblings are alike but not the same, clones are identical.

Warm-up and Worked Exam Questions

These warm-up questions cover some of the basics you'll need for the exam — use them to make sure you've learnt all the key information properly before you move on to tackling some exam questions.

Warm-up Questions

1) What translation would map the point (1, 3) onto (–2, 6)?

2) Two similar cones have volumes of $27 \, m^3$ and $64 \, m^3$.
   If the surface area of the smaller one is $36 \, m^2$, find the surface area of the larger cone.

3) From the diagram below, pick out:

   a) a pair of congruent shapes
   b) a pair of similar shapes

4) Triangles ABC and DEF are similar.
   a) Triangle DEF is an enlargement of triangle ABC.
      What is the scale factor of the enlargement?
   b) What is the length of DF?

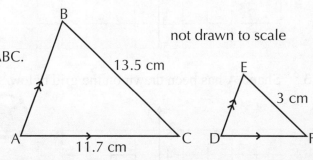

not drawn to scale

Worked Exam Question

I'm afraid this helpful blue writing won't be there in the exam, so if I were you I'd make the most of it and make sure you fully understand it now.

*1 *ABC* is a triangle. *FDEC* is a parallelogram such that *F* is the midpoint of *AC*, *D* is the midpoint of *AB* and *E* is the midpoint of *BC*.

This * tells you your quality of written communication is being tested — so you need to take extra care to explain everything you do clearly

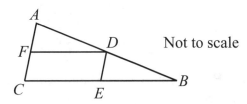

Not to scale

Prove that triangles *AFD* and *DEB* are congruent.

F is the midpoint of AC so AF = FC,
and opposite sides of a parallelogram are equal so DE = FC.
Therefore AF = DE.

E is the midpoint of CB so CE = EB,
and opposite sides of a parallelogram are equal so CE = FD.
Therefore FD = EB.

D is the midpoint of AB, so AD = DB.

Satisfies condition SSS so triangles are congruent.

[4 marks]

Exam Questions

2 In the diagram below, **B** is an image of **A**.

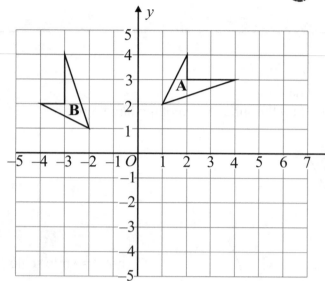

a) Describe fully the single transformation that maps **A** onto **B**.

....

....

....

[3 marks]

b) Translate shape **B** by the vector $\begin{pmatrix} -1 \\ -4 \end{pmatrix}$. Label the image as **C**.

[1 mark]

3 Shape **A** has been drawn on the grid below.

a) On the grid, reflect shape **A** in the *x*-axis. Label this image **B**.

[2 marks]

b) Rotate shape **B** 90° clockwise about the origin. Label this image **C**.

[2 marks]

c) Describe fully the single transformation which maps **A** onto **C**.

....

[2 marks]

4 Triangle **R** has been drawn on the grid below.

 Enlarge triangle **R** with centre (6, –3) and scale factor 4. Label your image **S**.

[3 marks]

Exam Questions

5 The shapes *ABCD* and *EFGH* are mathematically similar.

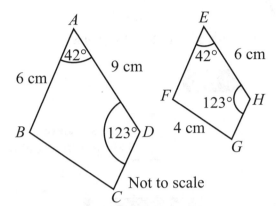

a) Find the length of *EF*.

.... cm
[2 marks]

b) Find the length of *BC*.

.... cm
[1 mark]

6 A regular hexagon has sides of length 16 cm.
It is an enlargement of another regular hexagon with sides of length 4 cm. Ⓐ

Write down the scale factor of the enlargement.

....
[1 mark]

*7 The diagram shows two overlapping circles, with centres *O* and *P*.
The circles intersect at *M* and *N*, and the centre of each circle is a point on the circumference
of the other circle. *KOPL* is a straight line. *KM* and *NL* are parallel to each other.

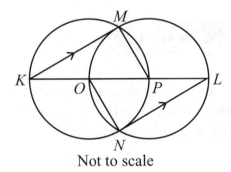

Not to scale

Prove that triangles *KMP* and *LNO* are congruent.

....

....

....

....
[4 marks]

8 **A**, **B** and **C** are three solid cones which are mathematically similar. The surface area of each
cone is given below. The perpendicular height of **A** is 4 cm. The volume of **C** is 135π cm³.

a) Calculate the volume of **A**.

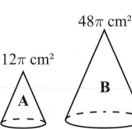

Not to scale

108π cm²

48π cm²

12π cm²

.... cm³
[4 marks]

b) Calculate the perpendicular height of **B**.

.... cm
[4 marks]

Projections

Projections are just different <u>views</u> of a 3D solid shape — looking at it from the <u>front</u>, the <u>side</u> and the <u>top</u>.

The Three Different Projections

There are three different types of projections — <u>front elevations</u>, <u>side elevations</u> and <u>plans</u> (elevation is just another word for projection).

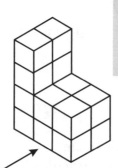

1) Front Elevation

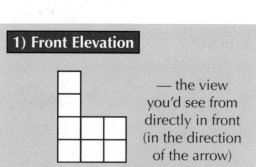

— the view you'd see from directly in front (in the direction of the arrow)

2) Plan

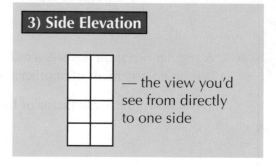

— the view you'd see from directly above

3) Side Elevation

— the view you'd see from directly to one side

Don't be thrown if you're given a diagram drawn on <u>isometric</u> (dotty) paper — it works in just the same way. You just <u>count</u> the <u>number of dots</u> to find the <u>dimensions</u> of the shape.

On isometric paper, the shape above would look like this

*Decide If You **Need** To Draw Projections **To Scale***

1) You'll often be given <u>grid paper</u> to draw your projections on — so make sure you get the <u>dimensions</u> right.

2) However, if you're asked to <u>sketch</u> a projection (and not given grid paper), it <u>doesn't</u> have to be perfectly to <u>scale</u>.

3) <u>Lines</u> on the projection should show any changes in <u>depth</u>.

A question might give you a plan and elevation and ask you to sketch the solid... Just piece together the original shape from the info given. And check your final sketch against the question.

EXAMPLE:

a) On the cm square grid, draw the side elevation of the prism from the direction of the arrow.

b) Draw a plan of the prism on the grid.

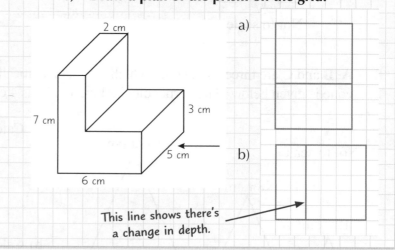

This line shows there's a change in depth.

You need to know what the three types of projection are

Projection questions aren't too bad — just take your time and sketch the diagrams carefully. Watch out for questions on isometric paper — they might look confusing, but they can be easier than other questions.

Areas

Be warned — there are lots of <u>area formulas</u> coming up on the next two pages for you to <u>learn</u>.
You should already know the formulas for the area of a <u>rectangle</u> ($A = l \times w$) and the area of a <u>square</u> ($A = l^2$).

Areas of *Triangles* and *Quadrilaterals*

LEARN these Formulas: Note that in each case the <u>height</u> must be
the <u>vertical height</u>, not the sloping height.

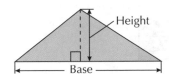

<u>Area of triangle</u> = ½ × base × vertical height

$$A = ½ \times b \times h_v$$

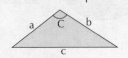
The alternative formula is:
<u>Area of triangle = ½ ab sin C</u>
This is covered on p147.

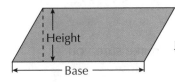

$\dfrac{\text{Area of}}{\text{parallelogram}}$ = base × vertical height

$$A = b \times h_v$$

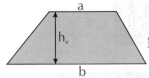

$\dfrac{\text{Area of}}{\text{trapezium}}$ = average of parallel sides × distance between them (vertical height)

$$A = ½(a + b) \times h_v$$

(This one's on the formula sheet
— but you should learn it anyway.)

Split *Composite Shapes* into *Easier Shapes*

<u>Composite shapes</u> are made up of different shapes <u>stuck together</u>. Finding their area is actually dead easy
— just <u>split them up</u> into <u>triangles</u> and <u>quadrilaterals</u> and work out the area of each bit.

EXAMPLE: **Lotte is painting one wall of her loft bedroom, with dimensions as shown
on the diagram. One pot of paint will cover 1.9 m².
How many pots of paint will she need?**

You need to work out the <u>area</u> of the wall —
so split it into two shapes (a <u>rectangle</u> and a <u>trapezium</u>):

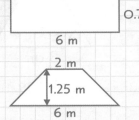

0.75 m   Find the area of the rectangle (dead easy):
Area = l × w = 6 × 0.75 = **4.5 m²**

Find the area of the trapezium (using the formula above):
Area = ½(a + b) × h = ½(6 + 2) × 1.25 = **5 m²**

So the <u>total area</u> of the wall is: 4.5 m² + 5 m² = **9.5 m²**
Each pot covers 1.9 m², so Lotte will need: 9.5 ÷ 1.9 = **5 pots of paint**

Did I say already — you must learn these formulas
Not much to say about this page really — LEARN the formulas and practise using them.

Areas

Another page of formulas, you know the drill: **LEARN these Formulas**

Area and *Circumference* of *Circles*

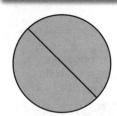

Area of circle = π × (radius)²
Remember that the radius is half the diameter.

$$A = \pi r^2$$

Circumference = π × diameter
= 2 × π × radius

$$C = \pi D = 2\pi r$$

For these formulas, use the π button on your calculator. For non-calculator questions, use π ≈ 3.14 (unless the question tells you otherwise).

Areas of *Sectors* and *Segments*

These next ones are a bit more tricky — before you try and <u>learn</u> the <u>formulas</u>, make sure you know what a <u>sector</u>, an <u>arc</u> and a <u>segment</u> are (they're labelled on the diagrams below).

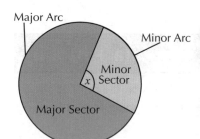
Major Arc
Minor Arc
Minor Sector
Major Sector

$$\underline{\text{Area of Sector}} = \frac{x}{360} \times \text{Area of full Circle}$$

$$\underline{\text{Length of Arc}} = \frac{x}{360} \times \text{Circumference of full Circle}$$

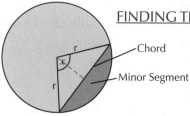
Chord
Minor Segment

<u>FINDING THE AREA OF A SEGMENT</u> is OK if you know the formulas.

1) Find the <u>area of the sector</u> using the above formula.
2) Find the area of the triangle, then <u>subtract it</u> from the sector's area. You can do this using the '½ ab sin C' formula for the area of the triangle (see previous page), which becomes: ½ r²sin x.

EXAMPLE: **Find the area of the shaded segment in the diagram on the right. The circle has radius 3 cm and the sector angle is 60°. Give your answer to 3 significant figures.**

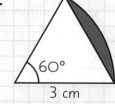
60°
3 cm

First, find the area of the <u>whole sector</u>:

area of sector = $\frac{x}{360} \times \pi r^2 = \frac{60}{360} \times \pi \times 3^2 = \frac{1}{6} \times \pi \times 9 = \frac{3}{2}\pi$ cm²

Then find the area of the <u>triangle</u>: area of triangle = $\frac{1}{2}r^2\sin x = \frac{1}{2} \times 3^2 \times \sin 60° = 3.897114...$ cm²

Finally, <u>subtract</u> the area of the triangle from the area of the sector:

$\frac{3}{2}\pi - 3.897114... = 0.815274... = 0.815$ cm² (3 s.f.)

Four more lovely formulas for you to LEARN

One more thing — if you're asked to find the perimeter of a semicircle or quarter circle, don't forget to add on the straight edges too. It's an easy mistake to make, and it'll cost you marks.

Surface Area

Time to move on to 3D shapes. First things first, nets and surface area:

Nets

A <u>NET</u> is just a hollow <u>3D shape</u> folded out flat.
Here are the nets of some <u>common shapes</u> — make sure you can recognise them.

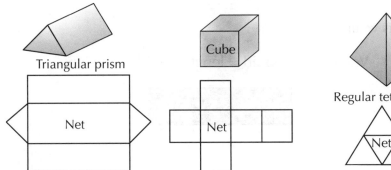
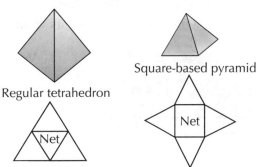

Triangular prism

Net

Cube

Net

Regular tetrahedron

Net

Square-based pyramid

Net

Note that these are just some of the nets for these shapes — there are
many other nets that will produce the same shapes (particularly for a cube).

Surface Area

1) <u>SURFACE AREA</u> only applies to 3D objects — it's simply the <u>total area</u> of all the <u>faces</u> added together.

2) <u>SURFACE AREA OF SOLID = AREA OF NET</u>. So if it helps, imagine the net and add up the area of <u>each bit</u>.

3) <u>SPHERES, CONES AND CYLINDERS</u> have surface area formulas that you need to <u>learn</u>:

Surface area of a SPHERE = $4\pi r^2$

curved area
of cone (*l* is the   area of
slant height)   circular base

Surface area of a CONE = $\pi rl + \pi r^2$

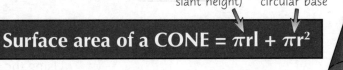

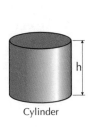
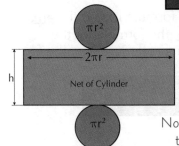

πr^2

$2\pi r$

Net of Cylinder

πr^2

Cylinder

Surface area of a CYLINDER = $2\pi rh + 2\pi r^2$

Note that the <u>length of the rectangle</u> is equal
to the <u>circumference</u> of the circular ends.

EXAMPLE: **Find the exact surface area of a hemisphere with radius 4 cm.**

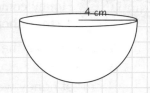

A hemisphere is <u>half a sphere</u> — so the surface area of
the <u>curved face</u> is: $4\pi r^2 \div 2 = 2\pi r^2 = 2 \times \pi \times 4^2 = 32\pi$ cm².

Don't forget the area of the <u>flat face</u> though —
this is just the area of a <u>circle</u> with radius 4 cm: $\pi r^2 = 16\pi$ cm².

So the <u>total surface area</u> is $32\pi + 16\pi = 48\pi$ cm².

You're asked for the exact value,
so leave your answer in terms of π.

To find the surface area of a solid just add up the area of each face

A net is just all the sides folded out flat, which makes it easier to see the shapes you need to find the areas of.

Volume

You might think you know some of this already, but I bet you don't know it all. There's only one thing for it...

LEARN these volume formulas...

(Another word for volume is capacity.)

Volumes of Cuboids

A cuboid is a rectangular block. Finding its volume is dead easy:

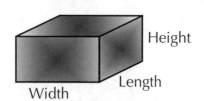

Height
Length
Width

Volume of Cuboid = length × width × height

$$V = L \times W \times H$$

Volumes of Prisms

A PRISM is a solid (3D) object which is the same shape all the way through
— i.e. it has a CONSTANT AREA OF CROSS-SECTION.

Triangular Prism

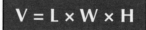

Constant Area
of Cross-section

Length

$$\text{VOLUME OF PRISM} = \text{CROSS-SECTIONAL AREA} \times \text{LENGTH}$$

$$V = A \times L$$

Cylinder (circular prism)

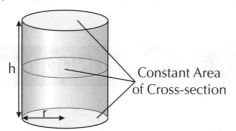

h

r

Constant Area
of Cross-section

Using the formula to find the area
of a circle, the formula for the
volume of a cylinder becomes:

$$V = \pi r^2 h$$

EXAMPLE: **Honey comes in cylindrical jars with radius 4.5 cm and height 12 cm.**
1 cm³ of honey weighs 1.4 g. Work out the mass of honey in this jar to 3 s.f.

First, work out the volume of the jar — just use the formula above:
$V = \pi r^2 h = \pi \times 4.5^2 \times 12 = 763.4070... \text{ cm}^3$

1 cm³ of honey weighs 1.4 g, so multiply the volume by 1.4:
mass of honey = 1.4 × 763.4070... = 1068.7698... = 1070 g (3 s.f.)

See p127 for more on density.

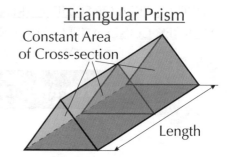

4.5 cm
12 cm
Honey

You have to remember what a prism is

It's the constant area of cross-section which is important — that's what makes a prism a prism. If you remember that, it makes perfect sense that to get the volume you just multiply that area by the length.

Volume

Volumes of Spheres

$$\text{Volume of Sphere} = \frac{4}{3}\pi r^3$$

A <u>hemisphere</u> is half a sphere. So the volume of a hemisphere is just half the volume of a full sphere, $V = \frac{2}{3}\pi r^3$.

Volumes of Pyramids and Cones

A pyramid is a shape that goes from a <u>flat base</u> up to a <u>point</u> at the top. Its base can be any shape at all. If the base is a circle then it's called a <u>cone</u> (rather than a circular pyramid).

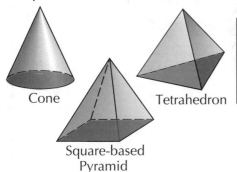

Cone

Tetrahedron

Square-based Pyramid

$$\text{Volume of Pyramid} = \frac{1}{3} \times \text{Base Area} \times \text{Vertical Height}$$
$$\text{Volume of Cone} = \frac{1}{3} \times \pi r^2 \times h_v$$

Make sure you use the <u>vertical</u> (<u>perpendicular</u>) <u>height</u> in these formulas — don't get confused with the <u>slant height</u>, which you used to find the <u>surface area</u> of a cone.

Volumes of Frustums

A <u>frustum of a cone</u> is what's left when the top part of a cone is cut off parallel to its circular base.

| VOLUME OF FRUSTUM | = | VOLUME OF ORIGINAL CONE | − | VOLUME OF REMOVED CONE |

$$= \frac{1}{3}\pi R^2 H - \frac{1}{3}\pi r^2 h$$

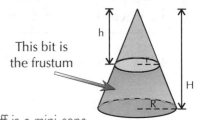

This bit is the frustum

The bit that's chopped off is a mini cone that's <u>similar</u> to the original cone.

EXAMPLE: A waste paper basket is the shape of a frustum formed by removing the top 10 cm from a cone of height 50 cm and radius 35 cm. Find the volume of the waste paper basket to 3 significant figures.

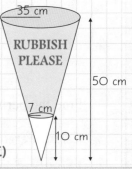

RUBBISH PLEASE

35 cm

50 cm

7 cm

10 cm

Volume of <u>original cone</u> = $\frac{1}{3}\pi R^2 H = \frac{1}{3} \times \pi \times 35^2 \times 50 = 64140.850... \text{ cm}^3$

Volume of <u>removed cone</u> = $\frac{1}{3}\pi r^2 h = \frac{1}{3} \times \pi \times 7^2 \times 10 = 513.126... \text{ cm}^3$

Volume of <u>frustum</u> = 64140.850... − 513.126... = 63627.723... = 63600 cm³ (3 s.f.)

Remember that a cone is just a pyramid with a round base

The cone formula is a variation on the pyramid formula because the area of the base = area of a circle = πr^2. So really just three formulas to learn here, and three important ones at that.

Warm-up and Worked Exam Questions

There are lots of formulas in this section. The best way to see what you know is to practise these questions. If you find you keep forgetting the formulas, you need more practice.

Warm-up Questions

1) From the isometric projection shown, draw:
   a) both side elevations
   b) front elevation
   c) plan view

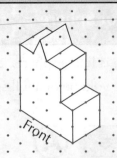

2) A woodworking template has the shape shown.
   a) Calculate the area of one of the round holes.
   b) Use this to calculate the area of the template.
   c) If the template is 4 mm thick, calculate its volume.

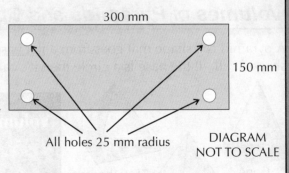

300 mm

150 mm

All holes 25 mm radius

DIAGRAM NOT TO SCALE

3) Calculate the volume of this triangular prism.

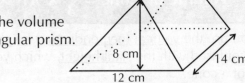

8 cm

14 cm

12 cm

4) Calculate the volume of a sphere with a radius of 4 metres. Give your answer to 3 s.f.

Worked Exam Question

Take a look at this worked exam question — it'll help you to prepare for the real exam:

1   Look at the sector shown in the diagram below. (A)

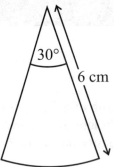

30°

6 cm

Diagram not accurately drawn

Find the perimeter of the sector. Give your answer to 3 significant figures.

Circumference of full circle = 2 × π × 6 cm = 12π cm

Length of arc = $\frac{30}{360}$ × circumference of circle = $\frac{30}{360}$ × 12π cm = π cm

Perimeter of sector = 6 cm + π cm + 6 cm = 15.14159... cm

.....15.1..... cm

[4 marks]

Exam Questions

2 The diagram shows a field. The farmer wants to spray weed killer on the field.
Weed killer costs £0.27 per 10 m².

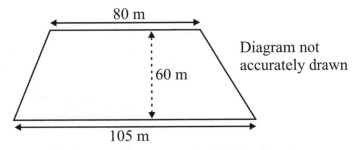

TIP: The formula for
the area of a trapezium
is on the formula sheet.

80 m

60 m

Diagram not
accurately drawn

105 m

How much will it cost the farmer to spray weed killer on the whole field?

£ ....
[4 marks]

3 The diagram shows a regular octahedron and one of its faces. Ⓒ
Each of the faces is an equilateral triangle.

Calculate the surface area of the octahedron.

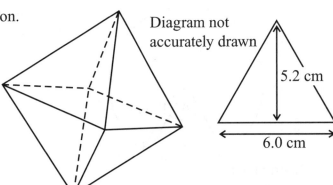

Diagram not
accurately drawn

5.2 cm

6.0 cm

.... cm²
[3 marks]

4 The cross-section of a prism is a regular hexagon.

Each side of the hexagon has a length of 8 cm.
The distance from the centre of the hexagon to
the midpoint of each side is 7 cm.
Calculate the volume of the prism.

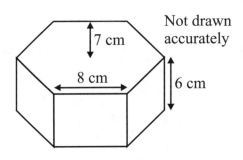

Not drawn
accurately

7 cm

8 cm

6 cm

.... cm³
[3 marks]

Exam Questions

5 The diagram below shows Amy's new paddling pool.
It has a diameter of 2 metres, and is 40 cm high.

Not drawn accurately

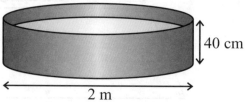

40 cm

2 m

The instructions that came with the pool say that it should only be filled three-quarters full.
What is the maximum volume of water that Amy can put in the pool?
(Give your answer to 2 decimal places.)

.... m³
[4 marks]

6 The circle below has a radius of 12 cm.
The sector *S* has a central angle of 50°.

Find the area of the sector *S* of the circle.
Give your answer to 3 significant figures.

50° 12 cm

S

Diagram not
accurately drawn

.... cm²
[4 marks]

7 The diagram below shows a wooden spinning top made from a hemisphere and a cone.

The hemisphere has a diameter of 14 cm.
The slanting length of the cone is 12 cm
and the radius of its base is 2 cm.

Work out the total surface area of the spinning top.
Give your answer to 3 significant figures.

.... cm²
[6 marks]

Density and Speed

Density and speed. They're both a matter of <u>learning the formulas</u>, bunging the <u>numbers</u> in and watching the <u>units</u>.

Density = *Mass ÷ Volume*

Density is the <u>mass per unit volume</u> of a substance. It's usually measured in <u>kg/m³</u> or <u>g/cm³</u>.
You might think this is physics, but density is specifically mentioned in the maths syllabus.

$$\text{DENSITY} = \frac{\text{MASS}}{\text{VOLUME}} \qquad \text{VOLUME} = \frac{\text{MASS}}{\text{DENSITY}} \qquad \text{MASS} = \text{DENSITY} \times \text{VOLUME}$$

A <u>formula triangle</u> is a mighty handy tool for remembering formulas like these.
Here's the one for density. To <u>remember the order of the letters</u> in
the formula triangle think D^MV or <u>DiMoV</u> (The Russian Agent).

E.g. to get the formula for density from the triangle, cover up D and you're left with $\frac{M}{V}$.

<u>HOW DO YOU USE FORMULA TRIANGLES?</u>
1) <u>COVER UP</u> the thing you want to find and <u>WRITE DOWN</u> what's left showing.
2) Now <u>PUT IN THE VALUES</u> for the other two things and <u>WORK IT OUT</u>.

EXAMPLE: **A giant 'Wunda-Choc' bar has a density of 1.3 g/cm³.**
If the bar's volume is 1800 cm³, what is the mass of the bar in kg?

First write down the <u>formula</u>: mass = density × volume
Put in the values and <u>calculate</u>: mass = 1.3 g/cm³ × 1800 cm³
                                             = 2340 g
Check you've given the
answer in the <u>correct units</u>: mass in kg = 2340 g ÷ 1000 = **2.34 kg**

Check your units match. If the density is in <u>g/cm³</u>, the volume must be in <u>cm³</u> and you'll get a mass in <u>g</u>.

Speed = *Distance ÷ Time*

Speed is the <u>distance travelled per unit time</u>, e.g. the number of <u>km per hour</u> or <u>metres per second</u>.

$$\text{SPEED} = \frac{\text{DISTANCE}}{\text{TIME}} \qquad \text{TIME} = \frac{\text{DISTANCE}}{\text{SPEED}} \qquad \text{DISTANCE} = \text{SPEED} \times \text{TIME}$$

Here's the <u>formula triangle</u> for speed —
this time, we have the words <u>SaD Times</u> to help
you remember the order of the letters (S^DT).
So if it's a question on speed, distance and time,
just say <u>SAD TIMES</u>.

The units you get out of a formula <u>DEPEND ENTIRELY</u> on the units you put in. So, if you put a <u>distance in cm</u> and a <u>time in seconds</u> into the speed formula, the answer comes out in <u>cm/second</u>.

EXAMPLE: **A car travels 9 miles at 36 miles per hour. How many minutes does it take?**

Write down the <u>formula</u>,
put in the values and <u>calculate</u>: time = $\frac{\text{distance}}{\text{speed}}$ = $\frac{9 \text{ miles}}{36 \text{ mph}}$ = 0.25 hours

<u>Convert</u> the time from hours to <u>minutes</u>: 0.25 hours × 60 = **15 minutes**

Density is mass per unit volume, speed is distance per unit time

Learn the formula triangles on this page — once you've got the formula triangle sorted, then you only need to cover up whichever letter you are trying to work out and the formula you need is right there.

Distance-Time Graphs

Distance-time (D/T) graphs deserve a page all to themselves — just to make sure you know all the vital details about them. The best thing about them is that they don't vary much.

Distance-Time Graphs

Distance-time graphs are pretty common in exams.

They're not too bad once you get your head around them — just remember these 3 important points:

1) At any point, GRADIENT = SPEED, but watch out for the UNITS.
2) The STEEPER the graph, the FASTER it's going.
3) FLAT SECTIONS are where it is STOPPED.

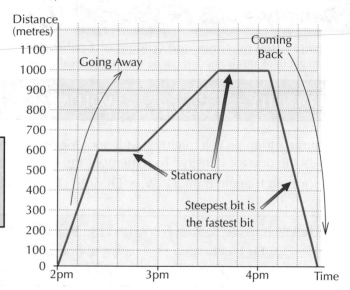

EXAMPLE: Henry went out for a ride on his bike. After a while he got a puncture and stopped to fix it. This graph shows the first part of Henry's journey.

a) **What time did Henry leave home?**

He left home at the point where the line starts.   **At 8:15**

b) **How far did Henry cycle before getting a puncture?**

The horizontal part of the graph is where Henry stopped.   **12 km**

c) **What was Henry's speed before getting a puncture?**

Using the speed formula is the same as finding the gradient.

$$\text{speed} = \frac{\text{distance}}{\text{time}} = \frac{12\,\text{km}}{0.5\,\text{hours}}$$
$$= 24\,\text{km/h}$$

d) **At 9:30 Henry turns round and cycles home at 24 km/h. Complete the graph to show this.**

You have to work out how long it will take Henry to cycle the 18 km home:

$$\text{time} = \frac{\text{distance}}{\text{speed}} = \frac{18\,\text{km}}{24\,\text{km/h}} = 0.75\,\text{hours}$$

Decimal times are yuck, so convert it to minutes.

$$0.75 \times 60\,\text{mins} = 45\,\text{mins}$$

45 minutes after 9:30 is 10:15, so that's the time Henry gets home. Now you can complete the graph.

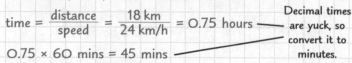

Gradients just mean something per something

Remember, on distance-time graphs the gradients represent distance per time (speed), so the steeper the line the faster the speed. The only way to get good at these distance-time graphs is to practise, practise, practise...

Unit Conversions

A nice easy page for a change — just some <u>facts</u> to learn. Hooray!

Metric Units

1) <u>Length</u>   mm, cm, m, km
2) <u>Area</u>   mm², cm², m², km²,
3) <u>Volume</u>   mm³, cm³, m³, ml, litres
4) <u>Weight</u>   g, kg, tonnes
5) <u>Speed</u>   km/h, m/s

MEMORISE THESE KEY FACTS:

1 cm = 10 mm	1 tonne = 1000 kg
1 m = 100 cm	1 litre = 1000 ml
1 km = 1000 m	1 litre = 1000 cm³
1 kg = 1000 g	1 cm³ = 1 ml

Imperial Units

1) <u>Length</u>   Inches, feet, yards, miles
2) <u>Area</u>   Square inches, square feet, square miles
3) <u>Volume</u>   Cubic inches, cubic feet, gallons, pints
4) <u>Weight</u>   Ounces, pounds, stones, tons
5) <u>Speed</u>   mph

IMPERIAL UNIT CONVERSIONS

1 Foot = 12 Inches
1 Yard = 3 Feet
1 Gallon = 8 Pints
1 Stone = 14 Pounds (lb)
1 Pound = 16 Ounces (oz)

Metric-Imperial Conversions

<u>LEARN THESE</u> — they don't promise to give you these in the exam and if they're feeling mean (as they often are), they won't.

To convert between units, <u>multiply or divide</u> <u>by the conversion factor</u>:

APPROXIMATE CONVERSIONS

2.2 pounds (lb) ≈ 1 kg
1 inch ≈ 2.5 cm
1 gallon ≈ 4.5 litres
5 miles ≈ 8 km

EXAMPLE:
a)   Convert 10 pounds into kg.

1 kg ≈ 2.2 lb, so 10 lb ≈ 10 ÷ 2.2 ≈ 4.5 kg ←

b)   Convert 12.25 gallons into litres.

1 gallon ≈ 4.5 litres, so 12.25 gallons ≈ 12.25 × 4.5 ≈ 55.1 litres

<u>ALWAYS CHECK IT LOOKS SENSIBLE</u>
1 kg ≈ 2.2 lb, so the number of pounds should be <u>about twice</u> the number of kg. If it's not, then chances are you divided instead of multiplied, or vice versa.

Convert Speeds in Two Steps

Speeds are made up of <u>two measures</u> — a <u>distance</u> and a <u>time</u>. To convert from, say, miles per hour to metres per second, you have to convert the distance unit and the time unit <u>separately</u>.

EXAMPLE: **A rabbit's top speed is 56 km/h. How fast is this in m/s?**

First convert from <u>km/h</u> to <u>m/h</u>:   56 km/h = (56 × 1000) m/h = 56 000 m/h

Now convert from <u>m/h</u> to <u>m/s</u>:   56 000 m/h = (56 000 ÷ 3600) m/s
                                                 = 15.6 m/s (1 d.p.)

1 minute = 60 seconds and 1 hour = 60 minutes
So 1 hour = 60 × 60 = 3600 seconds.

There's no way round it — you just have to learn all these factors

There's loads of conversion factors to learn here so keep scribbling them down until you remember every one. Then use your common sense to make sure you don't divide when you should be multiplying.

Unit Conversions

Converting areas and volumes from one unit to another is an exam disaster that you have to know how to avoid. 1 m² definitely does <u>NOT</u> equal 100 cm². Remember this and read on for why.

Converting **Area** and **Volume** Measurements

$$1 \text{ m}^2 = 100 \text{ cm} \times 100 \text{ cm} = 10\ 000 \text{ cm}^2$$
$$1 \text{ cm}^2 = 10 \text{ mm} \times 10 \text{ mm} = 100 \text{ mm}^2$$

$$1 \text{ m}^3 = 100 \text{ cm} \times 100 \text{ cm} \times 100 \text{ cm} = 1\ 000\ 000 \text{ cm}^3$$
$$1 \text{ cm}^3 = 10 \text{ mm} \times 10 \text{ mm} \times 10 \text{ mm} = 1000 \text{ mm}^3$$

EXAMPLES:

1) **Convert 9 m² to cm².**

   To change area measurements from m² to cm² multiply by 100 twice.

   9 × 100 × 100 = 90 000 cm²

2) **Convert 60 000 mm³ to cm³.**

   To change volume measurements from mm³ to cm³ divide by 10 three times.

   60 000 ÷ (10 × 10 × 10) = 60 cm³

Conversion Graphs

Conversion graphs themselves are <u>easy</u> to use. That's why examiners often wrap them up in tricky questions.

METHOD FOR USING CONVERSION GRAPHS:

1) <u>Draw a line</u> from a value on <u>one axis</u>.
2) Keep going until you <u>hit the LINE</u>.
3) Then <u>change direction</u> and go straight to <u>the other axis</u>.
4) <u>Read off the value</u> from this axis. The two values are <u>equivalent</u>.

EXAMPLE:

Sam went on holiday to Florida and paid $3.15 per gallon for petrol. How much is this in pounds (£) per litre?

You could also do this conversion the other way round (i.e. £ per gallon, then £ per litre).

You actually need to do <u>two conversions</u> here — first convert <u>$ per gallon</u> to <u>$ per litre</u>, then convert this to <u>£ per litre</u>.

This is a conversion you need to know off by heart.

Using 1 gallon = 4.5 litres, change 'per gallon' to 'per litre':

$3.15 per gallon ÷ 4.5 = $0.70 per litre

Now use the graph to <u>convert $0.70 to £</u>. It's difficult to read how many £ are equal to $0.70, so just find a point where you can <u>accurately read the values</u>.

$36 ≈ £22   (÷36)
$1 ≈ £0.61...
$0.70 ≈ £0.427...   (×0.70)

So $3.15 per gallon ≈ £0.43 per litre

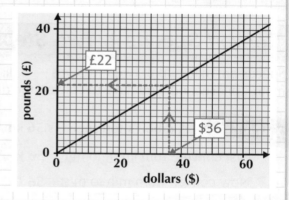

Conversion graphs are all about reading off equivalent amounts

Conversion graphs in exams can be for all sorts of units, but they all work the same way (like the one above). Converting areas and volumes can be tricky, so go through the methods on this page again if you need to.

Warm-up and Worked Exam Questions

Time to check all that lovely revision has sunk in. Try these first to make sure you've learnt the key stuff:

Warm-up Questions

1) A lump of lead, weighing 374 g has a volume of 33 cm³.
   What is the approximate density of the lead (to 3 s.f.)?

2) A solid plastic building block measures 5 cm × 4 cm × 6 cm.
   The density of the plastic is 0.8 g/cm³. What is the mass of the block?

3) A cheetah runs 100 m in 4 seconds. What is its average speed in km per hour?

4) A cyclist travels for ¾ hour at a speed of 12 km per hour. What distance does he travel?

5) The distance/time graph below shows Selby's bike ride from his house (**A**) to the zoo (**C**),
   which is 25 km away.
   a) After one hour Selby stops at a bench (**B**) to get his
      breath back. Find the gradient of the line between
      point **A** and point **B**.
   b) What does the gradient of the line between
      point **A** and point **B** represent?
   c) How long was Selby's journey to the zoo (**C**)
      from home (**A**)?
   d) How long did Selby spend at the zoo?
   e) After the zoo, Selby stopped at the shops (**E**) for
      30 minutes before cycling straight home.
      Given that he arrived home 7 hours after he first left, complete the graph above.
   f) How many hours did Selby spend cycling in total during the day?

6) a) Convert 12.7 kg into grams.   b) Convert 1430 cm into metres.

7) 22 lbs of apples weighs about how many kilograms?

8) Change 3 m³ to mm³.

Worked Exam Question

Make sure you really take this stuff in — read it thoroughly and then have a go yourself to check you've understood. You'll kick yourself if this comes up in the exam and you just gave it a quick glance.

1   The diagram shows a solid prism made from iron.

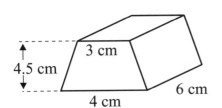

4.5 cm
3 cm
4 cm
6 cm
Not drawn accurately

Volume of a prism =
area of cross-section
× length.

a) Calculate the volume of the prism.

Area of cross section = ½ × (3 + 4) × 4.5
                      = 15.75 cm²
Volume = 15.75 × 6 = 94.5 cm³

.....94.5... cm³
[2 marks]

b) Iron has a density of 7.9 grams per cm³.
   Work out the mass of the prism.

Mass = Density × Volume

Use the volume you
found in part a)

Mass = 7.9 × 94.5 = 746.55 g

.....746.55.. g
[2 marks]

Exam Questions

2 Below is a conversion graph to change between temperatures in °C and °F.

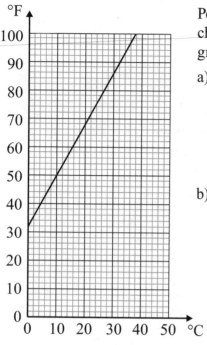

Peter wants to know how the temperature in his greenhouse changes during the day. He places a thermometer in the greenhouse and checks it at regular intervals.

a) At 7 o'clock in the morning, the thermometer recorded a temperature of 50 °F. What was the temperature in °C?

.... °C
[1 mark]

b) By noon, the temperature has risen by 15 °C.
What is the average hourly increase in temperature between 7 o'clock and 12 o'clock? Give your answer in °F.

.... °F
[3 marks]

3 The playing surface of a snooker table has an area of 39 200 cm².

Convert the area of the snooker table into m².

.... m²
[2 marks]

4 Adam has been caught speeding by a pair of average speed cameras.
The speed limit was 50 mph.

The cameras are 2500 m apart. The time taken for his car to pass between them was 102 seconds.

a) What was Adam's average speed between the cameras?
Give your answer to the nearest mph. Take 1 mile as 1.6 km.

.... mph
[3 marks]

b) If Adam had been travelling within the speed limit, what is the minimum time it should have taken him to pass between the cameras? Give your answer to the nearest second.

.... s
[2 marks]

Triangle Construction

How you construct a triangle depends on what <u>info you're given</u> about the triangle...

Three Sides — use a *Ruler and Compasses*

 **Construct the triangle ABC where AB = 6 cm, BC = 4 cm, AC = 5 cm.**

First, <u>sketch and label</u> a triangle so you know roughly what's needed. It doesn't matter which line you make the base line.

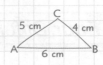

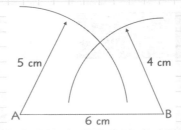

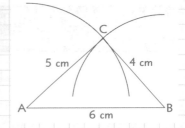

Draw the <u>base line</u> accurately. <u>Label</u> the ends A and B.

For AC, set the <u>compasses</u> to <u>5 cm</u>, put the point at A and <u>draw an arc</u>. For BC, set the <u>compasses</u> to <u>4 cm</u>, put the point at B and <u>draw an arc</u>.

Where the <u>arcs cross</u> is <u>point C</u>. Now you can finish your triangle.

Sides and Angles — use a *Ruler and Protractor*

 **Construct triangle DEF. DE = 5 cm, DF = 3 cm, and angle EDF = 40°.**

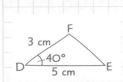

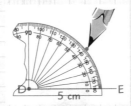

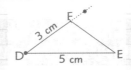

<u>Roughly sketch and label</u> the triangle again.

Draw the <u>base line</u> accurately. Then draw <u>angle EDF</u> (the angle at D) — place the centre of the protractor over D, measure <u>40°</u> and put a dot.

Measure <u>3 cm</u> towards the dot and label it F. Join up <u>D and F</u>. Now you've drawn the <u>two sides</u> and the <u>angle</u>. Just join up F and E to <u>complete</u> the triangle.

If you're given <u>3 pieces of information</u> about a triangle, there's usually only <u>one triangle</u> that you could draw.

SSS — 3 sides

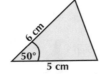

SAS — 2 sides and the angle between them.

ASA — 2 angles and the side between them.

RHS — right angle, the hypotenuse and another side.

However, if you're given <u>2 sides</u> and <u>an angle which isn't between them</u>, there are <u>TWO</u> possible triangles you could draw.

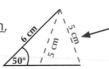

The 5 cm side could be in either of the positions shown.

Don't forget your compasses and protractor for the exam

Constructing a triangle isn't difficult, so long as you learn the methods on this page — and remember to take your ruler, compasses and protractor with you into the exam. You won't get far without them.

Loci and Constructions

A <u>LOCUS</u> (another ridiculous maths word) is simply:

> A LINE or REGION that shows <u>all the points which fit a given rule</u>.

Make sure you learn how to do these <u>PROPERLY</u> using a <u>ruler</u> and <u>compasses</u> as shown on the next few pages.

The **Four** Different Types of **Loci**

Loci is just the plural of locus.

1) The locus of points which are '<u>A FIXED DISTANCE</u> from a given <u>POINT</u>'.

This locus is simply a <u>CIRCLE</u>.

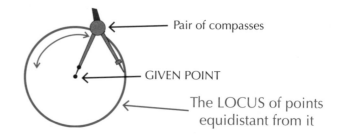

Pair of compasses

GIVEN POINT

The LOCUS of points equidistant from it

2) The locus of points which are '<u>A FIXED DISTANCE</u> from a given <u>LINE</u>'.

This locus is a <u>SAUSAGE SHAPE</u>.

It has <u>straight sides</u> (drawn with a <u>ruler</u>) and <u>ends</u> which are <u>perfect semicircles</u> (drawn with compasses).

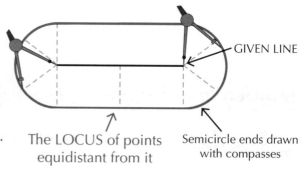

GIVEN LINE

The LOCUS of points equidistant from it

Semicircle ends drawn with compasses

3) The locus of points which are '<u>EQUIDISTANT</u> from <u>TWO GIVEN LINES</u>'.

1) Keep the compass setting <u>THE SAME</u> while you make <u>all four marks</u>.
2) Make sure you <u>leave</u> your compass marks <u>showing</u>.
3) You get <u>two equal angles</u> — i.e. this <u>LOCUS</u> is actually an <u>ANGLE BISECTOR</u>.

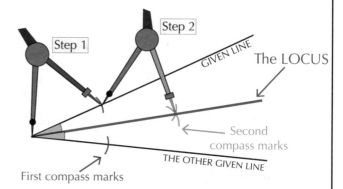

Step 1

Step 2

GIVEN LINE

The LOCUS

Second compass marks

THE OTHER GIVEN LINE

First compass marks

4) The locus of points which are '<u>EQUIDISTANT</u> from <u>TWO GIVEN POINTS</u>'.

<u>This LOCUS</u> is all points which are the <u>same distance</u> from A as they are from B.

This time the locus is actually the <u>PERPENDICULAR BISECTOR</u> of the line joining the two points.

The perpendicular bisector of line segment AB is a line at right angles to AB, passing through the midpoint of AB. This is the method to use if you're asked to draw it.

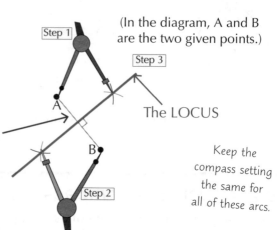

(In the diagram, A and B are the two given points.)

Step 1

Step 3

A

The LOCUS

B

Step 2

Keep the compass setting the same for all of these arcs.

Loci and Constructions

Don't just read the page through once and hope you'll remember it — get your ruler, compasses and pencil out and have a go. It's the only way of testing whether you really know this stuff.

Constructing *Accurate 60° Angles* C

1) They may well ask you to draw an <u>accurate 60° angle</u> without a protractor.

2) One thing they're needed for is constructing <u>equilateral triangles</u>.

3) <u>Follow the method</u> shown in this diagram (make sure you leave the compass settings the <u>same</u> for each step).

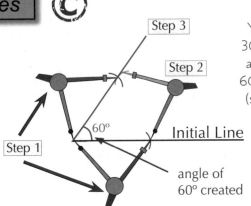

You can construct 30° angles and 45° angles by bisecting 60° and 90° angles (see previous page).

Constructing *Accurate 90° Angles* C

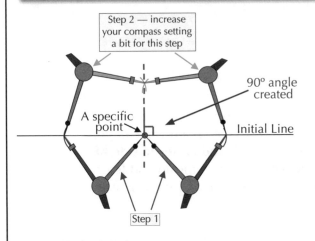

1) They might want you to construct an <u>accurate 90° angle</u>.

2) Make sure you can <u>follow the method</u> shown in this diagram.

The examiners <u>won't</u> accept any of these constructions done 'by eye' or with a protractor. You've got to do them the <u>proper way</u>, with <u>compasses</u>. <u>Don't</u> rub out your compass marks, or the examiner won't know you used the proper method.

Drawing the *Perpendicular* from a *Point* to a *Line* C

1) This is similar to the one above but <u>not quite the same</u> — make sure you can do <u>both</u>.

2) You'll be given a line and a point, like this: →

A ——— B

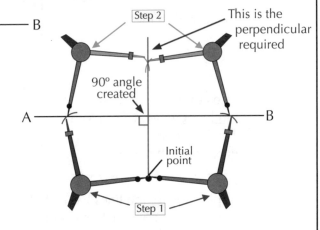

Constructing <u>TWO PERPENDICULARS</u> gives you
<u>PARALLEL LINES</u>

If you draw another line perpendicular to the line you've just drawn, it'll be parallel to the initial line:

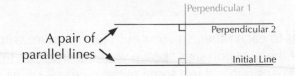

Constructions are basically tricks for maths drawings

There's nothing too 'mathsy' about this page. It's just a few simple tricks to use to draw different angles accurately — it's almost art. So get it learnt quick-smart so you can get back to the maths.

Loci and Constructions — Worked Examples

Now you know what <u>loci</u> are, and how to do all the <u>constructions</u> you need, it's time to put them all together.

Finding a **Locus** that Satisfies **Lots of Rules**

In the exam, you might be given a situation with <u>lots</u> of different <u>conditions</u>, and asked to find the <u>region</u> that satisfies <u>all</u> the conditions. To do this, just draw <u>each locus</u>, then see which bit you want.

EXAMPLE: **On the square below, shade the region that is within 3 cm of vertex A and closer to vertex B than vertex D.**

The <u>shaded area</u> is the region you want.

Construct a <u>quarter circle</u> <u>3 cm from A</u> using a pair of compasses — you want the region within it.

It's a square, so this diagonal is <u>equidistant</u> from B and D. The bit <u>above</u> the line is closer to B than D.

If it wasn't a square you'd have to <u>construct</u> the equidistant line with a <u>compass</u> using the method on p134.

You might be given the information as a <u>wordy problem</u> — work out what you're being asked for and draw it.

EXAMPLE: **Tessa is organising a village fete. The fete will take place on a rectangular field, shown in the diagram below. Tessa is deciding where an ice cream van can go. It has to be at least 1 m away from each edge of the field, and closer to side AB than side CD. There is a maypole at M, and the ice cream van must be at least 2 m away from the maypole. The diagram is drawn to a scale of 1 cm = 2 m. Show on it where the ice cream van can go.**

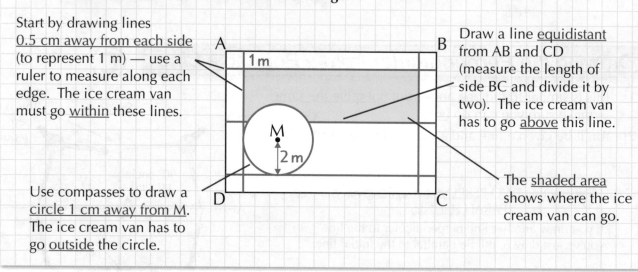

Start by drawing lines <u>0.5 cm away from each side</u> (to represent 1 m) — use a ruler to measure along each edge. The ice cream van must go <u>within</u> these lines.

Use compasses to draw a <u>circle 1 cm away from M</u>. The ice cream van has to go <u>outside</u> the circle.

Draw a line <u>equidistant</u> from AB and CD (measure the length of side BC and divide it by two). The ice cream van has to go <u>above</u> this line.

The <u>shaded area</u> shows where the ice cream van can go.

In the examples above, the lines were all at <u>right angles</u> to each other, so you could just measure with a <u>ruler</u> rather than do constructions with compasses. If the question says "<u>Leave your construction lines clearly visible</u>", you'll definitely need to <u>get your compasses out</u> and use some of the methods on p134-135.

If there are several rules, draw each locus, then find the bit you want

Don't panic if you get a wordy loci question — just deal with one condition at a time and work out which bit you need to shade at the end. Make sure you draw your loci accurately — it's really important.

Bearings

Bearings. They'll be useful next time you're off sailing. Or in your Maths exam.

Bearings

To find or plot a bearing you must remember <u>the three key words</u>:

1) 'FROM' <u>Find the word 'FROM' in the question</u>, and put your pencil on the diagram at the point you are going '<u>from</u>'.

2) NORTH LINE At the point you are going <u>FROM</u>, <u>draw in a NORTH LINE</u>. (There'll often be one drawn for you in exam questions.)

3) CLOCKWISE Now draw in the angle CLOCKWISE <u>from the north line to the line joining the two points</u>. This angle is the required bearing.

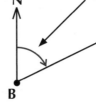

The bearing of A from B

EXAMPLE: **Find the bearing of Q from P.**

> ALL BEARINGS SHOULD BE GIVEN AS 3 FIGURES
> e.g. 176°, 034° (not 34°), 005° (not 5°), 018° etc.

1) 'From P'

2) North line at P

3) <u>Clockwise</u>, from the N-line. This angle is the bearing of Q from P. Measure it with your protractor: **245°**

EXAMPLE: **The bearing of Z from Y is 110°. Find the bearing of Y from Z.**

See page 99 for interior angles.

First sketch a diagram so you can see what's going on. Angles a and b are <u>interior angles</u>, so they add up to <u>180°</u>.

Angle b = 180° − 110° = 70°
So bearing of Y from Z = 360° − 70° = 290°.

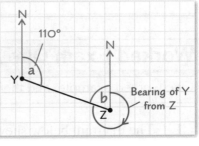

Bearings Questions and **Scale Drawings**

EXAMPLE: **A hiker walks 2 km from point A, on a bearing of 036°. If the scale of the map below is 2 cm to 1 km, how far is the hiker now from his car?**

First, draw a line at a <u>bearing of 036°</u> from point A. <u>1 km</u> is <u>2 cm</u> on the map and the hiker walks <u>2 km</u>, so make the line from A <u>4 cm</u> long.

You want the distance of the hiker from the car, so use a ruler to measure it on the map, then use the scale to work out the <u>real distance</u> it represents.

> Distance to car on map = 3 cm. 2 cm = 1 km, so 1 cm = 0.5 km, therefore 3 cm = 1.5 km.

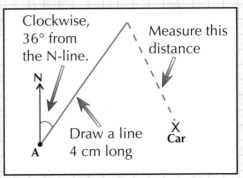

If you are asked to <u>CALCULATE</u> a distance or an angle, you'll need to use the <u>cosine or sine</u> rule (see p147).

FROM a point draw a NORTH LINE then draw the angle CLOCKWISE

Make sure you've learnt the three key words above and the method for using them — scribble them out from memory to check you've got them spot on, then have a go at some questions to practise <u>using</u> them.

Warm-up and Worked Exam Questions

You need to work through these one by one and make sure you really know what you're doing with your ruler and compasses. Look back over the last five pages if you get stuck.

Warm-up Questions

1) Using a compass and ruler, construct an equilateral triangle with sides of length 4 cm.

2) Construct a triangle with sides 3 cm, 4 cm and 5 cm. Check it by measuring the sides.

3) The gardens of a stately home are shown on the diagram below. The public can visit the gardens, but must stay at least 2 m away from the rectangular pond and at least 2 m away from each of the statues (labelled A and B). Make a copy of this diagram using a scale of 1 cm = 2 m and indicate on it the areas where the public can go.

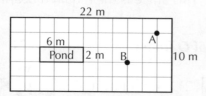

4) Construct four 90° angles to form a square with side length 5.5 cm.

5) Draw a line and a point and construct the perpendicular from the point to the line.

6) A ship sails 12 km on a bearing of 050°, then 20 km on a bearing of 100°.
   It then sails directly back to its starting position. Calculate this distance to 1 d.p.

Worked Exam Question

One worked example, and then it's over to you.

1 The diagram below shows a sketch of a field *ABCD*. A footpath *AC* runs across the field.

a) Make an accurate scale drawing of the field.
   Use a scale of 1 cm : 10 m.

   This is just like constructing two triangles.

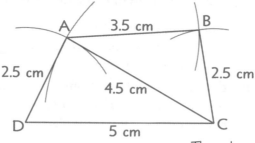

Not drawn accurately

Draw a 5 cm base line
(to represent 50 m),
and draw arcs from D
and C to find point A.

Then draw arcs from A and
C to find point B.

[3 marks]

b) Using your scale drawing, find the length of the line *BD* in the real field.

   On the diagram, BD = 5.2 cm, so in the real field BD = 5.2 × 10 = 52 m

   Remember the scale
   is 1 cm = 10 m.   ....52... m

   [2 marks]

Exam Questions

2 Two ships leave a port at the same time.
Ship *A* travels due west for 40 km. Ship *B* travels 60 km on a bearing of 110°.

   a) Using a scale of 1 cm = 10 km, draw the journeys of the two ships in the space below
      and clearly mark their final positions.

N

Port

[4 marks]

   b) Measure the final bearing of Ship *B* from Ship *A*.

.... °
[1 mark]

   c) Calculate the final bearing of Ship *A* from Ship *B*.

.... °
[2 marks]

3 *RS* is a straight line.

 Use a ruler and compasses to construct an angle of 60° to the line *RS* at the point *R*.
Show all of your construction lines.

*It's really important
that you don't rub out
your construction lines
in these questions —
you won't get all the
marks otherwise.*

R
                                  S

[2 marks]

4 *ABC* is a triangle.

Find and shade the region inside the triangle which is **both** closer to the line *AB* than
the line *BC*, **and** also more than 6.5 cm from the point *C*.

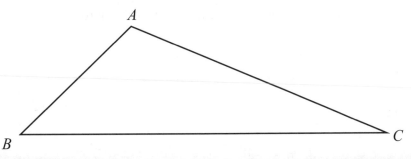

[4 marks]

Revision Questions for Section Four

There are lots of opportunities to show off your artistic skills here (as long as you use them to answer the questions).

* Try these questions and <u>tick off each one</u> when you <u>get it right</u>.
* When you've done <u>all the questions</u> for a topic and are <u>completely happy</u> with it, tick off the topic.

Angles and Polygons (p98-102) ☑

1) What do angles in a quadrilateral add up to?

2) Find the missing angles in the diagrams below.

a)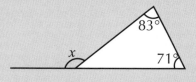
b)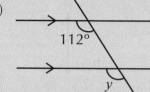
c)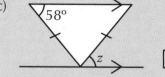

3) Find the exterior angle of a regular hexagon.

4) How many lines of symmetry does an equilateral triangle have?
What is its order of rotational symmetry?

Circle Geometry (p105-107) ☑

5) What angle is formed when a tangent meets a radius?

6) Find the missing angle in each of the diagrams below.

a)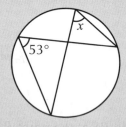
b)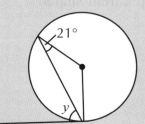
c)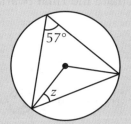

Transformations (p110-112) ☑

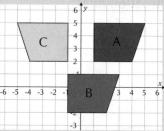

7) Describe the transformation that maps:
a) Shape A onto Shape B
b) Shape A onto shape C

8) Carry out the following transformations on the triangle X, which has vertices (1, 1), (4, 1) and (2, 3):

a) a rotation of 90° clockwise about (1, 1)   b) a translation by the vector $\begin{pmatrix} -3 \\ -4 \end{pmatrix}$
c) an enlargement of scale factor 2, centre (1, 1)

9) A shape with area 5 cm² is enlarged by a scale factor of 4. What is the area of the enlarged shape?

Congruence and Similarity (p113-114) ☑

10) State the four conditions you can use to prove that two triangles are congruent.

11) Prove that triangles ABC and ACD on the right are congruent.

12) The shapes on the right are similar.
What is the length of side x?

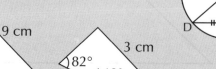

Revision Questions for Section Four

Projections (p118) ☑

13) What is a plan view?

14) On squared paper, draw the front elevation of the shape on the right.

Area, Surface Area and Volume (p119-123) ☑

15) What is the formula for finding the area of a trapezium?

16) Find the area of the shape on the right.

17) A circle has diameter 16 cm.
Find its exact circumference and area.

18) Find the area of the sector with radius 10 cm and angle 45° to 2 d.p.

19) What is the formula for finding the surface area of a sphere?

20) The shape on the right is made from a cylinder and a hemisphere.
Find its exact surface area.

21) Find the volume of a hexagonal prism with
a cross-sectional area 36 cm² and length 11 cm.

22) Find the volume of the solid on the right (to 2 d.p.):

Density, Speed and Distance-Time Graphs (p127-128) ☑

23) Find the volume of a snowman if its density is 0.4 g/cm³ and its mass is 5 kg.

24) Find the average speed of a car if it travels 63 miles in an hour and a half.

25) What does a horizontal line mean
on a distance-time graph?

26) The graph on the right shows
Ben's car journey.
What speed did he drive home at?

Unit Conversions (p129-130) ☑

27) Convert   a) 5.6 litres to cm³,   b) 8 pounds to kg,   c) 3 m/s to km/h,   d) 569 m² to cm².

28) Convert 12 km to miles. Construct a graph if you need to.

Constructions and Loci (p133-136) ☑

29) Construct triangle XYZ, where XY = 5.6 cm, XZ = 7.2 cm and angle YXZ = 55°.

30) Construct two triangles, ABC, with angle A = 40°, AB = 6 cm, BC = 4.5 cm.

31) What shape does the locus of points that are a fixed distance from a given point make?

32) Construct an accurate 45° angle.

33) Draw a square with sides of length 6 cm and label it ABCD. Shade the region
that is nearer to AB than CD and less than 4 cm from vertex A.

Bearings (p137) ☑

34) Describe how to find a bearing from point A to point B.

35) A helicopter flies 25 km on a bearing of 210°, then 20 km on a bearing of 040°.
Draw a scale diagram to show this. Use a scale of 1 cm = 5 km.

Pythagoras' Theorem

Pythagoras' theorem sounds hard but it's actually <u>dead simple</u>.
It's also dead important, so make sure you really get your teeth into it.

Pythagoras' Theorem — $a^2 + b^2 = c^2$

1) PYTHAGORAS' THEOREM only works for RIGHT-ANGLED TRIANGLES.

2) Pythagoras uses <u>two sides</u> to find the <u>third side</u>.

3) The <u>BASIC FORMULA</u> for Pythagoras is $a^2 + b^2 = c^2$

4) Make sure you get the numbers in the <u>RIGHT PLACE</u>. c is the <u>longest</u> side (called the hypotenuse) and it's always <u>opposite</u> the right angle.

5) Always <u>CHECK</u> that your answer is <u>SENSIBLE</u>.

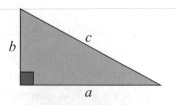

$$a^2 + b^2 = c^2$$

EXAMPLE: **ABC is a right-angled triangle. AB = 6 m and AC = 3 m. Find the exact length of BC.**

1) Write down the <u>formula</u>. → $a^2 + b^2 = c^2$

2) Put in the <u>numbers</u>. → $BC^2 + 3^2 = 6^2$

3) <u>Rearrange</u> the equation. → $BC^2 = 6^2 - 3^2 = 36 - 9 = 27$

4) Take <u>square roots</u> to find BC. → $BC = \sqrt{27} = 3\sqrt{3}$ m

5) '<u>Exact length</u>' means you should give your answer as a <u>surd</u> — <u>simplified</u> if possible.

It's not always c you need to find — loads of people go wrong here.

Remember to check the answer's <u>sensible</u> — here it's about <u>5.2</u>, which is between <u>3 and 6</u>, so that seems about right...

Use **Pythagoras** to find the **Distance Between Points**

You need to know how to find the straight-line <u>distance</u> between <u>two points</u> on a <u>graph</u>.
If you get a question like this, follow these rules and it'll all become breathtakingly simple:

> 1) Draw a <u>sketch</u> to show the <u>right-angled triangle</u>.
> 2) Find the <u>lengths of the shorter sides</u> of the triangle.
> 3) <u>Use Pythagoras</u> to find the <u>length of the hypotenuse</u>. (That's your answer.)

EXAMPLE: **Point P has coordinates (8, 3) and point Q has coordinates (–4, 8). Find the length of the line PQ.**

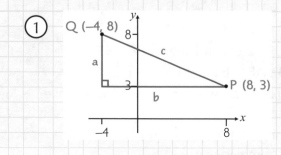

② Length of <u>side a</u> = 8 – 3 = 5
   Length of <u>side b</u> = 8 – –4 = 12

③ Use <u>Pythagoras</u> to find <u>side c</u>:
   $c^2 = a^2 + b^2 = 5^2 + 12^2 = 25 + 144 = 169$
   So: $c = \sqrt{169} = 13$

Finding lengths in a right-angled triangle? Pythagoras is your man

This is probably one of the most famous of all maths formulas. It will most likely be in your exam at some point, so don't risk losing important marks — learn the formula and practise some questions.

Trigonometry — Sin, Cos, Tan

Trigonometry — it's a big scary word. It's <u>important</u> and <u>always cropping up</u> in exams, but if you just follow the method below it won't be a big scary topic.

The 3 Trigonometry Formulas

There are three basic <u>trig formulas</u> — each one links <u>two sides and an angle</u> of a <u>right-angled triangle</u>.

$$\text{Sin } x = \frac{\text{Opposite}}{\text{Hypotenuse}} \qquad \text{Cos } x = \frac{\text{Adjacent}}{\text{Hypotenuse}} \qquad \text{Tan } x = \frac{\text{Opposite}}{\text{Adjacent}}$$

- The <u>Hypotenuse</u> is the <u>LONGEST SIDE</u>.
- The <u>Opposite</u> is the side <u>OPPOSITE</u> the angle <u>being used</u> (x).
- The <u>Adjacent</u> is the (other) side <u>NEXT TO</u> the angle <u>being used</u>.

1) Whenever you come across a trig question, work out which <u>two sides</u> of the triangle are involved in that question — then <u>pick the formula</u> that involves those sides.
2) <u>To find the angle — use the inverse</u>, i.e. press **SHIFT** or **2ndF**, followed by <u>sin</u>, <u>cos</u> or <u>tan</u> (and make sure your calculator is in DEG mode) — your calculator will display <u>sin⁻¹</u>, <u>cos⁻¹</u> or <u>tan⁻¹</u>.
3) Remember, you can only use sin, cos and tan on <u>right-angled triangles</u> — you may have to add lines to the diagram to create one.

There's more about formula triangles on p127 if you need to jog your memory.

Formula Triangles Make Things Simple

A handy way to tackle trig questions is to convert the formulas into <u>formula triangles</u>. Then you can use the <u>same method every time</u>, no matter which side or angle is being asked for.

1) <u>Label</u> the three sides <u>O, A and H</u> (Opposite, Adjacent and Hypotenuse).
2) Write down <u>from memory</u> 'SOH CAH TOA'.
3) Decide which <u>two sides</u> are <u>involved</u>: O,H A,H or O,A and select <u>SOH</u>, <u>CAH</u> or <u>TOA</u> accordingly.
4) Turn the one you choose into a <u>FORMULA TRIANGLE</u>:

5) <u>Cover up</u> the thing you want to find (with your finger), and write down whatever is left showing.
6) <u>Translate into numbers</u> and work it out.
7) Finally, <u>check</u> that your answer is <u>sensible</u>.

In the formula triangles, S represents sin x, C is cos x, and T is tan x.

H = longest, O = opposite, A = next to, and remember SOH CAH TOA

It's vital to practise exam questions, but don't make the mistake of thinking it's pointless learning these seven steps first. If you don't know them all thoroughly, you'll just keep on getting questions wrong.

Trigonometry — Sin, Cos, Tan

Here are some lovely examples to help you through the trials of trig.

Examples: Ⓑ

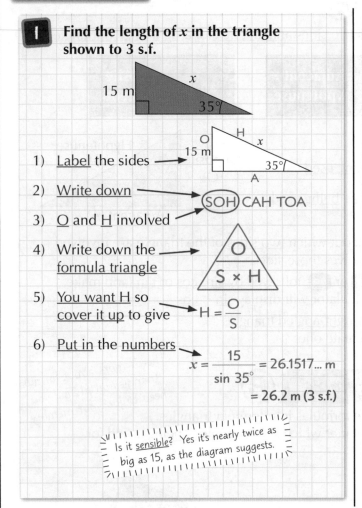

1 Find the length of x in the triangle shown to 3 s.f.

1) <u>Label</u> the sides ⟶

2) <u>Write down</u> ⟶ (SOH) CAH TOA

3) <u>O</u> and <u>H</u> involved

4) Write down the <u>formula triangle</u> ⟶

5) <u>You want H</u> so <u>cover it up</u> to give ⟶ $H = \dfrac{O}{S}$

6) <u>Put in</u> the <u>numbers</u> ⟶

$$x = \frac{15}{\sin 35°} = 26.1517... \text{ m}$$

$$= 26.2 \text{ m (3 s.f.)}$$

Is it <u>sensible</u>? Yes it's nearly twice as big as 15, as the diagram suggests.

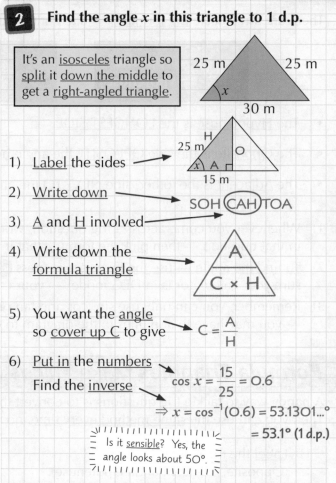

2 Find the angle x in this triangle to 1 d.p.

It's an <u>isosceles</u> triangle so <u>split</u> it <u>down the middle</u> to get a <u>right-angled triangle</u>.

1) <u>Label</u> the sides ⟶

2) <u>Write down</u> ⟶ SOH (CAH) TOA

3) <u>A</u> and <u>H</u> involved

4) Write down the <u>formula triangle</u> ⟶

5) You want the <u>angle</u> so <u>cover up C</u> to give ⟶ $C = \dfrac{A}{H}$

6) <u>Put in</u> the <u>numbers</u>
   Find the <u>inverse</u> ⟶ $\cos x = \dfrac{15}{25} = 0.6$

$$\Rightarrow x = \cos^{-1}(0.6) = 53.1301...°$$

$$= 53.1° \text{ (1 d.p.)}$$

Is it <u>sensible</u>? Yes, the angle looks about 50°.

Angles of *Elevation* and *Depression* Ⓑ

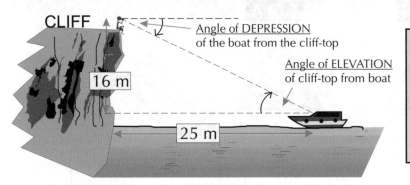

CLIFF

Angle of DEPRESSION of the boat from the cliff-top

Angle of ELEVATION of cliff-top from boat

16 m

25 m

1) The <u>Angle of Depression</u> is the angle <u>downwards</u> from the horizontal.

2) The <u>Angle of Elevation</u> is the angle <u>upwards</u> from the horizontal.

3) The angles of elevation and depression are <u>equal</u>.

You need to have learnt all seven steps on page 143

Here you can see the seven steps from the last page being put into action. You can see how easy it is to apply those steps, but only if you can remember them and practise using them — so practise.

Warm-up and Worked Exam Questions

Learning facts and practising exam questions is the only recipe for success.
That's what the questions on these pages are all about. All you have to do — is do them.

Warm-Up Questions

1) In a right-angled triangle, the two shorter sides are 10 cm and 8.4 cm. Find:
   a) the length of the longest side, correct to 3 significant figures.
   b) the smallest angle, correct to the nearest degree.
2) Find the length of x in the triangle to the right.

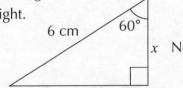

6 cm   60°

x Not to scale

Worked Exam Questions

There's a knack to using the facts you've stored away in your brain box to get marks in the exam.
These worked examples will really help you see how...

1 The diagram shows a right-angled triangle ABC.
AC is 4 cm long. BC is 8 cm long.

Calculate the length of AB.
Give your answer to 2 decimal places.

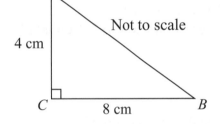

Not to scale

4 cm

C 8 cm B

$4^2 + 8^2 = AB^2$ Use Pythagoras' Theorem:
                        $a^2 + b^2 = c^2$
$16 + 64 = 80 = AB^2$

$\sqrt{80} = AB$, so $AB = 8.94427... = 8.94$ cm (to 2 d.p.)

........**8.94**........ cm
[3 marks]

2 The diagram shows a right-angled triangle.
Find the size of the angle marked x.
Give your answer to 1 decimal place.

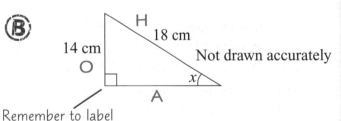

H
18 cm
14 cm
O   Not drawn accurately
            x
        A

Remember to label
your triangle

SOH CAH TOA

$\frac{O}{S \times H}$

$S = \dfrac{O}{H}$

$\sin x = \dfrac{14}{18}$, so $x = \sin^{-1}(14 \div 18) = 51.05755... = 51.1°$ (to 1 d.p.)

........**51.1**........ °
[3 marks]

Exam Questions

3   A triangle has a base of 10 cm. Its other two sides are both 13 cm long. **C**
     Calculate the area of the triangle.

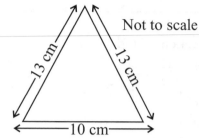

Not to scale

.... cm²
[4 marks]

4   In the triangle below, *AB* = *BC* = 10 m and angle *C* = 34°. **B**

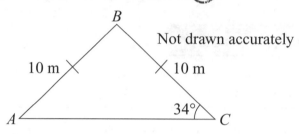

B

Not drawn accurately

10 m   10 m

A   34° *C*

a) Calculate the length *AC*.
    Give your answer to 2 decimal places.

.... m
[3 marks]

b) Calculate the height of the triangle.
    Give your answer to 2 decimal places.

.... m
[3 marks]

5   The diagram shows a kite *EFGH*.
     Diagonal *EG* bisects the diagonal *HF* at *M*. **B**
     EM = 5 cm, *MG* = 9 cm and *HF* = 12 cm.

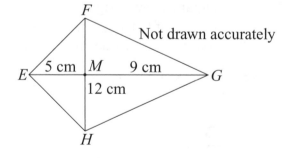

F

Not drawn accurately

E   5 cm *M*   9 cm   *G*

12 cm

H

a) Calculate the size of angle *FGM*.
    Give your answer to 1 decimal place.

...........................°
[3 marks]

b) Calculate the size of angle *FEH*.
    Give your answer to 1 decimal place.

...........................°
[3 marks]

The Sine and Cosine Rules

Normal trigonometry using SOH CAH TOA etc. can only be applied to <u>right-angled</u> triangles. Which leaves us with the question of what to do with other-angled triangles. Step forward the <u>Sine and Cosine Rules</u>...

Labelling *the Triangle*

This is very important. You must label the sides and angles properly so that the letters for the sides and angles correspond with each other. Use <u>lower case letters</u> for the <u>sides</u> and <u>capitals</u> for the <u>angles</u>.

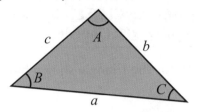

Remember, <u>side '*a*' is opposite angle *A*</u> etc.

It doesn't matter which sides you decide to call *a*, *b*, and *c*, just as long as the angles are then labelled properly.

Three Formulas to Learn:

The **Sine** Rule

$$\frac{a}{\sin A} = \frac{b}{\sin B} = \frac{c}{\sin C}$$

You don't use the whole thing with both '=' signs of course, so it's not half as bad as it looks — you just <u>choose the two bits</u> that you want:

e.g. $\dfrac{b}{\sin B} = \dfrac{c}{\sin C}$ or $\dfrac{a}{\sin A} = \dfrac{b}{\sin B}$

The **Cosine** Rule

The 'normal' form is...

$$a^2 = b^2 + c^2 - 2bc\,\cos A$$

...or this form is good for finding an angle (you get it by rearranging the 'normal' version):

$$\text{or} \quad \cos A = \frac{b^2 + c^2 - a^2}{2bc}$$

Area *of the Triangle*

This formula comes in handy when you know <u>two sides</u> and the <u>angle between them</u>:

Area of triangle = ½ *ab* sin *C*

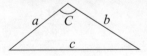

Of course, you already know a simple formula for calculating the area using the base length and height (see p119). The formula here is for when you don't know those values.

EXAMPLE:

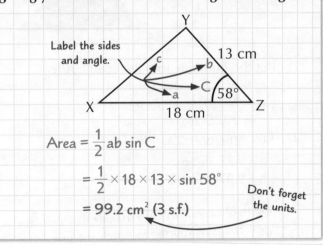

Triangle XYZ has XZ = 18 cm, YZ = 13 cm and angle XZY = 58°. Find the area of the triangle, giving your answer correct to 3 significant figures.

Label the sides and angle.

Area $= \dfrac{1}{2}$ ab sin C

$= \dfrac{1}{2} \times 18 \times 13 \times \sin 58°$

$= 99.2$ cm^2 (3 s.f.)

Don't forget the units.

Make sure you label each side and angle of the triangle correctly

The rearranged cosine rule won't be on the formula sheet in your exam — but the other 3 formulas will. It'll really help if you learn them all now, though. Even more importantly, you need to practise using them.

The Sine and Cosine Rules

Amazingly, there are only <u>FOUR</u> question types where the <u>sine</u> and <u>cosine</u> rules would be applied. So learn the exact details of these four examples and you'll be laughing.

The Four Examples

---

1 | <u>TWO ANGLES</u> given plus <u>ANY SIDE</u> — <u>SINE RULE</u> needed.

Find the length of _AB_ for the triangle below.

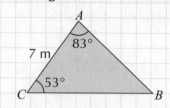

1) Don't forget the obvious...
   $B = 180° - 83° - 53° = 44°$

2) Put the <u>numbers</u> into the <u>sine rule</u>.
   $$\frac{b}{\sin B} = \frac{c}{\sin C} \Rightarrow \frac{7}{\sin 44°} = \frac{c}{\sin 53°}$$

3) <u>Rearrange</u> to find c.
   $$\Rightarrow c = \frac{7 \times \sin 53°}{\sin 44°} = 8.05 \text{ m (3 s.f.)}$$

---

2 | <u>TWO SIDES</u> given plus an <u>ANGLE NOT ENCLOSED</u> by them — <u>SINE RULE</u> needed.

Find angle _ABC_ for the triangle shown below.

1) Put the <u>numbers</u> into the <u>sine rule</u>.
   $$\frac{b}{\sin B} = \frac{c}{\sin C} \Rightarrow \frac{7}{\sin B} = \frac{8}{\sin 53°}$$

2) <u>Rearrange</u> to find $\sin B$.
   $$\Rightarrow \sin B = \frac{7 \times \sin 53°}{8} = 0.6988...$$

3) Find the <u>inverse</u>.
   $$\Rightarrow B = \sin^{-1}(0.6988...) = 44.3° \text{ (1 d.p.)}$$

---

3 | <u>TWO SIDES</u> given plus the <u>ANGLE ENCLOSED</u> by them — <u>COSINE RULE</u> needed.

Find the length _CB_ for the triangle to the right.

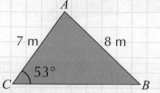

1) Put the <u>numbers</u> into the <u>cosine rule</u>.
   $a^2 = b^2 + c^2 - 2bc \cos A$
   $= 7^2 + 8^2 - 2 \times 7 \times 8 \times \cos 83°$
   $= 99.3506...$

2) Take <u>square roots</u> to find a.
   $a = \sqrt{99.3506...}$
   $= 9.97 \text{ m (3 s.f.)}$

---

4 | <u>ALL THREE SIDES</u> given but <u>NO ANGLES</u> — <u>COSINE RULE</u> needed.

Find angle _CAB_ for the triangle shown.

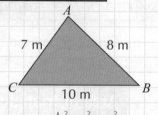

1) Use this version of the <u>cosine rule</u>.
   $$\cos A = \frac{b^2 + c^2 - a^2}{2bc}$$

2) <u>Put in</u> the <u>numbers</u>.
   $$= \frac{49 + 64 - 100}{2 \times 7 \times 8}$$

3) <u>Take the inverse</u> to find _A_.
   $$= \frac{13}{112} = 0.11607...$$
   $$\Rightarrow A = \cos^{-1}(0.11607...)$$
   $$= 83.3° \text{ (1 d.p.)}$$

You might come across a triangle that isn't labelled ABC — just relabel it yourself to match the sine and cosine rules...

Learn which rule you need for which question type

Rather than fret about which equation to use and how to do it, you just need to learn these four basic question types and practise them. It'll save you loads of time and stress on the big day.

3D Pythagoras

This is a 3D version of the 2D Pythagoras theorem you saw on page 142.
There's just <u>one simple formula</u> — learn it and the world's your oyster...

3D Pythagoras for Cuboids — $a^2 + b^2 + c^2 = d^2$ (A)

<u>Cuboids</u> have their own formula for calculating
the length of their <u>longest diagonal</u>:

$$a^2 + b^2 + c^2 = d^2$$

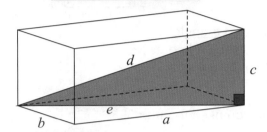

In reality it's nothing you haven't seen before
— it's just <u>2D Pythagoras' theorem</u> being used <u>twice</u>:

1) <u>a, b</u> and <u>e</u> make a <u>right-angled triangle</u> so

$$e^2 = a^2 + b^2$$

2) Now look at the <u>right-angled triangle</u>
formed by <u>e, c</u> and <u>d</u>:

$$d^2 = e^2 + c^2 = a^2 + b^2 + c^2$$

EXAMPLE: **Find the exact length of the diagonal BH for the cube in the diagram.**

1) Write down the <u>formula</u>. $a^2 + b^2 + c^2 = d^2$

2) Put in the <u>numbers</u>. $4^2 + 4^2 + 4^2 = BH^2$

3) Take the <u>square root</u> to find BH. $\Rightarrow BH = \sqrt{48} = 4\sqrt{3}$ cm

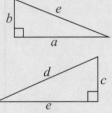

The Cuboid Formula can be used in Other 3D Shapes (A*)

EXAMPLE: **In the square-based pyramid shown, M is the midpoint of the base. Find the vertical height AM.**

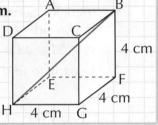

1) <u>Label N</u> as the midpoint of ED.

Then think of <u>EN, NM and AM</u> as three <u>sides</u> of a <u>cuboid</u>, and <u>AE</u> as the <u>longest diagonal</u> in the cuboid (like d in the section above).

2) Sketch the <u>full cuboid</u>.

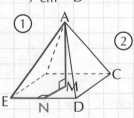

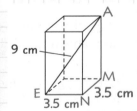

3) Write down the <u>3D Pythagoras formula</u>. $a^2 + b^2 + c^2 = d^2$

4) <u>Rewrite</u> it using <u>side labels</u>. $EN^2 + NM^2 + AM^2 = AE^2$

5) Put in the <u>numbers</u> and <u>solve for AM</u>. $\Rightarrow 3.5^2 + 3.5^2 + AM^2 = 9^2$

$$\Rightarrow AM = \sqrt{81 - 2 \times 12.25} = 7.52 \text{ cm (3 s.f.)}$$

$a^2 + b^2 + c^2 = d^2$ gives you the longest diagonal from the 3 side lengths

Finding the length of the longest diagonal of a cuboid is pretty easy as long as you learn the formula.
Other 3D shapes can be a little more tricky, but really you just need to work out where the formula fits.

3D Trigonometry

3D trig may sound tricky, and in many ways it is... but it's actually just using the <u>same old rules</u>.

Angle Between Line and Plane — Use a Diagram

Learn the 3-Step Method

1) Make a <u>right-angled triangle</u> between the line and the plane.

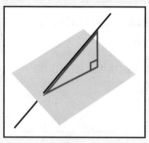

2) Draw a <u>simple 2D sketch</u> of this triangle and mark on the lengths of two sides (you might have to use <u>Pythagoras</u> to find one).

3) Use <u>trig</u> to find the angle.

Have a look at p142-144 to jog your memory about Pythagoras and trig.

EXAMPLE:

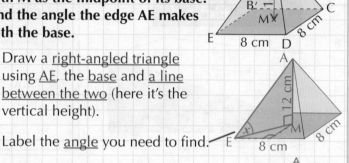

ABCDE is a square-based pyramid with M as the midpoint of its base. Find the angle the edge AE makes with the base.

1) Draw a <u>right-angled triangle</u> using <u>AE</u>, the <u>base</u> and <u>a line between the two</u> (here it's the vertical height).

Label the <u>angle</u> you need to find.

2) Now sketch this triangle in 2D and <u>label</u> it.

Use <u>Pythagoras</u> (on the <u>base</u> triangle) to <u>find EM</u>.

$$EM^2 = 4^2 + 4^2 = 32$$
$$\Rightarrow EM = \sqrt{32} \text{ cm}$$

3) Finally, use <u>trigonometry</u> to find <u>x</u> — you know the <u>opposite</u> and <u>adjacent</u> sides so use <u>tan</u>.

$$\tan x = \frac{12}{\sqrt{32}} = 2.1213...$$
$$x = \tan^{-1}(2.1213...)$$
$$= 64.8° \text{ (1 d.p.)}$$

The Sine Rule and Cosine Rule can also be used in 3D

For <u>triangles</u> inside 3D shapes that <u>aren't right-angled</u> you can use the <u>sine and cosine rules</u>. This sounds mildly terrifying but it's actually OK — just use the <u>same formulas</u> as before (see p147-8).

EXAMPLE: **Find the size of angle AEH in the cuboid on the right.**

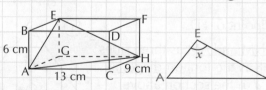

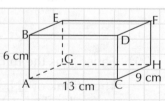

1) <u>Draw the triangle</u> AEH and label angle AEH as x.

2) Use <u>Pythagoras'</u> theorem to find the lengths of <u>AH, AE and EH</u>.

$$AH^2 = 13^2 + 9^2 = 250 \Rightarrow AH = \sqrt{250}$$
$$AE^2 = 6^2 + 9^2 = 117 \Rightarrow AE = \sqrt{117}$$
$$EH^2 = 6^2 + 13^2 = 205 \Rightarrow EH = \sqrt{205}$$

3) <u>Find x using the <u>cosine rule</u>:

Put in the <u>numbers</u>.

<u>Rearrange</u> and take the <u>inverse</u> to find x.

$$AH^2 = AE^2 + EH^2 - 2 \times AE \times EH \times \cos x$$
$$250 = 117 + 205 - 2\sqrt{117}\sqrt{205} \cos x$$
$$x = \cos^{-1}\left(\frac{117 + 205 - 250}{2\sqrt{117 \times 205}}\right) = 76.6° \text{ (1 d.p.)}$$

You can use the 2D trigonometry rules in 3D shapes too

The hard part is working out where to apply the rules you already know. Look for where you can make a triangle, then see which lengths and angles you've got, and which ones you need to find.

Vectors

Vectors represent a movement of a certain <u>size</u> in a certain <u>direction</u>.
They might seem a bit weird at first, but there are really just a few facts to get to grips with...

The Vector **Notations**

There are several ways to <u>write</u> vectors...

They're represented on a diagram by an <u>arrow</u>.

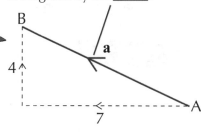

1) <u>Column</u> vectors: $\begin{pmatrix} 2 \\ -5 \end{pmatrix}$ — 2 units right, 5 units down $\begin{pmatrix} -7 \\ 4 \end{pmatrix}$ — 7 units left, 4 units up

2) **a** ———— <u>exam questions</u> use <u>bold</u> like this

3) $\underline{a}$ or $\underset{\sim}{a}$ — <u>you</u> should always <u>underline</u> them
   (unless you have a magical bolding pen...)

4) $\overrightarrow{AB}$ ———— this means the vector <u>from point A to point B</u>

Multiplying a Vector *by a Scalar*

Multiplying a vector by a <u>positive</u> number <u>changes</u> the vector's <u>size</u> but <u>not its direction</u> — it <u>scales</u> the vector. If the number's <u>negative</u> then the <u>direction gets switched</u>.

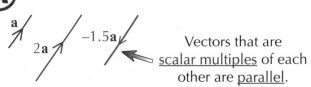

Vectors that are <u>scalar multiples</u> of each other are <u>parallel</u>.

Adding and *Subtracting* Vectors

You can describe movements between points by <u>adding and subtracting known vectors</u>. <u>All vector exam questions</u> are based around this.

"$\underset{\sim}{a} + \underset{\sim}{b}$" means 'go along $\underset{\sim}{a}$ then $\underset{\sim}{b}$'.

In the diagrams, $\overrightarrow{PR} = \underset{\sim}{a} + \underset{\sim}{b}$ and $\overrightarrow{XZ} = \underset{\sim}{c} - \underset{\sim}{d}$.

"$\underset{\sim}{c} - \underset{\sim}{d}$" means 'go along $\underset{\sim}{c}$ then backwards along $\underset{\sim}{d}$' (the <u>minus</u> sign means go the <u>opposite</u> way).

EXAMPLE:

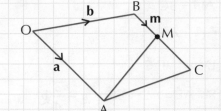

In the diagram below, M is the midpoint of BC.
Find vectors $\overrightarrow{AM}$, $\overrightarrow{OC}$ and $\overrightarrow{AC}$ in terms of **a**, **b** and **m.**

To obtain the <u>unknown vector</u> just '<u>get there</u>' by any route <u>made up of known vectors.</u>

$\overrightarrow{AM} = -\underset{\sim}{a} + \underset{\sim}{b} + \underset{\sim}{m}$ ——— A to M via O and B

$\overrightarrow{OC} = \underset{\sim}{b} + 2\underset{\sim}{m}$ ——— O to C via B and M — M's half-way between B and C so $\overrightarrow{BC} = 2\mathbf{m}$

$\overrightarrow{AC} = -\underset{\sim}{a} + \underset{\sim}{b} + 2\underset{\sim}{m}$ ——— A to C via O, B and M

That's three vital vector facts done

But they're only really 'done' if you've learnt them. So be sure you know how vectors can be written, what multiplying a vector by a scalar does and how to add and subtract vectors — then you're done.

Vectors

Extra bits and pieces can crop up in vector questions — these examples will show you how to tackle them...

Vectors Along a Straight Line

1) You can use <u>vectors</u> to <u>show</u> that <u>points lie on a straight line</u>.

2) You need to show that the <u>vectors</u> along <u>each part of the line</u> point in the <u>same direction</u> — i.e. they're <u>scalar multiples</u> of each other.

If XYZ is a straight line then $\overrightarrow{XY}$ must be a scalar multiple of $\overrightarrow{YZ}$.

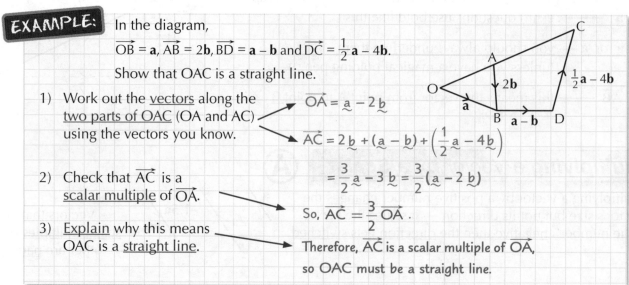

EXAMPLE:

In the diagram,
$\overrightarrow{OB} = \mathbf{a}$, $\overrightarrow{AB} = 2\mathbf{b}$, $\overrightarrow{BD} = \mathbf{a} - \mathbf{b}$ and $\overrightarrow{DC} = \frac{1}{2}\mathbf{a} - 4\mathbf{b}$.

Show that OAC is a straight line.

1) Work out the <u>vectors</u> along the <u>two parts of OAC</u> (OA and AC) using the vectors you know.

$\overrightarrow{OA} = \underset{\sim}{a} - 2\underset{\sim}{b}$

$\overrightarrow{AC} = 2\underset{\sim}{b} + (\underset{\sim}{a} - \underset{\sim}{b}) + \left(\frac{1}{2}\underset{\sim}{a} - 4\underset{\sim}{b}\right)$

2) Check that $\overrightarrow{AC}$ is a <u>scalar multiple</u> of $\overrightarrow{OA}$.

$= \frac{3}{2}\underset{\sim}{a} - 3\underset{\sim}{b} = \frac{3}{2}(\underset{\sim}{a} - 2\underset{\sim}{b})$

So, $\overrightarrow{AC} = \frac{3}{2}\overrightarrow{OA}$.

3) <u>Explain</u> why this means OAC is a <u>straight line</u>.

Therefore, $\overrightarrow{AC}$ is a scalar multiple of $\overrightarrow{OA}$, so OAC must be a straight line.

Vector Questions Can Involve Ratios

<u>Ratios</u> are used in vector questions to tell you the <u>lengths</u> of different <u>sections of a straight line</u>. If you know the vector along part of that line, you can use this information to <u>find other vectors along the line</u>.

E.g. $X \bullet \quad Y \bullet \quad Z \bullet$ XY : YZ = 2 : 3 tells you that $\overrightarrow{XY} = \frac{2}{5}\overrightarrow{XZ}$ and $\overrightarrow{YZ} = \frac{3}{5}\overrightarrow{XZ}$.

EXAMPLE:

ABCD is a parallelogram, with AB parallel to DC and AD parallel to BC.

Point E lies on DC, such that DE : EC = 3 : 1.
$\overrightarrow{BC} = \mathbf{a}$ and $\overrightarrow{BA} = \mathbf{b}$.
Find $\overrightarrow{AE}$ in terms of **a** and **b**.

1) Write $\overrightarrow{AE}$ as a <u>route</u> along the <u>parallelogram</u>.

$\overrightarrow{AE} = \overrightarrow{AD} + \overrightarrow{DE}$

2) Use the <u>parallel sides</u> to find $\overrightarrow{AD}$ and $\overrightarrow{DC}$.

$\overrightarrow{AD} = \overrightarrow{BC} = \underset{\sim}{a}$

$\overrightarrow{DC} = \overrightarrow{AB} = -\underset{\sim}{b}$

3) Use the <u>ratio</u> to find $\overrightarrow{DE}$.

$\overrightarrow{DE} = \frac{3}{4}\overrightarrow{DC}$

4) Now use $\overrightarrow{AD}$ and $\overrightarrow{DE}$ to find $\overrightarrow{AE}$.

So $\overrightarrow{AE} = \overrightarrow{AD} + \overrightarrow{DE} = \underset{\sim}{a} - \frac{3}{4}\underset{\sim}{b}$

Remember — parallel vectors are scalar multiples of each other

For these types of questions, just use the vectors you're given to find what you're asked for. It's worth learning how to do these questions, because very similar ones are likely to come up on the exam.

Warm-up and Worked Exam Questions

Trigonometry and vector questions can be pretty tricky until you get your head around the basics. That's what these warm-up questions are all about — work through them carefully and check any bits you don't know.

Warm-up Questions

1) In this triangle, find the length of AC, correct to 1 decimal place.

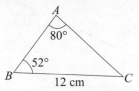

2) A triangle has sides of 4 cm, 6 cm and 8 cm. Calculate the largest angle, correct to 1 d.p.

3) The diagram to the right shows a cuboid $ABCDEFGH$. $FG = 5$ cm, $CD = 2$ cm and $CG = 8$ cm. Calculate the size of the angle FDG.

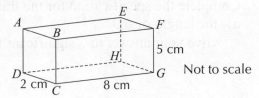

Not to scale

4) $ABCD$ is a parallelogram. $\overrightarrow{AB} = 2\mathbf{a}$ and $\overrightarrow{AD} = 2\mathbf{d}$. L is the midpoint of AC, and M is the midpoint of BC. Write each of the following in terms of $\mathbf{a}$ and $\mathbf{d}$.
   a) $\overrightarrow{CD}$ b) $\overrightarrow{AC}$ c) $\overrightarrow{BL}$

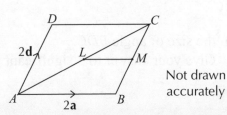

Not drawn accurately

Worked Exam Question

Take the time to go through this example and make sure you understand it all.
If any of the facts are baffling you, it's not too late to take another peek over the section.

1 In the triangle below, $AB = 10$ cm, $BC = 7$ cm and angle $ABC = 85°$. Ⓐ

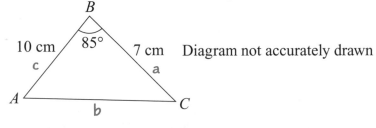

Label the sides of the triangle.

Diagram not accurately drawn

a) Calculate the length of AC.
   Give your answer to 3 significant figures.
   Use the cosine rule to find b:
   $b^2 = a^2 + c^2 - 2ac \cos B,$
   $AC^2 = 7^2 + 10^2 - (2 \times 7 \times 10 \times \cos 85°)$
   $AC = \sqrt{149 - 140 \times \cos 85°} = 11.6907... = 11.7$ cm (to 3 s.f.)

   ....11.7...... cm
   [3 marks]

b) Calculate the area of triangle ABC.
   Give your answer to 3 significant figures.

   You know the length of two sides and the angle between them, so use the area formula from p147.

   $\text{Area} = \dfrac{1}{2}ac \sin B$
   $= \dfrac{1}{2} \times 7 \times 10 \times \sin 85°$
   $= 34.86681... = 34.9$ cm^2 (to 3 s.f)

   ....34.9...... cm^2
   [2 marks]

Exam Questions

2 The diagram below is a sketch of a metal framework.
Some of the information needed to manufacture the framework has been lost.

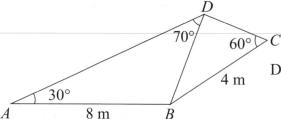

Diagram not accurately drawn

Complete the specification for the framework by calculating:

a) the length of *BD*.
Give your answer to 3 significant figures.

.... m
[3 marks]

b) the size of angle *BDC*.
Give your answer to 3 significant figures.

°
....
[3 marks]

3 In the triangle below, *AB* = 12 cm, *BC* = 19 cm and *AC* = 14 cm. Ⓐ
Calculate the area of the triangle.

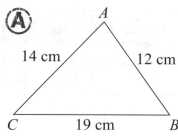

Diagram not accurately drawn

.... cm²
[5 marks]

4 The diagram below is a cuboid *ABCDEFGH*. Ⓐ
The cuboid has sides of length
6 cm, 4 cm and 3 cm.

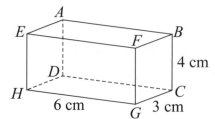

Not to scale

Calculate the length of the diagonal *BH*.
Give your answer to 3 significant figures.

.... cm
[3 marks]

Exam Questions

5 *ABCD* is a parallelogram. $\overrightarrow{AB} = 2\mathbf{a}$ and $\overrightarrow{AD} = 2\mathbf{d}$.
   L is the midpoint of *AC*, and *M* is the midpoint of *BC*.

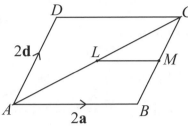

Not drawn accurately

Write in terms of **a** and **d**:

a) $\overrightarrow{CD}$

....
[1 mark]

b) $\overrightarrow{AC}$

....
[1 mark]

c) $\overrightarrow{BL}$

....
[1 mark]

*6 *ABCD* is a quadrilateral.

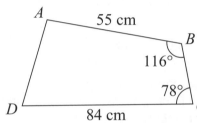

Diagram not accurately drawn

AB = 55 cm.
DC = 84 cm.
Angle *ABC* = 116°.
Angle *BCD* = 78°.

Given that *AC* = 93 cm, work out the area of *ABCD* to 3 significant figures.
Show clearly how you get your answer.

You need to be really clear with
your working here — the * means
you're being tested on your quality
of written communication.

.... cm²
[8 marks]

7 *ABCD* is a parallelogram. $\overrightarrow{AB} = 3\mathbf{a}$, and $\overrightarrow{BW} = \mathbf{b}$.
   M is the midpoint of *CD* and *AX* = 2*XC*.
   BW : *WC* = 1 : 5

a) Find $\overrightarrow{BX}$ in terms of **a** and **b**.

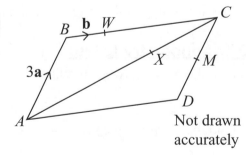

Not drawn
accurately

....
[4 marks]

b) Hence show that *B*, *X* and *M* are three points on a straight line.

[4 marks]

Revision Questions for Section Five

There are a good few facts and formulas in this section, so use this page to check you've got them all sorted.

- Try these questions and <u>tick off each one</u> when you <u>get it right</u>.
- When you've done <u>all the questions</u> for a topic and are <u>completely happy</u> with it, tick off the topic.

Pythagoras' Theorem (p142) ☑

1) What is the formula for Pythagoras' theorem? What do you use it for?

2) A museum has a flight of stairs up to its front door (see diagram).
A ramp is to be put over the top of the steps for wheelchair users.
Calculate the length that the ramp would need to be to 3 s.f.

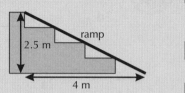

3) Point P has coordinates (–3, –2) and point Q has coordinates (2, 4).
Calculate the length of the line PQ to 1 d.p.

Trigonometry — Sin, Cos, Tan (p143-144) ☑

4) Write down the three trigonometry formula triangles.

5) Find the size of angle *x* in triangle ABC to 1 d.p.

6) Find the length of side XZ of triangle XYZ to 3 s.f.

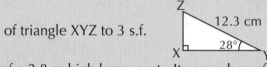

7) A seagull is sitting on top of a 2.8 m high lamp-post. It sees a bag of chips on the ground,
7.1 m away from the base of the lamp-post. Calculate the angle of depression of the chips
from the top of the lamp-post, correct to 1 d.p.

The Sine and Cosine Rules (p147-148) ☑

8) Write down the sine and cosine rules and the formula (involving sin) for the area of any triangle.

9) List the 4 different types of sine/cosine rule questions and which rule you need for each.

10) Triangle JKL has side JK = 7 cm, side JL = 11 cm and angle JLK = 32°. Find angle JKL.

11) In triangle FGH side FH = 8 cm, side GH = 9 cm and angle FHG = 47°. Find the length of side FG.

12) Triangle PQR has side PQ = 12 cm, side QR = 9 cm and angle PQR = 63°. Find its area.

3D Pythagoras (p149) ☑

13) What is the formula for finding the length of the longest diagonal in a cuboid?

14) Find the length of the longest diagonal in the cuboid measuring 5 m × 6 m × 9 m.

3D Trigonometry (p150) ☑

15) Find the angle between the line BH and the plane ABCD in this cuboid.

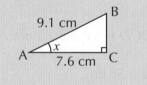

16) Find the size of angle WPU in the cuboid shown to the nearest degree.

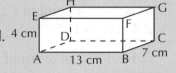

Vectors (p151-152) ☑

17) What is the effect of multiplying a vector by a scalar?

18) ABCD is a quadrilateral.
AXC is a straight line with AX : XC = 1 : 3.
   a) Find $\overrightarrow{AX}$.
   b) Find $\overrightarrow{DX}$ and $\overrightarrow{XB}$.
   c) Is DXB a straight line? Explain your answer.

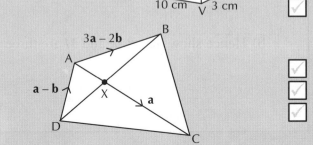

Sampling and Bias

To carry out any statistical investigation, you need to collect data. Ideally, you'd get data from <u>every single member</u> of the '<u>population</u>' you're interested in. Alas, in reality you usually have to make do with a <u>sample</u> of them instead — and you need to be careful when <u>choosing</u> your sample. Read on...

Be Careful — Sample Data Must be Representative

1) The <u>whole group</u> you want to find out about is called the <u>POPULATION</u>.
   It can be a group of anything — people, plants, penguins, you name it.

2) Often you <u>can't survey</u> the <u>whole</u> population, e.g. because it's <u>too big</u>.
   So you <u>select a smaller group</u> from the population, called a <u>SAMPLE</u>, instead.

3) It's really <u>important</u> that your <u>sample fairly represents</u> the <u>WHOLE</u> population.
   This allows you to <u>apply</u> any <u>conclusions</u> from your survey to the <u>whole population</u>.

   For a <u>sample</u> to be <u>representative</u>, it needs to be:

   1 A <u>RANDOM SAMPLE</u>
   — which means <u>every member</u> of the <u>population</u> has an <u>equal chance</u> of being in it.

   2 <u>BIG ENOUGH</u> for the size of the population.

See the next page for random sampling methods.

You Need to Spot Problems with Sampling Methods

A <u>BIASED</u> sample (or survey) is one that <u>doesn't properly represent</u> the <u>whole population</u>.

To <u>SPOT BIAS</u>, you need to <u>think about</u>:
> 1) **WHEN**, **WHERE** and **HOW** the sample is taken.
> 2) **HOW MANY** members are in it.

If certain groups are <u>excluded</u>, the <u>SAMPLE ISN'T RANDOM</u>. And that can lead to <u>BIAS</u> from things like <u>age</u>, <u>gender</u>, different <u>interests</u>, etc. If the <u>sample</u> is <u>too small</u>, it's also likely to be <u>biased</u>.

 **Tina wants to find out how often people travel by train. She decides to ask the people waiting for trains at her local train station one morning. Give one reason why this might not be a suitable sample to choose.**

Think about <u>when</u>, <u>where</u> and <u>how</u> Tina selects her sample:

The sample is biased because it excludes people who never use the train and is likely to include a lot of people who use the train regularly.

You could also say that the sample is only taken at one particular place and time, so won't represent the whole population.

 **Samir's school has 800 pupils. Samir is interested in whether these pupils would like to have more music lessons. For his sample he selects 10 members of the school orchestra. Explain why Samir's sample is likely to be biased.**

Firstly, a sample of 10 is too small to represent the whole school. The sample isn't random — only members of the orchestra are included, so it's likely to be biased in favour of more music lessons.

Always watch out for sampling bias
Make sure you understand why samples should be representative and how to spot when they're not — always think about the two key points above when you're looking for bias.

Sampling Methods

To get a <u>representative sample</u>, you need to use <u>random sampling</u>. Here are two methods you can use.

Simple Random Sampling — *choosing a Random Sample*

One way to get a random sample is to use '<u>simple random sampling</u>'.

To SELECT a SIMPLE RANDOM SAMPLE...

1. <u>Assign a number</u> to <u>every member</u> of the population.
2. Create a <u>list</u> of <u>random numbers</u>, e.g. by using a computer, calculator or picking numbers out of a bag.
3. <u>Match</u> the random numbers to members of the population.

Use **Stratified Sampling** if there are different **Groups**

Sometimes the population can be split into <u>groups</u> where the members have something <u>in common</u>, e.g. age groups or gender. In these cases you can use <u>STRATIFIED SAMPLING</u>.

With this method, <u>each group's share</u> of the <u>sample</u> is calculated based on its <u>share of the population</u> — so bigger groups get more representation, and smaller groups get less.

To calculate the NUMBER of SAMPLE MEMBERS from EACH GROUP...

1. Find the <u>proportion of the population</u> contained in the group. $\longrightarrow$ $\dfrac{\text{Number in group}}{\text{Total population}}$
2. <u>Multiply</u> by the <u>sample size</u>.

Once you've calculated the numbers, use <u>simple random sampling</u> within each group to create the sample.

EXAMPLE: **The table on the right shows information about some of the students at Eastfield Secondary School.**

	Year 9	Year 10	Year 11
Boys	206	219	120
Girls	194	181	80

a) **A sample of 50 students is taken, stratified by year group and gender. Calculate the number of Year 10 girls in the sample.**

1. Find the <u>proportion of students</u> that are <u>Year 10 girls</u>: $\dfrac{181}{206 + 219 + 120 + 194 + 181 + 80} = \dfrac{181}{1000}$ or 0.181 $\longleftarrow$ Total population

2. <u>Multiply</u> by the <u>sample size</u>: $0.181 \times 50 = 9.05$

Round to the nearest whole number $\longrightarrow$ There are 9 Year 10 girls.

b) **A second sample of 100 students is taken, stratified by year group. How many Year 11 students are in this sample?**

1. Now you want the <u>proportion of students</u> in <u>Year 11</u>: $\dfrac{120 + 80}{1000} = \dfrac{2}{10}$ or 0.2

2. <u>Multiply</u> by the <u>sample size</u>: $0.2 \times 100 = 20$ Year 11 students

Stratified sampling can give you a more representative sample

Two sampling strategies to learn on this page which shouldn't be too hard to get your head round. Remember — stratified sampling is about having the same <u>proportions</u> in the sample as in the population.

Collecting Data

Data is often collected to test a <u>hypothesis</u> (or theory). One way to do this is by using <u>questionnaires</u>. But your <u>questions</u> must be <u>crystal clear</u>, and you need to be able to <u>record answers easily and accurately</u>.

You can **Organise** your **Data** into **Classes**

1) Data can be <u>qualitative</u> (<u>words</u>), or <u>quantitative</u> (<u>numbers</u>). <u>Quantitative</u> data is either <u>discrete</u> — can only take certain exact values, or <u>continuous</u> — can take any value in a range.

Primary data is data you've collected <u>yourself</u>, <u>secondary</u> data is collected by <u>others</u>.

2) To collect <u>quantitative</u> data, you often need to <u>group</u> it into <u>classes</u>. <u>Discrete</u> data classes should have '<u>gaps</u>' between them, e.g. '<u>0-1 goals</u>', '<u>2-3 goals</u>' (jump from 1 to 2 — there are no values in between). <u>Continuous</u> data classes should have <u>no 'gaps'</u>, so are often written using <u>inequalities</u> (see p166).

3) Whatever the data you have, make sure <u>none of the classes overlap</u> and they <u>cover all the possible values</u>.

EXAMPLE: **Jonty wants to find out about the ages (in whole years) of people who use his local library. Design a data-collection sheet he could use to collect his data.**

Include <u>columns</u> for: the <u>data values</u>, '<u>Tally</u>' to record the answers and '<u>Frequency</u>' to show the totals.

Use <u>non-overlapping</u> classes — with <u>gaps</u> because the data's <u>discrete</u>.

You can have gaps here, e.g. between 39 and 40, because the ages are all whole numbers, so you don't have to fit 39.5 in.

Age (whole years)	Tally	Frequency
0-19		
20-39		
40-59		
60-79		
80 or over		

Include classes like '<u>...or over</u>', '<u>...or less</u>' or '<u>other</u>' to <u>cover all options</u> in a sensible number of classes.

Design your **Questionnaire Carefully**

You need to be able to <u>say what's wrong</u> with questionnaire <u>questions</u> and <u>write</u> your own <u>good questions</u>. A <u>GOOD</u> question is:

1 <u>CLEAR</u> and <u>EASY TO UNDERSTAND</u> ✓
WATCH OUT FOR:
<u>confusing wording</u> or <u>no time frame</u> ✗

How much do you spend on food? ☐ a little ☐ average amount ☐ a lot

BAD: Wording is vague and no time frame is specified (e.g. each week or month).

BAD: Response boxes might be interpreted differently by different people.

2 <u>EASY TO ANSWER</u> ✓
WATCH OUT FOR:
<u>response boxes</u> that <u>overlap</u>, or <u>don't allow</u> for <u>all possible answers</u> ✗

How many pieces of fruit do you eat a day on average? ☐ 1-2 ☐ 2-3 ☐ 3-4 ☐ 4-5 ☐ > 5

BAD: Response boxes overlap and don't allow an answer of zero.

3 <u>FAIR</u> — <u>NOT LEADING</u> or <u>BIASED</u> ✓
WATCH OUT FOR:
wording that <u>suggests</u> an answer ✗

Do you agree that potatoes taste better than cabbage? ☐ Yes ☐ No

BAD: This is a leading question — you're more likely to say 'Yes'.

4 <u>EASY TO ANALYSE</u> afterwards ✓
WATCH OUT FOR:
<u>open-ended</u> questions, with no limit on the possible answers ✗

What is your favourite food? ....

BAD: Every answer could be different — it would be better to include response boxes to choose from.

Learn the 4 key points for writing good questions

It's easy to ask daft questions, because <u>you</u> know what you mean — but put yourself in the reader's shoes.

Warm-up and Worked Exam Questions

Two lovely warm-up questions here on sampling. If you have any problems with these,
flick back and have another look at the last few pages before looking at the exam questions.

Warm-up Questions

1) Dr Smith wants to survey a sample of 50 of his patients. In total he has 300 patients:
   90 are children, 100 are men and 110 are women.
   He wants the sample to represent the proportion of each group.
   a) What type of sampling procedure should he use?
   b) How many women should be in this sample?

2) The following situation involves a population and a sample.
   Identify both and also identify the source of probable bias:

   A flour company wants to know what proportion of Birmingham households bake some
   or all of their own bread. A sample of 600 residential addresses in Birmingham is taken
   and interviewers are sent to these addresses. The interviewers are employed during regular
   working hours on weekdays and interview only during these hours.

Worked Exam Question

Take a good look at this worked exam question. There are usually loads of different correct answers
for questions like this one, so have a think about other answers you could give.

1   Leah is doing a questionnaire at her school to find Ⓒ
    out how popular after school activities are.

    a) Design a question for Leah to include in her questionnaire.
       You should include suitable response boxes.

       How often do you attend after school activities?   Think about the four key
                                                                   points on p159.
            Never   About once per month

             ☐   ☐

        About once per week   More than once per week

             ☐   ☐

                                                                   [2 marks]

    Leah asks pupils at an after school drama club to complete her questionnaire.

    b) Write down **one** reason why this might not be a suitable sample.

       <u>The results of her survey are likely to be biased as she is only asking people who</u>

       <u>attend an after school activity.</u>
                                                                   [1 mark]
           The key idea here is "bias" — the results of her survey are likely to
           be an unfair representation of what all pupils at the school think.

Exam Questions

2 Mike wants to find out how often people in his year group go to football matches. Ⓒ

He includes the question below in a survey.

How often do you attend football matches?
Sometimes ☐   A lot ☐

a) Write down **one** thing that is wrong with this question.

....

....

[1 mark]

There are 100 people in Mike's year group.

b) Describe a method he could use to take a random sample of these people.

....

....

[2 marks]

3 Dougie is investigating the heights of pupils in his school. There are 720 pupils Ⓐ in the school. The table below shows the number of pupils in each year.

Year	7	8	9	10	11
Number of pupils	167	162	150	125	116

Dougie takes a sample of 75 pupils, stratified by year.
Work out how many pupils from Year 11 are in the sample.

You should answer with a whole number.

....

[2 marks]

4 The table below shows the number of students in two different schools. Ⓐ

School	Male	Female	Total
Appleborough School	435	487	922
Warringpool High	568	543	1111
Total	1003	1030	2033

Cheng wants to take a sample of 150 students, stratified by school and gender.
Work out how many females from Appleborough School should be in his sample.

....

[2 marks]

Mean, Median, Mode and Range

Mean, median, mode and range pop up all the time in statistics questions
— make sure you know what they are.

The Four Definitions

MODE = MOST common
MEDIAN = MIDDLE value (when values are in order of size)
MEAN = TOTAL of items ÷ NUMBER of items
RANGE = Difference between highest and lowest

REMEMBER:

Mode = most (emphasise the 'mo' in each when you say them)

Median = mid (emphasise the m*d in each when you say them)

Mean is just the average, but it's mean 'cos you have to work it out.

The Golden Rule:

There's one vital step for finding the median that lots of people forget:

Always REARRANGE the data in ASCENDING ORDER

(and check you have the same number of entries!)

You absolutely must do this when finding the median,
but it's also really useful for working out the mode too.

EXAMPLE: Find the median, mode, mean, and range of these numbers:

2, 5, 3, 2, 6, –4, 0, 9, –3, 1, 6, 3, –2, 3

Check that you still have the same number of entries after you've rearranged them.

The MEDIAN is the middle value (when they're arranged in order of size)
— so first, rearrange the numbers.

When there are two middle numbers,
the median is halfway between the two.

–4, –3, –2, 0, 1, 2, (2, 3) 3, 3, 5, 6, 6, 9
← seven numbers this side ↑ seven numbers this side →

Median = 2.5

An even number of values means there will be two middle numbers.

MODE (or modal value) is the most common value. ——→ Mode = 3

Some data sets have more than one mode, or no mode at all.

$$\text{MEAN} = \frac{\text{total of items}}{\text{number of items}} \longrightarrow \frac{-4-3-2+0+1+2+2+3+3+3+5+6+6+9}{14}$$

$$= 31 \div 14 = 2.214... = 2.21 \text{ (3 s.f.)}$$

RANGE = distance from lowest to highest value, i.e. from –4 up to 9. ——→ 9 – (–4) = 13

Choose the Best Average

The mean, median and mode
all have their advantages and
disadvantages — LEARN THEM:

	Advantages	Disadvantages
Mean	Uses all the data. Usually most representative.	Isn't always a data value. May be distorted by extreme data values.
Median	Easy to find in ordered data. Not distorted by extreme data values.	Isn't always a data value. Not always a good representation of the data.
Mode	Easy to find in tallied data. Always a data value (when it exists).	Doesn't always exist or sometimes more than one. Not always a good representation of the data.

Mean, median, mode & range — easy marks for learning four words

The maths involved in working these out is so simple that you'd be mad not to learn the definitions.
If you remember which is which and don't make careless arithmetic errors, there's marks to be had.

Averages and Spread

Measures of <u>spread</u> tell you <u>how spread out</u> data is. The <u>range</u> (see the previous page) is a measure of spread over all the data values. The <u>interquartile range</u> tells you the <u>spread</u> of the <u>middle 50%</u> of values.

Quartiles *Divide the Data into* **Four Equal Groups**

1) The quartiles are the <u>lower quartile</u> Q_1, the <u>median</u> Q_2 and the <u>upper quartile</u> Q_3.

2) If you put the data in <u>ascending order</u>, the quartiles are <u>25%</u> (¼), <u>50%</u> (½) and <u>75%</u> (¾) of the way through the list. So if a data set has n values, you work out the <u>positions</u> of the quartiles using these <u>formulas</u>:

Q_1 position number $= (n + 1)/4$
Q_2 position number $= 2(n + 1)/4$
Q_3 position number $= 3(n + 1)/4$

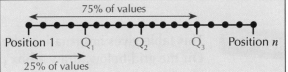

3) The <u>INTERQUARTILE RANGE</u> (IQR) is the <u>difference</u> between the <u>upper quartile</u> and the <u>lower quartile</u> and contains the <u>middle 50%</u> of values.

EXAMPLE:

Here are the ages, in months, of a number of fine cheeses:
7, 12, 5, 4, 3, 9, 5, 11, 6, 5, 7
Find the interquartile range of the ages.

1. Put the data in <u>order of size</u>. → 3, 4, 5, 5, 5, 6, 7, 7, 9, 11, 12 ← *Check you've got the right number of values — 11 ✓*

2. Find Q_1 — $n = 11$, so Q_1 is in position $(11 + 1)/4 = 3$. So $Q_1 = \underline{5}$.

3. Find Q_3 — Q_3 is in position $3(11 + 1)/4 = 9$. So $Q_3 = \underline{9}$.

4. <u>Subtract</u> Q_1 from Q_3 — IQR $= Q_3 - Q_1 = 9 - 5 = 4$ months

Careful — the formulas tell you the position of the quartile, not its value.

Read Off Measures *from* **Stem and Leaf Diagrams**

An <u>ordered stem and leaf diagram</u> can be used to show a set of data in <u>order of size</u>. And that makes it easy to read off values like the <u>median</u> and <u>quartiles</u>.

EXAMPLE:

Here are the scores for 15 dogs in an agility test:
26, 16, 29, 7, 12, 32, 29, 24, 13, 17, 20, 23, 24, 31, 34

a) **Draw an ordered stem and leaf diagram to show the data.**

1. First, put the data <u>in order</u>. ────→ 7, 12, 13, 16, 17, 20, 23, 24, 24, 26, 29, 29, 31, 32, 34

2. <u>Group</u> the data into rows — you can group these values by 'number of tens'.

3. Remember to include a <u>key</u>.

```
0 | 7
1 | 2 3 6 7          Key: 2|3 = 23
2 | 0 3 4 4 6 9 9
3 | 1 2 4
```

Write the first digit (number of tens) here... → ...write the second digit for each value (number of units) here.

b) **Find the median score and range of scores.**

1. Find the <u>position</u> of the <u>middle</u> value and read off from the diagram. — Median is in position $2(n + 1)/4 = 2(15 + 1)/4 = 8$ So median score = 24

2. The <u>range</u> is just the <u>highest minus the lowest</u>. — Range $= 34 - 7 = 27$

Interquartile range — the middle 50% of the data

The interquartile range is used to describe the spread of data, just like the range — but it's much less affected than the range by single values a long way from the rest of the data ("outliers").

Averages and Spread

The humble <u>box plot</u> might not look very fancy, but it tells you lots about the <u>spread</u> of data.

Box Plots *show the* Interquartile Range *as a* Box

1) Box plots give a good <u>summary</u> of the <u>spread</u> of a data set — they show a few <u>key measures</u>, rather than all the individual data values.

2) Make sure you can <u>draw</u> and <u>interpret</u> them.

[Diagram showing box plot with IQR labelled above the box, Lowest value, Lower quartile, Median, Upper quartile, Highest value pointing to the plot. Scale labelled Height (cm): 140, 150, 160, 170, 180, 190, 200, 210]

EXAMPLE: **This table gives information about the numbers of rainy days last year in some cities. On the grid below, draw a box plot to show the information.**

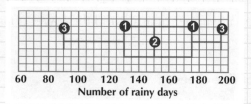

Number of rainy days (scale: 60, 80, 100, 120, 140, 160, 180, 200)

❶ Mark on the <u>quartiles</u> and <u>draw the box</u>.

❷ Draw a <u>line</u> at the <u>median</u>.

❸ Mark on the <u>minimum</u> and <u>maximum</u> points and <u>join them to the box</u> with horizontal lines.

Minimum number	90
Maximum number	195
Lower quartile	130
Median	150
Upper quartile	175

Compare Data *using* Averages *and* Spread

To <u>compare</u> two sets of data, you should look at:

You could also compare other key values like quartiles or min/max values.

❶ **AVERAGES** — <u>MEAN</u>, <u>MEDIAN</u> or <u>MODE</u>

Say which data set has the <u>higher/lower</u> value and <u>what that means</u> in the context of the data.

❷ **SPREAD** — <u>RANGE</u> or <u>INTERQUARTILE RANGE</u>

Say which data set has the <u>larger/smaller</u> value. A <u>larger spread</u> means the values are <u>less consistent</u> or there is <u>more variation</u> in the data.

If the data contains extreme values, it's better to use the IQR than the range.

EXAMPLE: **An animal park is holding a 'guess the weight of the baby hippo' competition. These box plots show information about the weights guessed by a group of school children.**

Compare the weights guessed by the boys and the girls.

[Box plots labelled Boys and Girls. Scale: Weight guessed in whole kg: 10, 20, 30, 40, 50, 60]

1. Compare <u>averages</u> by looking at the <u>median</u> values.
   The median for the boys is higher than the median for the girls.
   So the boys generally guessed heavier weights.

2. Compare the <u>spreads</u> by working out the <u>range</u> and <u>IQR</u> for each data set:
   Boys' range = 58 − 16 = 42 and IQR = 50 − 32 = 18.
   Girls' range = 52 − 12 = 40 and IQR = 44 − 30 = 14.
   Both the range and the IQR are smaller for the girls' guesses,
   so there is less variation in the weights guessed by the girls.

You can use box plots to compare different sets of data

It's easy to read the median off a box plot, and to use it to find the range and the interquartile range. Make sure you always think carefully about what the value of the average/spread actually means.

Frequency Tables — Finding Averages

The word <u>FREQUENCY</u> means <u>HOW MANY</u>, so a frequency table is just a <u>'How many in each category'</u> table. You saw how to find <u>averages and range</u> on p162 — it's the same ideas here, but with the data in a table.

Find *Averages* from *Frequency Tables*

1) The <u>MODE</u> is just the <u>CATEGORY with the MOST ENTRIES</u>.

2) The <u>RANGE</u> is found from the <u>extremes of the first column</u>.

3) The <u>MEDIAN</u> is the <u>CATEGORY</u> of the <u>middle value in the second column</u>.

4) To find the <u>MEAN</u>, you have to <u>WORK OUT A THIRD COLUMN</u> yourself.

The <u>MEAN</u> is then: **3rd Column Total ÷ 2nd Column Total**

Categories   How many

Number of cats	Frequency	
0	17	
1	22	
2	15	
3	7	

Mysterious 3rd column...

EXAMPLE: **Some people were asked how many sisters they have. The table opposite shows the results.**
Find the mode, the range, the mean and the median of the data.

Number of sisters	Frequency
0	7
1	15
2	12
3	8
4	4
5	0

❶ The <u>MODE</u> is the <u>category</u> with the <u>most entries</u> — i.e. the one with the <u>highest frequency</u>:

The highest frequency is 15 for '1 sister', so <u>MODE</u> = 1

❷ The <u>RANGE</u> is the <u>difference</u> between the highest and lowest numbers of sisters — that's 4 sisters (no one has 5 sisters) and no sisters, so:

<u>RANGE</u> = 4 – 0 = 4

You can label the first column x and the frequency column f, then the third column is f × x.

❸ To find the <u>MEAN</u>, <u>add a 3rd column</u> to the table showing '<u>number of sisters × frequency</u>'. <u>Add up</u> these values to find the <u>total number of sisters</u> of all the people asked.

3rd column total

$$\text{MEAN} = \frac{\text{total number of sisters}}{\text{total number of people asked}}$$

$$= \frac{79}{46} = 1.72 \text{ (3 s.f.)}$$

2nd column total

Number of sisters (x)	Frequency (f)	No. of sisters × Frequency (f × x)
0	7	0
1	15	15
2	12	24
3	8	24
4	4	16
5	0	0
Total	46	79

❹ The <u>MEDIAN</u> is the <u>category</u> of the <u>middle</u> value. Work out its <u>position</u>, then <u>count through</u> the 2nd column to find it.

It helps to imagine the data set out in an ordered list:
0000000111111111111111222222222222333333334444

median

There are 46 values, so the middle value is halfway between the 23rd and 24th values. There are a total of (7 + 15) = 22 values in the first two categories, and another 12 in the third category takes you to 34. So the 23rd and 24th values must both be in the category '2 sisters', which means the <u>MEDIAN</u> is 2.

Remember — mode is most

Exam questions will often ask you to find the mean, median, mode or range from a frequency table. As long as you have learnt the stuff on this page, you shouldn't run into any trouble.

Grouped Frequency Tables

<u>Grouped frequency tables</u> group together the data into <u>classes</u>. They look like ordinary frequency tables, but they're a <u>slightly trickier</u> kettle of fish... See p159 for grouped discrete data.

NON-OVERLAPPING CLASSES

- Use <u>inequality symbols</u> to cover all possible values.
- Here, <u>10</u> would go in the <u>1st</u> class, but <u>10.1</u> would go in the <u>2nd</u> class.

Height (*h* millimetres)	Frequency
$5 < h \leq 10$	12
$10 < h \leq 15$	15

To find MID-INTERVAL VALUES:

- Add together the <u>end values</u> of the <u>class</u> and <u>divide by 2</u>.
- E.g. $\dfrac{5 + 10}{2} = \underline{7.5}$

Find **Averages** *from* **Grouped Frequency Tables**

Unlike with ordinary frequency tables, you <u>don't know the actual data values</u>, only the <u>classes</u> they're in. So you have to <u>ESTIMATE THE MEAN</u>, rather than calculate it exactly. Again, you do this by <u>adding columns</u>:

> 1) Add a <u>3RD COLUMN</u> and enter the <u>MID-INTERVAL VALUE</u> for each class.
>
> 2) Add a <u>4TH COLUMN</u> to show '<u>FREQUENCY × MID-INTERVAL VALUE</u>' for each class.

And you'll be asked to find the <u>MODAL CLASS</u> and the <u>CLASS CONTAINING THE MEDIAN</u>, not exact values.

EXAMPLE: This table shows information about the weights, in kilograms, of 60 school children.

a) Write down the <u>modal class</u>.
b) Write down the <u>class containing the median</u>.
c) Calculate an <u>estimate for the mean weight</u>.

Weight (*w* kg)	Frequency
$30 < w \leq 40$	8
$40 < w \leq 50$	16
$50 < w \leq 60$	18
$60 < w \leq 70$	12
$70 < w \leq 80$	6

a) The <u>modal class</u> is the one with the <u>highest frequency</u>.

Modal class is 50 < w ≤ 60

b) Work out the <u>position</u> of the <u>median</u>, then <u>count through</u> the <u>2nd column</u>.

There are 60 values, so the median is halfway between the 30th and 31st values. Both these values are in the third class, so the class containing the median is 50 < w ≤ 60.

c) Add extra columns for 'mid-interval value' and 'frequency × mid-interval value'. Add up the values in the 4th column to estimate the <u>total weight</u> of the 60 children.

Weight (*w* kg)	Frequency (*f*)	Mid-interval value (x)	fx
$30 < w \leq 40$	8	35	280
$40 < w \leq 50$	16	45	720
$50 < w \leq 60$	18	55	990
$60 < w \leq 70$	12	65	780
$70 < w \leq 80$	6	75	450
Total	60	—	3220

Don't add up the mid-interval values.

$$\text{Mean} \approx \frac{\text{total weight}}{\text{number of children}} \quad \begin{array}{l}\leftarrow \text{4th column total} \\ \leftarrow \text{2nd column total}\end{array}$$

$$= \frac{3220}{60}$$

$$= 53.7 \text{ kg (3 s.f.)}$$

This time there are two columns to add

With frequency tables there was just one column to add, with grouped frequency tables there are two. It's still easy enough though as long as you remember what the columns are and how to find them.

Cumulative Frequency

Cumulative frequency just means <u>adding it up as you go along</u> — i.e. the <u>total frequency so far</u>. A cumulative frequency <u>graph</u> shows <u>cumulative frequency</u> up the <u>side</u> and the <u>range of data values</u> along the <u>bottom</u>. You need to be able to <u>draw the graph</u>, <u>read it</u> and <u>make estimates</u> from it.

EXAMPLE: **The table below shows information about the heights of a group of people.**
   a)   **<u>Draw</u> a <u>cumulative frequency graph</u> for the data.**
   b)   **Use your graph to <u>estimate</u> the <u>median</u> and <u>interquartile range</u> of the heights.**

Height (h cm)	Frequency	Cumulative Frequency
$140 < h \leq 150$	4	4
$150 < h \leq 160$	9	4 + 9 = <u>13</u>
$160 < h \leq 170$	20	13 + 20 = <u>33</u>
$170 < h \leq 180$	33	33 + 33 = <u>66</u>
$180 < h \leq 190$	36	66 + 36 = <u>102</u>
$190 < h \leq 200$	15	102 + 15 = <u>117</u>
$200 < h \leq 210$	3	117 + 3 = <u>120</u>

Total number of people surveyed

To **Draw** the **Graph**...

1) Add a 'CUMULATIVE FREQUENCY' COLUMN to the table — and fill it in with the <u>RUNNING TOTAL</u> of the <u>frequency column</u>.

2) <u>PLOT</u> points using the <u>HIGHEST VALUE in each class</u> and the <u>CUMULATIVE FREQUENCY</u>. (150, 4), (160, 13), etc.

3) <u>Join</u> the points with a <u>smooth curve</u>.

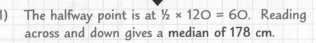
If you join the points with straight lines, it's a cumulative frequency polygon. If a question doesn't specify to draw a curve or a polygon, you can do either.

To **Find** the **Vital Statistics**...

1) <u>MEDIAN</u> — go <u>halfway up</u> the side, <u>across</u> to the <u>curve</u>, then <u>down</u> and read off the bottom scale.

2) <u>LOWER AND UPPER QUARTILES</u> — go ¼ and ¾ up the side, <u>across</u> to the <u>curve</u>, then <u>down</u> and read off the bottom scale.

3) <u>INTERQUARTILE RANGE</u> — the <u>distance between</u> the lower and upper quartiles.

1) The halfway point is at ½ × 120 = 60. Reading across and down gives a **median of 178 cm**.

2) ¼ of the way up is at ¼ × 120 = 30. Reading across and down gives a lower quartile of <u>169 cm</u>. ¾ of the way up is at ¾ × 120 = 90. Reading across and down gives an upper quartile of <u>186 cm</u>.

3) The interquartile range = 186 − 169 = 17 cm.

Plot zero at the lowest value in the first class.

Interquartile range

More **Estimating**...

To use the graph to <u>estimate</u> the number of values that are <u>less than</u> or <u>greater than</u> a given value:

Go <u>along</u> the bottom scale to the given value, <u>up</u> to the curve, then <u>across</u> to the cumulative frequency.

Remember — you can also join the points with straight lines

In the example above, if you were asked to estimate the number of people who are 176 cm or shorter, you would read along the bottom to 176, go up to meet the curve and across to find the answer is 52.

Warm-up and Worked Exam Questions

By the time the big day comes you need to know all the facts in this mini-section like the back of your hand. It's not easy, but the only way to get good marks is to practise with these questions.

Warm-up Questions

1) Write down the 4 basic definitions of the following: Mode, Median, Mean and Range.

2) The data shows the number of cars owned by 124 households in a survey. Find the:
   a) Mean;   b) Median;   c) Mode;   d) Range.

Number of cars	0	1	2	3	4	5	6
Frequency	1	24	36	31	22	9	1

3) The grouped frequency table below represents data from 79 random people.

Height (cm)	$145 \leq x < 155$	$155 \leq x < 165$	$165 \leq x < 175$	$175 \leq x < 185$
Frequency	18	22	24	15

   a) Estimate the mean.
   b) Which group contains the median?
   c) State the modal group.

Worked Exam Question

There's no better preparation for exam questions than doing, err... practice exam questions. Hang on, what's this I see...

1   During a science experiment 10 seeds were planted and their growth measured to the nearest cm after 12 days. The results were recorded in the table below. ©

Growth in cm	Number of plants
$0 \leq x \leq 2$	2
$3 \leq x \leq 5$	4
$6 \leq x \leq 8$	3
$9 \leq x \leq 11$	1

   a) Use the table to find:
   i) the group which contains the median.
      (10 + 1) ÷ 2 = 5.5, so the median is halfway between the 5th and 6th values, so it lies in the group containing the 5th and 6th values.
      ....$3 \leq x \leq 5$...............
      [1 mark]

   ii) an estimate of the mean growth.
      [(①× 2) + (④× 4) + (⑦× 3) + (⑩ × 1)] ÷ 10 = 49 ÷ 10 = 4.9 cm

   These are the mid-interval values. You could add a couple of extra columns to the table if you wanted — one for the mid-interval values and another for frequency × mid-interval value.
      ....4.9............... cm
      [4 marks]

   b) Explain why you can only find an estimate of the mean.
      As we do not have original data we do not know the exact data values and have to approximate using the mid-interval values.
      [1 mark]

Exam Questions

2 The table shows the number of pets owned by each pupil in class 7F. **(D)**

Number of pets	Frequency
0	8
1	3
2	5
3	8
4	4
5	1

a) How many pupils are there in class 7F?

....
[2 marks]

b) Find the total number of pets owned by pupils in class 7F.

....
[2 marks]

c) Work out the mean number of pets per pupil in class 7F.

....
[2 marks]

3 Declan is training to take part in a 10 km race.
He runs the same distance every day for 30 days.

For the first 20 days, his mean running time was 56.2 minutes.
His mean running time for all 30 days was 54.4 minutes.

Work out Declan's mean running time for the last 10 days of his training. **(C)**

.... minutes
[3 marks]

4 Liz sells earrings. The prices in pounds of 12 pairs of earrings are given below.

3   4   8   10   11   5   7   4   12   8   9   5

a) Draw an ordered stem and leaf diagram to show this information. **(D)**
You must include a key.

[3 marks]

b) Liz reduces all her prices by 50p. Will the interquartile range of the new prices **(B)**
be less than, greater than or the same as the interquartile range of the old prices?
Give a reason for your answer.

....

....
[1 mark]

Exam Questions

5   The cumulative frequency table below gives information about the length of time it takes to travel between Udderston and Trundle on the main road each morning.

Journey Time (*t* mins)	$0 < t \leq 20$	$0 < t \leq 25$	$0 < t \leq 30$	$0 < t \leq 35$	$0 < t \leq 45$	$0 < t \leq 60$
Cumulative Frequency	7	22	36	45	49	50

a) On the graph paper below, draw a cumulative frequency graph for the table.

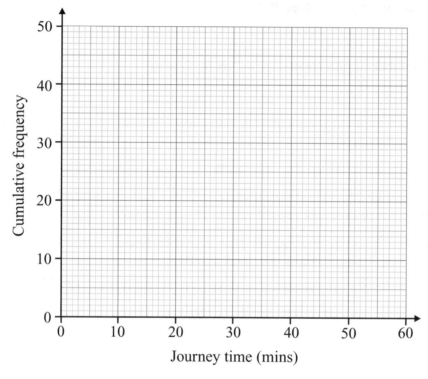

Journey time (mins)

[2 marks]

b) Use your graph to estimate the number of journeys that took between 27 and 47 minutes.

.... *journeys*
[2 marks]

c) Use your graph to estimate the percentage of journeys that took longer than 40 minutes.

.... %
[2 marks]

The minimum journey time was 12 minutes and the maximum journey time was 52 minutes.

d) Using this information and the graph above, draw a box plot on the grid below to show the journey times between Udderston and Trundle.

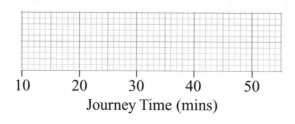

Journey Time (mins)

[3 marks]

Histograms and Frequency Density

A <u>histogram</u> is just a bar chart where the bars can be of <u>different widths</u>. This changes them from nice, easy-to-understand diagrams into seemingly incomprehensible monsters (and an examiner's favourite).

Histograms Show *Frequency Density*

1) The <u>vertical</u> axis on a histogram is always called <u>frequency density</u>. You work it out using this formula:

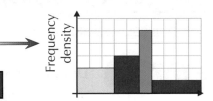

> **Frequency Density = Frequency ÷ Class Width**

> Remember... '<u>frequency</u>' is just another way of saying 'how much' or 'how many'.

2) You can rearrange it to work out <u>how much</u> a bar represents.

> **Frequency = Frequency Density × Class Width = AREA of bar**

EXAMPLE: **The table and the histogram below show the lengths of beetles found in a garden.**

Length (mm)	Frequency
$0 < x \le 10$	32
$10 < x \le 15$	36
$15 < x \le 18$	
$18 < x \le 22$	28
$22 < x \le 30$	16

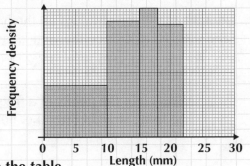

a) **Use the histogram to find the missing entry in the table.**

1. Add a <u>frequency density</u> column to the table and fill in what you can using the formula.

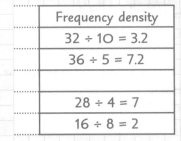

Frequency density
32 ÷ 10 = 3.2
36 ÷ 5 = 7.2
28 ÷ 4 = 7
16 ÷ 8 = 2

2. Use the frequency densities to <u>label</u> the <u>vertical axis</u> of the graph.

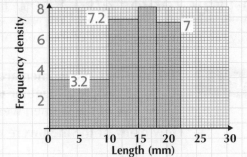

3. Now use the <u>3rd bar</u> to find the frequency for the class "$15 < x \le 18$".

Frequency density = 8 and class width = 3.
So frequency = frequency density × class width = 8 × 3 = 24

b) **Use the table to add the bar for the class "$22 < x \le 30$" to the histogram.**

Frequency density = Frequency ÷ Class Width = $\frac{16}{8}$ = 2

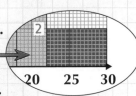

c) **Estimate the number of beetles between 7.5 mm and 12.5 mm in length.**

Use the formula <u>frequency = frequency density × class width</u> — multiply the frequency density of the <u>class</u> by the width of the <u>part of that class</u> you're interested in.

So the estimated number of beetles between 7.5 mm and 12.5 mm is:
3.2 × (10 − 7.5) + 7.2 × (12.5 − 10) = 3.2 × 2.5 + 7.2 × 2.5 = 8 + 18 = 26

You need to use the height and width of a bar to find its frequency

Make sure you get your head around the method above — otherwise you'll struggle with histograms.

Other Graphs and Charts

You're nearly at the end of graphs and charts now. Nearly... but not quite.

Frequency Polygons Show Frequencies

A <u>frequency polygon</u> is used to show the information from a frequency table.

EXAMPLE: **Draw a frequency polygon to show the information in the table.**

Age (*a*) of people at concert	Frequency	mid-interval value
20 < *a* ≤ 30	12	(20 + 30) ÷ 2 = 25
30 < *a* ≤ 40	21	(30 + 40) ÷ 2 = 35
40 < *a* ≤ 50	18	(40 + 50) ÷ 2 = 45
50 < *a* ≤ 60	10	(50 + 60) ÷ 2 = 55

1. Add a column to the table to show the <u>mid-interval values</u>.

2. Plot the <u>mid-interval values</u> on the <u>horizontal axis</u> and the <u>frequencies</u> on the <u>vertical axis</u>.

So plot the points (25, 12), (35, 21), (45, 18) and (55, 10).

> **Always join the points of a <u>frequency polygon</u> using <u>straight lines</u> (i.e. <u>not</u> a curve).**

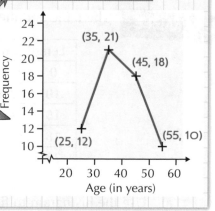

Two-Way Tables Also Show Frequencies

<u>Two-way tables</u> show <u>two</u> types of information in the same table.

EXAMPLE: **200 men and 200 women are asked whether they are left-handed or right-handed.**
- **63 people altogether were left-handed.**
- **164 of the women were right-handed.**

How many of the men were right-handed?

1. Draw a table to show the info from the question — this is in the blue cells.

2. Then fill in the gaps by <u>adding</u> and <u>subtracting</u>.

> When there's only <u>one</u> thing in a row or column that you don't know, you can <u>always</u> work it out.

	Women	Men	Total
Left-handed	200 − 164 = 36	63 − 36 = 27	63
Right-handed	164	200 − 27 = 173	164 + 173 = 337
Total	200	200	200 + 200 = 400

So **173** men were right-handed.

Two-way tables have row and column totals and a grand total

These tables and graphs aren't too complicated, just take your time and don't make any silly mistakes. Always use straight lines for frequency polygons, and double-check the addition in two-way tables.

Scatter Graphs

The last kind of graph in this section is <u>scatter graphs</u> — they're nice, so make the most of them.

Scatter Graphs — *Correlation* and *Line of Best Fit*

1) A <u>scatter graph</u> tells you <u>how closely</u> two things are <u>related</u> — the fancy word for this is <u>CORRELATION</u>.

2) If you can draw a <u>line of best fit</u> pretty close to <u>most</u> of your scatter of points, then the two things are <u>correlated</u>.

A line of best fit doesn't have to go through any of the points exactly, but it should go fairly close to most of them.

<u>Strong correlation</u> is when your points make a <u>fairly straight line</u>. This means the two things are <u>closely related</u> to each other.

<u>Weak correlation</u> means your points <u>don't line up</u> quite so nicely (but you still need to be able to see where you'd draw a line of best fit).

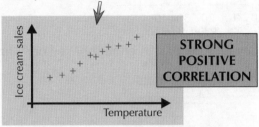

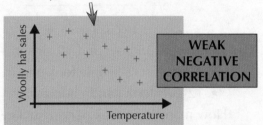

If the points form a line sloping <u>uphill</u> from left to right, then there is <u>positive correlation</u> — this means that both things increase or decrease <u>together</u>.

If the points form a line sloping <u>downhill</u> from left to right, then there is <u>negative correlation</u> — this just means that as one thing <u>increases</u> the other <u>decreases</u>.

3) If the points are <u>randomly scattered</u>, and it's <u>impossible</u> to draw a sensible line of best fit, then there's <u>no correlation</u>. Here, newspaper sales and temperature <u>aren't correlated</u>.

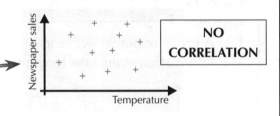

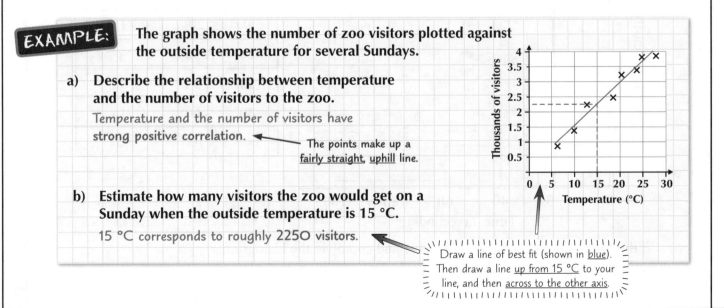

EXAMPLE: **The graph shows the number of zoo visitors plotted against the outside temperature for several Sundays.**

a) **Describe the relationship between temperature and the number of visitors to the zoo.**

Temperature and the number of visitors have strong positive correlation. ← The points make up a <u>fairly straight</u>, <u>uphill</u> line.

b) **Estimate how many visitors the zoo would get on a Sunday when the outside temperature is 15 °C.**

15 °C corresponds to roughly 2250 visitors.

Draw a line of best fit (shown in <u>blue</u>). Then draw a line <u>up from 15 °C</u> to your line, and then <u>across to the other axis</u>.

If you can draw a line of best fit you have correlation

If you use your line of best fit to estimate a value <u>outside</u> your data range, it's important to remember that the estimate might not be reliable as you don't know if the pattern continues beyond the range.

Warm-up and Worked Exam Questions

There are some lovely warm-up questions here covering scatter graphs and two-way tables.
Now's the time to go back over any bits you're not sure of — in the exam it'll be too late.

Warm-up Questions

1) Decide what type of correlation best describes the two scatter graphs below.

a)

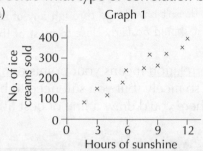

Graph 1

b)

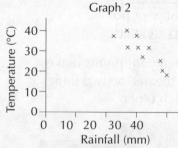

Graph 2

2) There were 35 boys and 30 girls in a PE lesson. They all took part in either hockey or swimming.

- A total of 32 people took part in swimming.
- 12 girls took part in hockey.

How many boys took part in hockey?

Worked Exam Question

It's no good learning all the facts in the world if you can't put them into practice in the exam.
These worked examples show how to make all those facts into good answers — and earn yourself marks.

1   A group of pupils were each given a potato. The table below gives some information about how long it took the pupils to peel their potato.

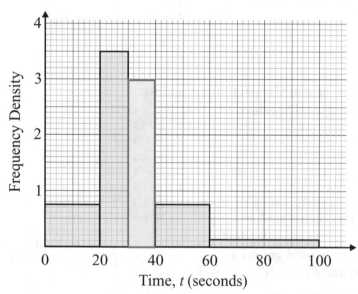

Time, t (s)	Frequency
$0 < t \leq 20$	15
$20 < t \leq 30$	35
$30 < t \leq 40$	30
$40 < t \leq 60$	15
$60 < t \leq 100$	5

Fill in the missing entry from the table and complete the histogram.

Work out the area of the bar for 20 < t ≤ 30 to find the missing frequency:

For 20 < t ≤ 30, frequency = frequency density × class width = 3.5 × 10 = 35

Find the height of the bar for 30 < t ≤ 40 and draw it on the graph:

For 30 < t ≤ 40, frequency density = frequency ÷ class width = 30 ÷ 10 = 3

[2 marks]

Exam Questions

2 The frequency polygon shows the time (*t* hours) that some students spent doing homework in one week.

Calculate an estimate of the mean amount of time spent on homework.

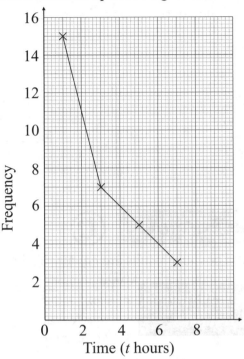

.... hours
[3 marks]

3 A furniture company is looking at how effective their advertising is.
They are comparing how much they spent on advertising in random months with their total sales value for that month. This information is shown on the graph below. **D**

The table shows the amount spent on advertising and the value of sales for three more months.

Amount spent on advertising (thousands of pounds)	0.75	0.15	1.85
Sales (thousands of pounds)	105	60	170

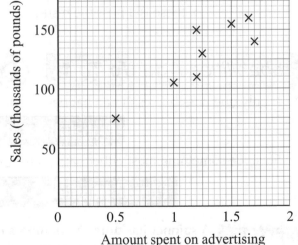

a) Plot the information from the table on the scatter graph.
[1 mark]

b) Describe the relationship between the amount spent on advertising and the value of sales.

....
[1 mark]

c) Use your graph to estimate how much the company would need to spend on advertising in order to sell £125 000 worth of furniture in one month.

£ ....
[3 marks]

Probability Basics

A lot of people reckon <u>probability</u> is pretty tough. But learn the <u>basics</u> well, and it'll all make sense.

All *Probabilities* are *Between 0 and 1*

Probabilities are <u>always</u> between 0 and 1. The <u>higher</u> the probability of something, the <u>more likely</u> it is.

- A probability of <u>ZERO</u> means it will <u>NEVER HAPPEN</u>.
- A probability of <u>ONE</u> means it <u>DEFINITELY WILL</u>. ← *You can't have a probability bigger than 1.*

Impossible	Unlikely	Evens	Likely	Certain
0	¼	½	¾	1
0	0.25	0.5	0.75	1
0%	25%	50%	75%	100%

Probabilities can be given as <u>fractions</u>, <u>decimals</u> or <u>percentages</u>.

You Can Find *Some* Probabilities Using a *Formula*

A <u>word of warning</u>... the following formula only works if <u>all</u> the possible results are <u>equally likely</u>.

$$\text{Probability} = \frac{\text{Number of ways for something to happen}}{\text{Total number of possible results}}$$

Words like '<u>fair</u>' and '<u>at random</u>' show possible results are all equally likely. '<u>Biased</u>' and '<u>unfair</u>' mean the opposite.

EXAMPLE: **Work out the probability of randomly picking a letter 'P' from the tiles below.**

A P P L E   P I E

1. There are <u>3 P's</u> — so there are <u>3 different ways</u> to 'pick a letter P'.
2. And there are <u>8 tiles</u> altogether — each of these is a <u>possible result</u>.

$$\text{Probability} = \frac{\text{number of ways to pick a P}}{\text{total number of possible results}}$$
$$= \frac{3}{8} \text{ (or 0.375)}$$

Probabilities *Add Up To 1*

1) If <u>only one</u> possible result can happen at a time, then the probabilities of <u>all</u> the results <u>add up to 1</u>.

Probabilities always ADD UP to 1.

2) So since something must either <u>happen</u> or <u>not happen</u> (i.e. <u>only one</u> of these can happen at a time):

P(event happens) + P(event doesn't happen) = 1

EXAMPLE: **A spinner has different numbers of red, blue, yellow and green sections. What is the probability of spinning green?**

Colour	red	blue	yellow	green
Probability	0.1	0.4	0.3	

<u>Only one</u> of the results can happen at a time, so all the probabilities must <u>add up to 1</u>.

P(green) = 1 − (0.1 + 0.4 + 0.3) = 0.2

Probabilities are between 0 and 1

If this page hasn't totally sunk in, go back through it again — you need to get the basics clear in your head.

Listing Outcomes and Expected Frequency

With a lot of probability questions, a good place to start is with a list of all the <u>things that could happen</u> (also known as <u>outcomes</u>). Once you've got a list of outcomes, the rest of the question is easy.

Listing *All Outcomes*: *2 Coins, Dice, Spinners*

A <u>sample space diagram</u> is a good way to show all the possible outcomes if there are <u>two activities</u> going on (e.g. two coins being tossed, or a dice being thrown and a spinner being spun, etc.).

EXAMPLE: **The spinners on the right are spun, and the scores added together.**

a) Make a sample space diagram showing all the possible outcomes.

1. All the scores from one spinner go <u>along the top</u>. All the scores from the other spinner go <u>down the side</u>.

2. <u>Add</u> the two scores together to get the different possible totals (the <u>outcomes</u>).

+	3	4	5
1	4	5	6
2	5	6	7
3	6	7	8

There are 9 outcomes here — even though some of the actual totals are repeated.

b) Find the probability of spinning a total of 6.

There are <u>9 possible outcomes</u> altogether, and <u>3 ways</u> to score 6.

$$P(\text{total} = 6) = \frac{\text{ways to score 6}}{\text{total number of possible outcomes}}$$
$$= \frac{3}{9} = \frac{1}{3}$$

'P(outcome)' just means the probability of that outcome.

Use Probability to Find an *"Expected Frequency"*

You can <u>estimate</u> how often you'd <u>expect</u> something to happen if you carry out an experiment *n* times.

> **Expected times outcome will happen = probability × number of trials**

EXAMPLE: **A game involves throwing a fair six-sided dice.**
The player wins if they score either a 5 or a 6.
If one person plays the game 180 times, estimate the number of times they will win.

1. First calculate the probability that they win <u>each game</u>.

$$\text{Probability of winning} = \frac{\text{number of ways to win}}{\text{total number of possible results}}$$
$$= \frac{2}{6} = \frac{1}{3}$$

2. Then <u>estimate</u> the number of times they'll win in <u>180</u> separate attempts.

$$\text{Expected number of wins} = \text{probability of winning} \times \text{number of trials}$$
$$= \frac{1}{3} \times 180$$
$$= 60$$

Expected frequency is how many times you'd expect something to happen

Make sure you can remember the formula for expected frequency in the box above. Don't be fooled by complicated statistics terms — for example, a 'sample space diagram' is basically just a table.

SECTION SIX — STATISTICS AND PROBABILITY

The AND / OR Rules

This page is also about when you have <u>more than one</u> thing happening at a time.

Combined Probability — Two or More Events

1) Always break down a complicated-looking probability question into <u>A SEQUENCE</u> of <u>SEPARATE SINGLE EVENTS</u>.
2) Find the probability of <u>EACH</u> of these <u>SEPARATE SINGLE EVENTS</u>.
3) Apply the <u>AND/OR</u> rule.

And now for the rules. Say you have <u>two events</u> — call them A and B...

The **AND Rule** gives **P(Both Events Happen)**

$$P(A \text{ and } B) = P(A) \times P(B)$$

This only works when the two events are <u>independent</u>, i.e. the result of one event <u>does not affect</u> the other event.

This says: The probability of <u>Event A AND Event B BOTH happening</u> is equal to the two separate probabilities <u>MULTIPLIED</u> together.

EXAMPLE: **Dave picks one ball at random from each of bags X and Y. Find the probability that he picks a yellow ball from both bags.**

1. Write down the <u>probabilities</u> of the different events.

   P(Dave picks a yellow ball from bag X) = $\frac{4}{10}$ = 0.4.

   P(Dave picks a yellow ball from bag Y) = $\frac{2}{8}$ = 0.25.

2. Use the <u>formula</u>.

   So P(Dave picks a yellow ball from both bags) = 0.4 × 0.25 = 0.1

The **OR Rule** gives **P(At Least One Event Happens)**

$$P(A \text{ or } B) = P(A) + P(B)$$

This says: The probability of <u>EITHER Event A OR Event B happening</u> is equal to the two separate probabilities <u>ADDED</u> together.

This only works when the two events <u>can't both happen</u> at the same time.

EXAMPLE: **A spinner with red, blue, green and yellow sections was spun — the probability of it landing on each colour is shown in the table. Find the probability of spinning either red or green.**

Colour	red	blue	yellow	green
Probability	0.25	0.3	0.35	0.1

1. Write down the <u>probabilities</u> of the different events.

   P(lands on red) = 0.25 and P(lands on green) = 0.1.

2. Use the <u>formula</u>.

   So P(Lands on either red or green) = 0.25 + 0.1 = 0.35

Three steps and two rules to learn here

You won't go far if you don't learn the AND/OR rules. The way to remember them is that it's the wrong way round — you'd want AND to go with '+' but it doesn't. It's 'AND with ×' and 'OR with +'.

Tree Diagrams

Learn these basic details (which apply to <u>ALL</u> tree diagrams). Then you'll be ready for the one in the exam.

Remember These **Four** Key **Tree Diagram Facts**

1) On any set of branches which meet at a point, the probabilities must <u>add up to 1</u>.

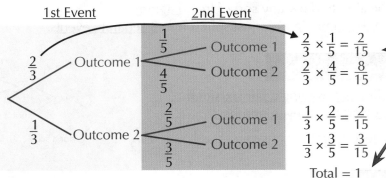

2) <u>Multiply along</u> the branches to get the <u>end probabilities</u>.

3) Check your diagram — the end probabilities must <u>add up to 1</u>.

4) To answer any question, <u>add up</u> the relevant end probabilities (see below).

$$\frac{2}{3} \times \frac{1}{5} = \frac{2}{15}$$
$$\frac{2}{3} \times \frac{4}{5} = \frac{8}{15}$$
$$\frac{1}{3} \times \frac{2}{5} = \frac{2}{15}$$
$$\frac{1}{3} \times \frac{3}{5} = \frac{3}{15}$$
Total = 1

EXAMPLES:

1. A box contains 5 red discs and 3 green discs. One disc is taken at random and its colour noted before <u>being replaced</u>. A second disc is then taken. Find the probability that both discs are the same colour.

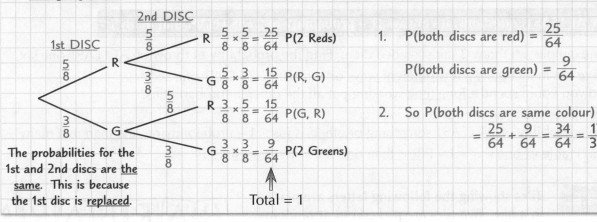

The probabilities for the 1st and 2nd discs are <u>the same</u>. This is because the 1st disc is <u>replaced</u>.

1. P(both discs are red) = $\frac{25}{64}$

   P(both discs are green) = $\frac{9}{64}$

2. So P(both discs are same colour)
   = $\frac{25}{64} + \frac{9}{64} = \frac{34}{64} = \frac{17}{32}$

2. A box contains 5 red discs and 3 green discs. Two discs are taken at random <u>without replacement</u>. Find the probability that both discs are the same colour.

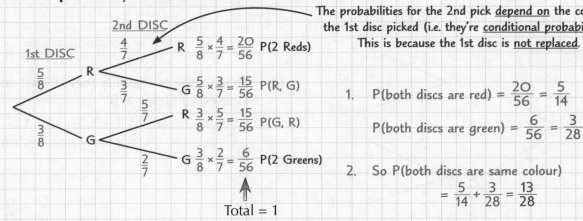

The probabilities for the 2nd pick <u>depend on</u> the colour of the 1st disc picked (i.e. they're <u>conditional probabilities</u>). This is because the 1st disc is <u>not replaced</u>.

1. P(both discs are red) = $\frac{20}{56} = \frac{5}{14}$

   P(both discs are green) = $\frac{6}{56} = \frac{3}{28}$

2. So P(both discs are same colour)
   = $\frac{5}{14} + \frac{3}{28} = \frac{13}{28}$

The tree's the key

The tree diagram is the top toy when it comes to probability questions. Even if the question doesn't specifically ask for a tree diagram you should draw one straight away so you know what's going on.

Tree Diagrams

Here's another page all about tree diagrams. This is excellent news, as tree diagrams are <u>really</u> useful.

Four Extra Details *for the* Tree Diagram *Method:*

1) Always break up the question into a <u>sequence</u> of separate events.

You need a <u>sequence</u> of events to be able to draw any sort of <u>tree diagram</u>.
For example... '<u>3 coins are tossed at the same time</u>' — just split it into <u>3 separate events</u>.

2) <u>Don't</u> feel you have to draw <u>complete</u> tree diagrams.

For example... '<u>What is the probability of throwing a fair six-sided dice 3 times and getting 2 sixes followed by an even number?</u>'

The diagram on the right is all you need to get the answer: $\frac{1}{6} \times \frac{1}{6} \times \frac{1}{2} = \frac{1}{72}$

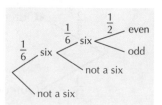

3) Watch out for <u>conditional probabilities</u>.

This is where the <u>probabilities</u> on a set of branches <u>change</u>, depending on the result of <u>the previous event</u>. For example... if you're picking things at random (e.g. cards from a pack, or balls out of a bag) <u>without replacing</u> your earlier picks.

See the last example on p179.

4) With '<u>AT LEAST</u>' questions, it's always (1 – probability of 'LESS THAN that many'):

For example... 'I throw 3 fair six-sided dice. <u>Find the probability of throwing AT LEAST one six.</u>'

There are in fact <u>quite a few different ways</u> of 'throwing AT LEAST one six', and you could spend a <u>long time</u> working out all the different probabilities.

The clever trick you should know is this:

The probability of 'AT LEAST something or other' is just: 1 – probability of '<u>less than</u> that many'.

So... P(<u>at least one</u> six) = 1 – P(<u>less than one</u> six) = 1 – P(<u>no sixes</u>).

EXAMPLE: Tiles showing the following letters are placed in a hat. Two tiles are picked out at random and their letters noted, without replacement.

BARBARA

a) **Complete the tree diagram below to show whether or not each of the letters picked is a 'B'.**

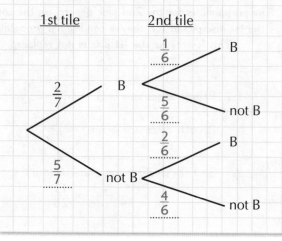

1st tile   2nd tile

The probabilities for the 2nd tile depend on what you pick for the 1st tile — so these are <u>conditional probabilities</u>.

b) **Calculate the probability that at least one of the selected tiles is a 'B'.**

P(at least 1 tile is B) = 1 – P(less than 1 tile is B)

$= 1 - $ P(neither tile is B)

$= 1 - \left(\frac{5}{7} \times \frac{4}{6} \right)$

$= 1 - \frac{20}{42} = \frac{22}{42} = \frac{11}{21}$

See how useful tree diagrams are

With probability questions that seem hard, drawing a tree diagram can be a good place to start.
It takes some thinking to decide how to draw it and which bits you need, but after that it's plain sailing.

Relative Frequency

Relative frequency is nothing too difficult — it's just a way of working out <u>probabilities</u>.

Fair or Biased?

The probability of rolling a three on a normal dice is $\frac{1}{6}$ — you know that each of the 6 numbers on the dice is <u>equally likely</u> to be rolled, and there's <u>only 1 three</u>.

BUT this only works if it's a <u>fair dice</u>. If the dice is a bit <u>wonky</u> (the technical term is '<u>biased</u>') then each number <u>won't</u> have an equal chance of being rolled. This is where <u>relative frequency</u> comes in — you can use it to <u>estimate</u> probabilities when things might be wonky.

Do the Experiment Again and Again and Again...

You need to do an experiment <u>over and over again</u> and count how often an outcome happens (its <u>frequency</u>). Then you can do a quick calculation to find the <u>relative frequency</u> of something.

$$\text{Relative frequency} = \frac{\text{Frequency}}{\text{Number of times you tried the experiment}}$$

An experiment could just mean rolling a dice.

You can use the <u>relative frequency</u> of an outcome to <u>estimate</u> its <u>probability</u>.

EXAMPLE: The spinner on the right was spun 100 times. Use the results in the table below to estimate the probability of getting each of the scores.

Score	1	2	3	4	5	6
Frequency	10	14	36	20	11	9

<u>Divide</u> each of the frequencies by 100 to find the <u>relative frequencies</u>.

Score	1	2	3	4	5	6
Relative Frequency	$\frac{10}{100} = 0.1$	$\frac{14}{100} = 0.14$	$\frac{36}{100} = 0.36$	$\frac{20}{100} = 0.2$	$\frac{11}{100} = 0.11$	$\frac{9}{100} = 0.09$

The <u>more times</u> you do the experiment, the <u>more accurate</u> your estimate of the probability will be. If you spun the above spinner 1000 times, you'd get a <u>better estimate</u> of the probability of each score.

If your answers are <u>far away</u> from what you'd expect, then you can say that the dice is probably <u>biased</u>.

EXAMPLE: Do the above results suggest that the spinner is biased?

<u>Yes</u>, because the relative frequency of 3 is <u>much higher</u> than you'd expect, while the relative frequencies of 1, 5 and 6 are <u>much lower</u>.

For a <u>fair</u> 6-sided spinner, you'd expect all the relative frequencies to be about $1 \div 6 = 0.17$(ish).

More experiments mean a more accurate probability estimate

In the exam, the relative frequencies might be shown on a diagram instead of in a table. Don't panic — you treat them in exactly the same way. And remember that even with a fair dice you're unlikely to get exactly the expected result, but the more experiments you do, the closer to the true probability you'll get.

Warm-up and Worked Exam Questions

Probability is really not that difficult once you get the hang of it, but it's important to get loads of practice, so try these warm-up questions. Take a look back at anything you're unsure about.

Warm-up Questions

1) What is the probability of rolling a six three times in a row with a six-sided dice?

2) A sweet is picked out of a bag containing 4 cola bottles and 3 toffees. It is then put back in and a sweet picked out again. What is the probability of getting a cola bottle both times?

3) A playing card is dropped 3 times.
   What is the probability of it landing face up all three times?

4) Three balls are picked randomly from a bag containing 3 blue and 4 red balls.
   The balls are not replaced. What is the probability of getting a ball of each colour?

Worked Exam Question

Take a look at this worked exam question. It's not too hard but it should give you a good idea of what to write. You'll usually get at least one probability question in the exam.

1 Jo and Heather are meeting for coffee.

The probability that Jo will wear burgundy trousers is $\frac{2}{5}$. **(A)**

There is a one in four chance that Heather will wear burgundy trousers.

The two events are independent.

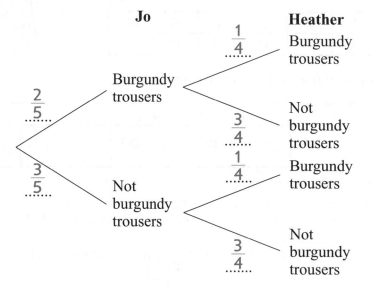

Check that the probabilities on each set of branches add up to 1.

a) Complete the tree diagram above.   *[2 marks]*

b) What is the probability that neither of them wear burgundy trousers?

$$\text{Probability neither wear burgundy trousers} = \frac{3}{5} \times \frac{3}{4}$$

$$= \frac{3 \times 3}{5 \times 4}$$

$$= \frac{9}{20}$$

$\frac{9}{20}$
....
[2 marks]

Exam Questions

2   There are 10 counters in a bag.
Four of the counters are blue and the rest are red.
One counter is picked out at random.

 a) Work out the probability that the counter picked is red.
   Give your answer as a fraction in its lowest terms.

....
[2 marks]

   b) What is the probability that the counter picked is green?

....
[1 mark]

3   Alvar has a fair six sided dice and a set of five cards numbered 2, 4, 6, 8 and 10. Ⓒ
He rolls the dice and chooses a card at random.
Alvar adds the number on the dice to the number on the card to calculate his total score.

   a) Complete the table below to show all of the possible scores.

Cards

		2	4	6	8	10
	1				9	11
	2			8	10	12
Dice	**3**			9	11	13
	4		8	10	12	14
	5	7	9	11	13	15
	6	8	10	12	14	16

[2 marks]

   b) Find the probability that Alvar will score exactly 9.

....
[2 marks]

   Alvar decides to play a game with the dice and cards against his friends
Zynah and Colin. If the total score is less than 8 Colin will win, if the
total score is more than 11 Alvar will win. Otherwise Zynah will win.

   c) Find the probability that Zynah will win the game.

....
[2 marks]

Exam Questions

4 Eimear has a bag containing a large number of counters.
Each counter is numbered either 1, 2, 3, 4 or 5.

She selects one counter from the bag, makes a note of its number, and then puts it back in the bag. Eimear does this 100 times. She records her results in the table below.

Number on counter	1	2	3	4	5
Frequency	23	25	22	21	9
Relative Frequency					

a) Complete the table, giving the relative frequencies
   of the number of times each counter is selected.

[2 marks]

b) Elvin says that he thinks that the bag contains the same number of counters
   with each number. Do you agree? Give a reason for your answer.

....
[1 mark]

c) Using Eimear's results, estimate the probability of selecting an odd number
   when **one** counter is picked from the bag.

....
[2 marks]

5 A couple are both carriers of a recessive gene that causes a hereditary disease.
If they have a child, the probability that the child will suffer from the disease is 0.25. Ⓐ
The couple plan to have two children.

If the couple have two children, find the probability
that at least one of them will have the disease.

....
[4 marks]

6 Rebecca buys a bag of beads to make a necklace. Ⓐ*
The bag contains 8 brown beads and 12 orange beads.
She picks three beads from the bag and puts them onto a string.

Work out the probability that she puts 2 orange beads and
one brown bead onto her string, in **any** order.

TIP: this is without replacement, so the total number of beads in the bag goes down each time.

....
[4 marks]

Revision Questions for Section Six

Here's the inevitable list of straight-down-the-middle questions to test how much you know.

- Have a go at each question... but <u>only tick it off</u> when you can get it right <u>without</u> cheating.
- And when you think you could handle pretty much <u>any</u> statistics question, tick off the whole topic.

Sampling and Collecting Data (p157-159) ☑

1) What is a sample and why does it need to be representative?

2) Say what is meant by a random sample.

3) This table shows information about some students. If a stratified sample of 50 students is taken, how many boys should be in the sample?

Boys	Girls
80	120

4) List the four key things you should bear in mind when writing questionnaire questions.

Finding Averages and Spread (p162-164) ☑

5) Write down the definitions for the mode, median, mean and range.

6) a) Find the mode, median, mean and range of this data: 2, 8, 11, 15, 22, 24, 27, 30, 31, 31, 41

   b) For the above data, find the lower and upper quartiles and the interquartile range.

7) These box plots show information about how long it took someone to get to work in summer and winter one year. Compare the travel times in the two seasons.

Frequency Tables and Cumulative Frequency (p165-167) ☑

8) For this grouped frequency table showing the lengths of some pet alligators:

   a) find the modal class,

   b) find the class containing the median,

   c) estimate the mean.

Length (y, in m)	Frequency
$1.4 \leq y < 1.5$	4
$1.5 \leq y < 1.6$	8
$1.6 \leq y < 1.7$	5
$1.7 \leq y < 1.8$	2

9) Draw a cumulative frequency graph for the data in the above grouped frequency table.

More Graphs and Charts (p171-173) ☑

10) How do you work out what frequency a bar on a histogram represents?

11) Draw a frequency polygon to show the data in the table on the right.

12) 125 boys and 125 girls were asked if they prefer Maths or Science. 74 of the boys said they prefer Maths, while 138 students altogether said they prefer Science. How many girls said they prefer Science?

Time (t, in secs) taken to run 100 m	Frequency
$10 \leq t < 12$	2
$12 \leq t < 14$	8
$14 \leq t < 16$	7
$16 \leq t < 18$	3

13) Sketch graphs to show:

   a) weak positive correlation, b) strong negative correlation, c) no correlation

Easy Probability (p176-177) ☑

14) I pick a random number between 1 and 50. Find the probability that my number is a multiple of 6.

15) What do the probabilities of all possible outcomes of an experiment add up to (if none of them can happen together)?

16) Write down the formula for estimating how many times you'd expect something to happen in n trials.

Harder Probability (p178-181) ☑

17) I throw a fair six-sided dice twice. Find P(I throw a 6 and then an even number).

18) I throw a fair six-sided dice. Find P(I throw either a 5 or a multiple of 3).

19) I pick a card at random from a normal pack of cards. I make a note of it, but don't replace it before I then pick a second card. Use a tree diagram to find the probability of me getting two kings.

20) When might you need to use relative frequency to find a probability?

Practice Exam 1: Non-calculator
As final preparation for the exams, we've included two full practice papers to really put your Maths skills to the test. Paper 1 is a non-calculator paper — Paper 2 (on page 197) requires a calculator. There's a formula sheet for both papers on page 213. Good luck...

Watch step-by-step solutions on video
Your free Online Edition of this book includes videos of our expert Maths tutors explaining the answers to this whole Exam Paper. (If you haven't accessed your Online Edition yet, you can find out how to get it at the front of this book.)

Candidate Surname		Candidate Forename(s)

Centre Number	Candidate Number	Candidate Signature

GCSE

Mathematics   **Higher Tier**
Paper 1 (Non-Calculator)

Practice Paper
Time allowed: 1 hour 30 minutes

You must have:
Pen, pencil, eraser, ruler, protractor, pair of compasses.
You may use tracing paper.

You are **not allowed** to use a calculator.

Instructions to candidates
- Use **black** ink to write your answers.
- Write your name and other details in the spaces provided above.
- Answer **all** questions in the spaces provided.
- In calculations show clearly how you worked out your answers.
- Do all rough work on the paper.

Information for candidates
- The marks available are given in brackets at the end of each question.
- You may get marks for method, even if your answer is incorrect.
- There are 17 questions in this paper. There are no blank pages.
- There are 70 marks available for this paper.
- In questions labelled with an asterisk (*), you will be assessed on the quality of your written communication — take particular care here with spelling, punctuation and the quality of explanations.

Answer ALL the questions.

Write your answers in the spaces provided.

You must show all of your working.

1 **(a)** Here are the first 5 terms in a sequence.

$$2 \quad 13 \quad 24 \quad 35 \quad 46$$

1 **(a) (i)** Write an expression for the nth term of this sequence.

....

....

Answer ....

1 **(a) (ii)** Find the 8th term of the sequence.

....

....

Answer .... *[3 marks]*

1 **(b)** The nth term of another sequence is $2n + 2$.

Rita says that the number 65 will be in the sequence.
Is she correct? Explain your answer.

....

....

....

....

....

[2 marks]

1

5

2 A regular polygon has 7 sides.

2 (a) Write down the sum of the exterior angles of the polygon.

....

Answer ....° *[1 mark]*

2 (b) Calculate the sum of the interior angles of the polygon.

....

....

Answer ....° *[2 marks]*

*3 A Youth Centre decides to organise a trip to a theme park.
They plan to hire a coach that costs £100 for the day.
The cost to get into the theme park is £15 per person.

The Youth Centre will charge £23 per person for the trip,
which includes the coach journey and entry to the theme park.

The trip can only go ahead if the Youth Centre makes enough money to cover its costs.
Work out how many people need to go on the trip for it to go ahead.

....

....

....

....

....

Answer .... *[4 marks]*

4 Work out $3\frac{3}{7} - 2\frac{1}{5}$

....

....

....

Answer .... *[3 marks]*

2

5 A large supermarket chain is planning to open a new store in a town called Digton.
Residents of Digton are asked to complete a questionnaire to give their views on this idea.

Here is one of the questions from the questionnaire:

'There is nowhere in Digton that sells a good range of products
— so Digton needs a new supermarket. Do you agree?'

5 **(a)** Write down one criticism of this question.

....

....

[1 mark]

5 **(b)** Suggest a more suitable question that could be used instead.

....

....

[1 mark]

Another question on the questionnaire is:

'How far are you willing to travel to buy your food shopping each week?'

☐ Not far ☐ Quite far ☐ Very far

5 **(c)** Write down one criticism of this question.

....

....

[1 mark]

5 **(d)** Rewrite the question with more suitable response options.

....

....

[2 marks]

3

15

6 Fully factorise the following expressions.

6 **(a)** $4e - 6ef$

....

Answer .... *[1 mark]*

6 **(b)** $g^2 - 16$

....

....

Answer .... *[1 mark]*

*7 Michael and Jojo are going out for a steak dinner.
Their three favourite restaurants are advertising the following special offers.

The Big Grill	Steak 'a' Lot	Danny's Steak House
STEAK – £16 each	STEAK – £18 each	STEAK – £21 each
Buy 1 get the second half price	Buy 2 and get 20% off the total price.	Buy 2 and get a third off the total price.

Which restaurant should Michael and Jojo go to for the best deal on steak?
Show all of your working.

....

....

....

....

....

....

....

Answer .... *[5 marks]*

4

8 **(a)** Write 56^2 as a product of its prime factors.

....

Answer .... [2 marks]

8 **(b)** Find the highest common factor of 56 and 72.

....

....

Answer .... [1 mark]

9 *RUT* and *SUV* are straight lines that intersect at *U*.

RS and *VT* are parallel.

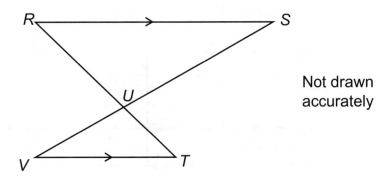

Not drawn
accurately

Show that triangles *RSU* and *TVU* are similar.

....

....

....

[3 marks]

13

10 In the diagram below, shape **B** is a transformation of shape **A**.

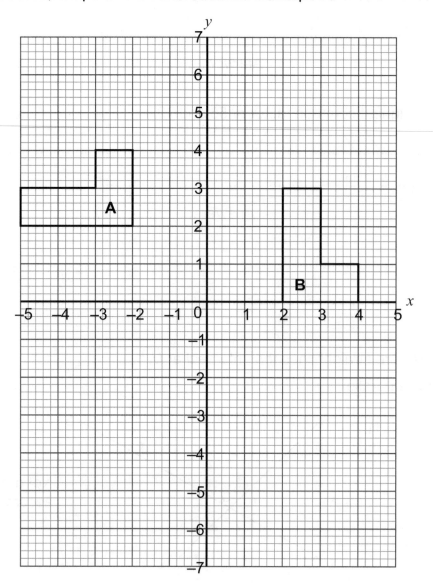

10 (a) Describe fully the transformation that maps shape **A** onto shape **B**.

....

....

....

[3 marks]

10 (b) Enlarge shape **B** by a scale factor of $-\dfrac{3}{2}$ from the centre (2, −1).
Label the enlargement **C**.

[3 marks]

6

11 A chocolate manufacturer trials a new shape of box for one of its products.

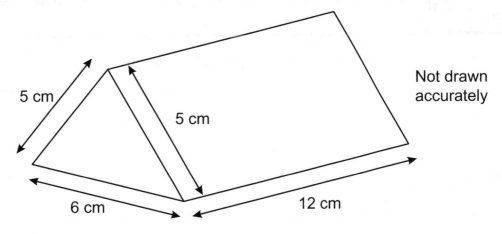

5 cm

5 cm

Not drawn
accurately

6 cm

12 cm

11 (a) Find the surface area of the box.

....

....

....

Answer .... cm² *[3 marks]*

11 (b) Find the volume of the box.

....

....

Answer .... cm³ *[2 marks]*

12 Solve the simultaneous equations

$$5y + 6x = 7$$
$$4y - 3x = 16$$

....

....

....

....

$x = $ ....

$y = $ ....

[3 marks]

14

13 Simplify these algebraic fractions as much as possible.

13 **(a)** $\dfrac{4x + 10}{6x + 14}$

....

....

Answer .... *[2 marks]*

13 **(b)** $\dfrac{x^2 - 2x - 15}{x^2 + 10x + 21}$

....

....

....

Answer .... *[3 marks]*

14 The diagram below shows the rectangle *ABCD*.

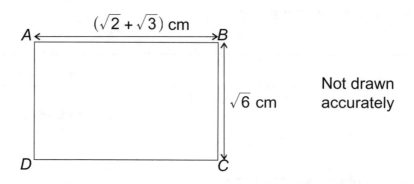

Not drawn accurately

Calculate the area of the rectangle, giving your answer in the form $(a\sqrt{3} + b\sqrt{2})$ cm².

....

....

....

Answer .... cm² *[3 marks]*

15 In the diagram below, *O* is the centre of the circle. The angle *a* is 36°.

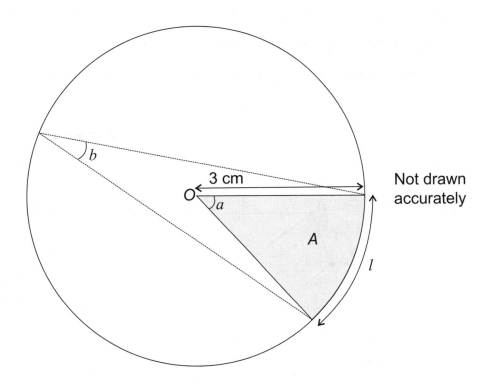

3 cm

Not drawn
accurately

15 (a) What is the size of angle *b*?

....

Answer .... ° *[1 mark]*

15 (b) Calculate the area of the minor sector A.
Leave your answer in terms of π.

....

....

....

Answer .... cm² *[3 marks]*

15 (c) Calculate the length of the minor arc, *l*, in terms of π.
Give your answer as a fraction in its lowest terms.

....

....

....

Answer .... cm *[3 marks]*

15

9

16 Write $x^2 + 6x - 8$ in the form $(x + a)^2 + b$

....

....

....

....

Answer .... *[3 marks]*

17

ABCD is a parallelogram.

$\overrightarrow{QP}$ = **b** and $\overrightarrow{QD}$ = **a**.

Triangles *PQD* and *ACD* are similar.

$AD:PD = 5:3$

17 (a) Find $\overrightarrow{CA}$ in terms of **a** and **b**.

....

....

Answer .... *[1 mark]*

17 (b) *R* is a point on *AC* so that $5\overrightarrow{AR} = 2\overrightarrow{AC}$.

Show that $\overrightarrow{PR}$ is parallel to $\overrightarrow{DQ}$.

....

....

....

....

....

Answer .... *[4 marks]*

8

Practice Exam 2: Calculator
Right, here's Exam Paper 2 — you'll need a calculator for this one. Don't forget there's
a formula sheet on page 213 if you need it (you'll get one of these in the real exam too).

Watch step-by-step solutions on video
Your free Online Edition of this book includes videos of our expert Maths tutors
explaining the answers to this whole Exam Paper. (If you haven't accessed your
Online Edition yet, you can find out how to get it at the front of this book.)

Candidate Surname		Candidate Forename(s)

Centre Number	Candidate Number	Candidate Signature

GCSE

Mathematics
Paper 2 (Calculator)

Higher Tier

Practice Paper
Time allowed: 2 hours

You must have:
Pen, pencil, eraser, ruler, protractor, pair of compasses.
You may use tracing paper.

You **may use** a calculator.

Instructions to candidates
*   Use **black** ink to write your answers.
*   Write your name and other details in the spaces provided above.
*   Answer **all** questions in the spaces provided.
*   In calculations show clearly how you worked out your answers.
*   Do all rough work on the paper.
*   Unless a question tells you otherwise, take the value of π to be 3.14,
    or use the π button on your calculator.

Information for candidates
*   The marks available are given in brackets at the end of each question.
*   You may get marks for method, even if your answer is incorrect.
*   There are 21 questions in this paper. There are no blank pages.
*   There are 105 marks available for this paper.
*   In questions labelled with an asterisk (*), you will be assessed
    on the quality of your written communication — take particular
    care here with spelling, punctuation and the quality of explanations.

Answer ALL the questions.

Write your answers in the spaces provided.

You must show all of your working.

1   Here is a pattern made of equilateral triangles.

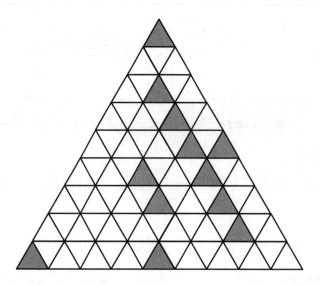

Shade 12 more triangles to make a pattern with rotational symmetry of order 3.   *[3 marks]*

2   In a class of 26 children, 12 are boys and the rest are girls.

2   **(a)** Work out the ratio of boys to girls.
          Give your answer in its simplest form.

....

....

....

Answer .... *[2 marks]*

2   **(b)** In another class the ratio of boys to girls is 2 : 3.
          There are 25 children in the class.

          Work out how many girls are in the class.

....

....

....

Answer .... girls *[2 marks]*

7

3 Alice walks to the garage to pick up her car.
Her journey is shown on the distance-time graph below.

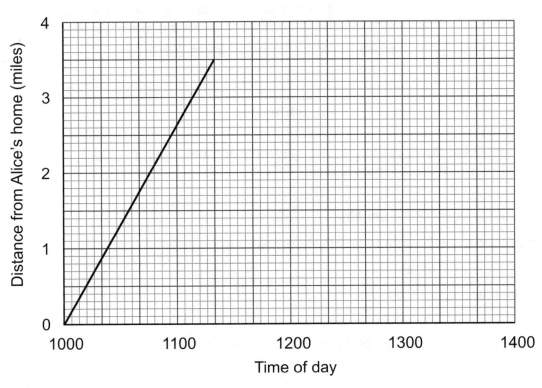

3 **(a)** How far is it from Alice's house to the garage?

....

Answer .... miles *[1 mark]*

3 **(b)** At what speed does she walk to the garage?

....

....

Answer .... mph *[2 marks]*

Alice spends 20 minutes at the garage, and then drives home at a speed of 21 mph.

3 **(c)** Complete the graph to show the time that Alice spends at the garage
and her return journey.

[3 marks]

3 **(d)** How long was Alice away from home for in total?

....

Answer .... *[1 mark]*

2

4   A painter wants to calculate the cost of painting the four outside walls of a warehouse. The diagram below gives the dimensions of the warehouse.

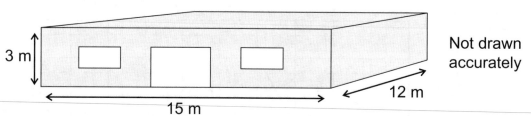

3 m

15 m

12 m

Not drawn accurately

There are 5 windows in the warehouse that each measure 2 m by 1 m and a door that measures 3 m by 2.5 m.

The paint covers 13 m² per litre.

The paint can be bought in tins that contain 5 litres or 2.5 litres.

5 litre tins cost £20.99

2.5 litre tins cost £12.99

Calculate the cheapest price for painting the warehouse. You must show all your working.

....

....

....

....

....

....

                                        Answer £ .... *[6 marks]*

5   The equation $x^3 - x - 4 = 0$ has a solution between 1 and 2.

Use trial and improvement to find this solution.
Give your answer correct to one decimal place.

You must show **ALL** of your working.

....

....

....

....

                                        x = ... *[4 marks]*

3

17

6 Rearrange the equations below to make b the subject in each case.

6 **(a)** $a = \frac{1}{2}bc^2$

....

....

Answer .... *[2 marks]*

6 **(b)** $12 = \dfrac{bx + 8}{by - 4}$

....

....

....

Answer .... *[3 marks]*

7 Two children play a game. Each round, Eva throws an ordinary unbiased 6-sided dice, and Finn spins a fair 3-sided spinner, labelled 1 to 3, twice and adds his scores together.

To win a round they have to score 6.

7 **(a)** Who is most likely to win a round? You must show your working.

....

....

....

Answer .... *[2 marks]*

7 **(b)** Eva and Finn decide to change the rules to increase their chances of winning a round. To win now, the score has to be 5 or more. They play 54 games in total.

Estimate the number of games in which Eva and Finn both score 5 or more.

....

....

....

....

Answer .... *[3 marks]*

4

202

8 Mrs Jones is trying to sell her house. She decides to advertise her house with an estate agent, with an asking price of £190 000. She asks two estate agents what fees they will charge.

Shirleys	Tibbersons
Fees for selling your house with us: Fixed Price £3700	Our selling fees are 1.95% of the actual selling price

* **8 (a)** Mrs Jones expects the actual selling price of her house to be 10% below her asking price.

Which estate agent will be cheapest to use if this happens?

....

....

....

....

[3 marks]

8 (b) Mrs Jones finds a house she wants to buy. It has an asking price of £212 500. She is told that the asking price was dropped by 15% six months ago.

What was the price of the house before the asking price was dropped?

....

....

....

....

....

Answer £ .... *[3 marks]*

5

16

PRACTICE PAPER 2

9   The table below gives information about the heights of the children in Class A.

Height in cm (h)	Frequency
$130 \leq h < 140$	5
$140 \leq h < 150$	10
$150 \leq h < 160$	14
$160 \leq h < 170$	8
$170 \leq h < 180$	3

9   **(a)**   Calculate an estimate for the mean height of the children in Class A.

....

....

....

....

Answer .... cm *[4 marks]*

* **9**   **(b)**   Below are two frequency polygons showing the heights
of the children in Classes A and B.

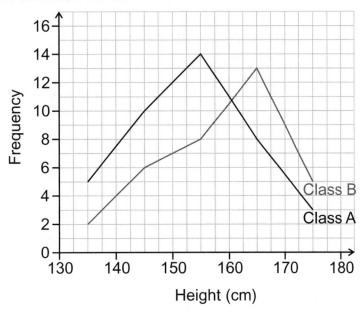

Compare the heights in the two classes.

....

....

....

....

[3 marks]

6

10 Reena inherits £4500. She decides to place the money in a savings account, and is considering two different accounts.

Account 1 pays an interest rate of 2% per year, with interest added at the end of the year.
Account 2 pays an interest rate of 0.4%, with interest added at the end of each month.

Reena wants to invest her money for 1 year.

In which account will her savings grow the most in this time?
Show your working clearly.

....

....

....

....

....

....

....

....

....

....

....

Answer .... *[5 marks]*

12

11 On the grid below, shade the region that satisfies all three of these inequalities:

$$x \leq 3 \qquad y > -4 \qquad y \leq x + 2$$

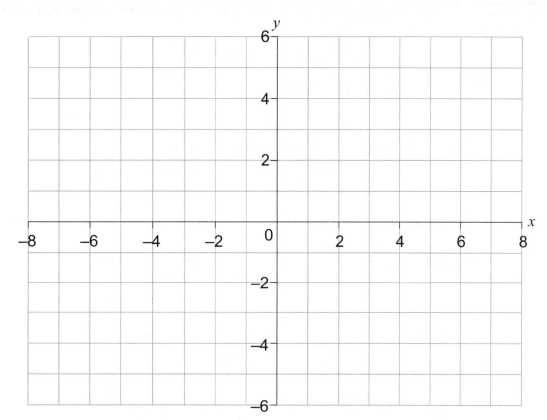

[4 marks]

12 A sweet shop sells cylindrical tubs of sherbet.
The cylindrical tubs have an internal diameter of 3.8 cm and are 4.9 cm tall.

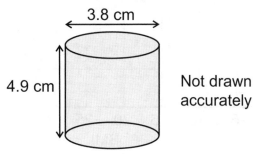

3.8 cm

4.9 cm

Not drawn accurately

1 cm³ of sherbet weighs 0.63 g.

Calculate the weight, in grams, of sherbet in a full tub.
Give your answer correct to 2 decimal places.

....

....

....

....

Answer .... g *[3 marks]*

13 Megan is the manager of a health club. She wants to know if the BMIs (Body Mass Indexes) of the female members have improved since she last surveyed them. She intends to publish her findings in an information leaflet.
The table below shows the new data she's collected from the 40 female members.

BMI (b)	Frequency
$15 < b \le 20$	4
$20 < b \le 25$	14
$25 < b \le 30$	12
$30 < b \le 35$	5
$35 < b \le 40$	3
$40 < b \le 45$	2

13 (a) Use this information to draw a cumulative frequency graph on the axes below.

[2 marks]

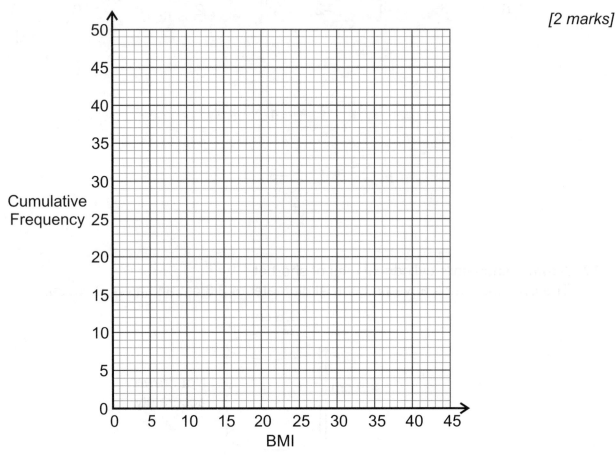

13 (b) Estimate the median BMI.

....

Answer .... [1 mark]

13 (c) Estimate the interquartile range (IQR).

....

Answer .... [2 marks]

12

* **13** **(d)** Megan also wants to include a comparison of the BMIs of the male and female members of the health club in her information leaflet.

A box plot giving information on the BMIs of the male health club members is shown below.

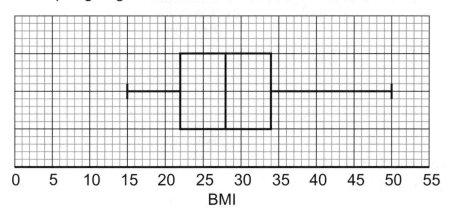

Compare the BMIs of the women to the BMIs of the men.

....

....

....

[2 marks]

14 In February 2010, the UK population was estimated to be 62 000 000 people.

The UK national debt is the money that the UK government owes to people who have bought government bonds. In February 2010, the debt was calculated to be £8.494 × 10^{11}.

Use this information to estimate the national debt per person in the UK in February 2010. Give your answer in standard form.

....

....

....

....

Answer £ .... *[2 marks]*

15 **(a)** Factorise fully

15 **(a)** **(i)** $3y - 6y^2z$

....

Answer .... [1 mark]

15 **(a)** **(ii)** $6x^2 - 8x - 8$

....

Answer .... [2 marks]

15 **(b)** Solve the equation $x^2 - 8x + 3 = 0$
Give your answer in surd form.

....

....

Answer .... [3 marks]

16 The value of y is inversely proportional to the cube of x.
When $y = 60$, $x = 2$.

16 **(a)** Write down a formula connecting y and x.

....

....

....

Answer .... [3 marks]

16 **(b)** What is the value of x when $y = 100$?
Give your answer correct to 2 decimal places.

....

....

Answer .... [2 marks]

11

15

17 The histogram below shows information about the length of time 100 cars were parked in a supermarket car park.

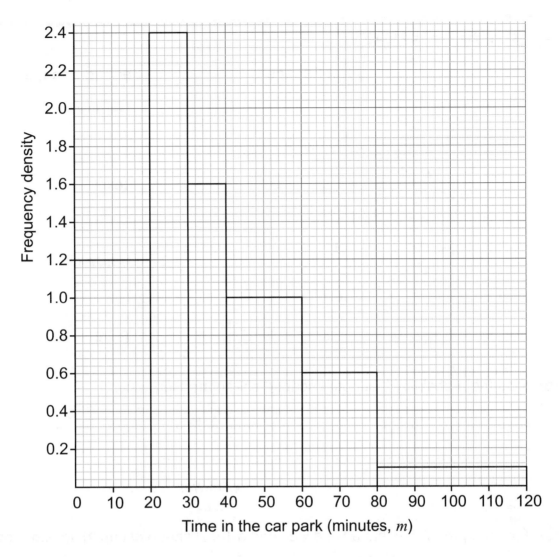

17 **(a)** Estimate how many cars were parked for more than 70 minutes.

....

....

Answer .... *[2 marks]*

17 **(b)** Calculate an estimate of the mean length of time the cars were parked for.

....

....

....

Answer .... minutes *[3 marks]*

12

18 A field contains 4 Herdwick sheep and 3 Texel sheep. One random sheep escapes from the field. Later on, another random sheep escapes.

18 (a) Complete the tree diagram.

First Escape   Second Escape   *[2 marks]*

$\frac{4}{7}$ Herdwick

.... Herdwick

.... Texel

$\frac{3}{7}$ Texel

.... Herdwick

.... Texel

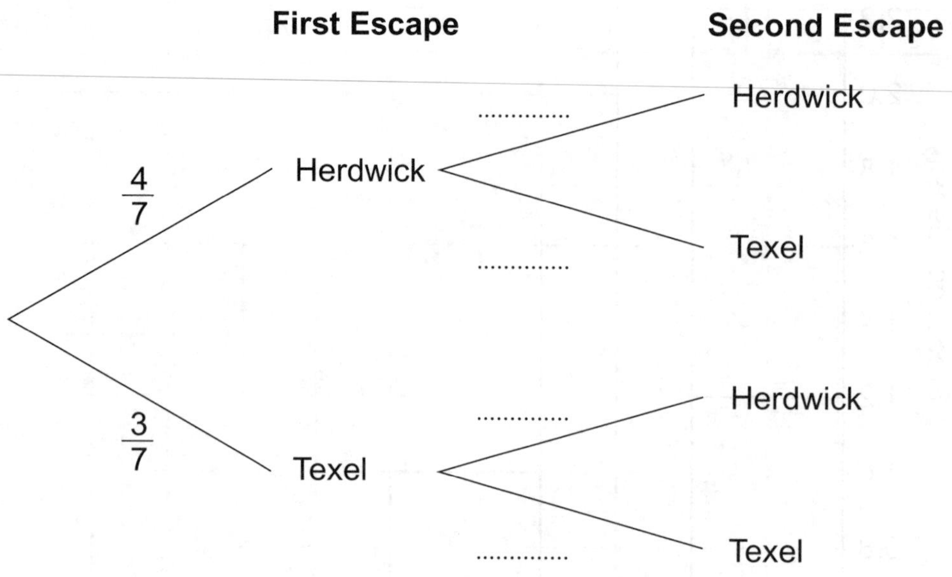

18 (b) Find the probability that both escaped sheep are Herdwicks

....

....

Answer .... *[2 marks]*

18 (c) Find the probability that a Herdwick and a Texel sheep escaped, in either order.

....

....

Answer .... *[2 marks]*

11

19 The height, h metres, of a stone shot by a catapult is related to its horizontal distance from the catapult, d metres, as described by the equation $h = 2d - 0.02d^2$.

19 (a) Complete this table of values for $h = 2d - 0.02d^2$.

d	0	20	40	50	60	80	100
h	0		48		48	32	0

[2 marks]

19 (b) Draw the graph of $h = 2d - 0.02d^2$ on the grid.

[2 marks]

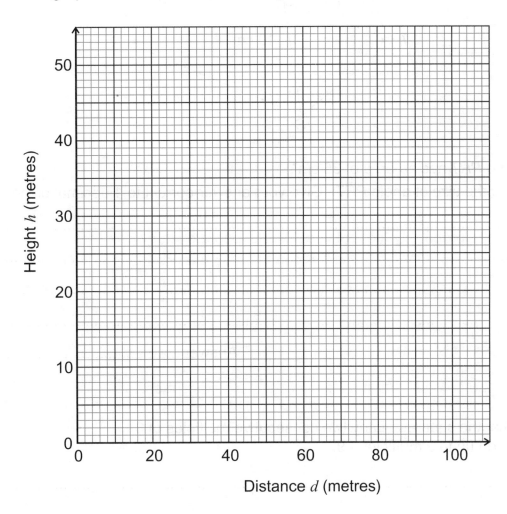

Distance d (metres)

19 (c) The catapult shoots a stone up a hill with a gradient of 1 in 10.

By drawing an appropriate line on the graph, find the horizontal distance travelled by the stone before it hits the hill.

....

....

....

Answer .... m *[3 marks]*

20 The diagram below shows pyramid *PQRST*.

PR is 8.5 cm and the diagonal *RT* is 10 cm.

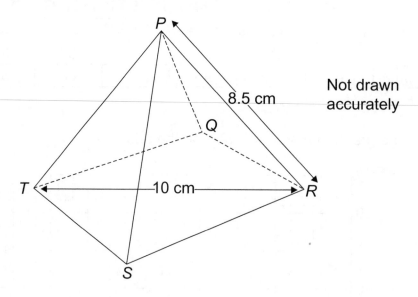

Not drawn accurately

The plane *PRT* has an area of 35 cm².

Calculate the size of angle *PRT*. Give your answer correct to 1 decimal place.

....

....

....

....

Answer ....° *[3 marks]*

*21 Prove that the squares of any two consecutive multiples of 3
always add up to a multiple of 9.

....

....

....

....

....

....

[5 marks]

15

FORMULA SHEET: HIGHER TIER

Volume of prism = area of cross-section × length

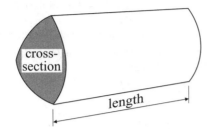

Area of trapezium $= \frac{1}{2}(a + b)h$

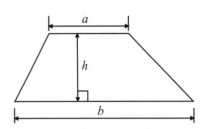

Volume of sphere $= \frac{4}{3}\pi r^3$

Surface area of sphere $= 4\pi r^2$

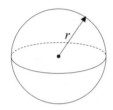

Volume of cone $= \frac{1}{3}\pi r^2 h$

Curved surface area of cone $= \pi r l$

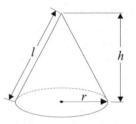

For any triangle *ABC*:

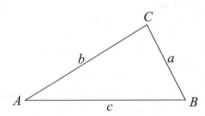

Sine rule: $\dfrac{a}{\sin A} = \dfrac{b}{\sin B} = \dfrac{c}{\sin C}$

Cosine rule: $a^2 = b^2 + c^2 - 2bc \cos A$

Area of triangle $= \frac{1}{2}ab \sin C$

The Quadratic Equation:

The solutions of $ax^2 + bx + c = 0$, where $a \neq 0$, are given by

$$x = \frac{-b \pm \sqrt{(b^2 - 4ac)}}{2a}$$

Section One — Numbers

Page 8 (Warm-up Questions)

1 a) 1, 4, 9   b) 1, 8   c) 2, 3, 5, 7
2 a) 36   b) There aren't any   c) 31, 37
3 $231 \div 3 = 77$ or $231 \div 7 = 33$ or $231 \div 11 = 21$.
   So 231 has more than 2 factors.
4 1, 2, 4, 5, 8, 10, 20, 40
5 $2 \times 2 \times 2 \times 5$ (or $2^3 \times 5$)

Page 9 (Exam Questions)

3 Take $a = 2$ and $b = 3$
   a) $2 + 3 = 5$ *[1 mark]*
   b) $2 \times 3 = 6$ *[1 mark]*
   c) $2^2 + 3^2 = 4 + 9 = 13$ *[1 mark]*
4 a) $2 \times 3 \times 5 \times 7$
      [2 marks available — 1 mark for a correct method, 1 mark for all prime factors correct]
   b) $3 \times 3 \times 5 \times 5 \times 7 \times 7$
      [2 marks available — 1 mark for a correct method, 1 mark for all prime factors correct]
      "A correct method" here is either using a factor tree or just repeatedly dividing the factors until you get primes.
5 a) $2 \times 2 \times 2 \times 3 \times 3$
      [2 marks available — 1 mark for a correct method, 1 mark for all prime factors correct]
   b) Factors of 54 are: 1, 2, 3, 6, 9, ⑱, 27, 54
      Factors of 72 are: 1, 2, 3, 4, 6, 8, 9, 12, ⑱, 24, 36, 72
      So the HCF is 18 *[1 mark]*
6 The first car takes 30 seconds to complete a circuit, the second car takes 70 seconds to complete a circuit.
   Multiples of 30 are: 30, 60, 90, 120, 150, 180, ⑳210, 240, ...
   Multiples of 70 are: 70, 140, ㉒210, 280, ...
   So it will be 210 seconds or 3.5 minutes until they are side by side on the start line.
   [2 marks available — 1 mark for a correct method, 1 mark for the correct answer]

Page 16 (Warm-up Questions)

1 a) $\frac{4}{15}$ b) $\frac{2}{5} \times \frac{3}{2} = \frac{6}{10} = \frac{3}{5}$
   c) $\frac{6}{15} + \frac{10}{15} = \frac{16}{15} = 1\frac{1}{15}$ d) $\frac{10}{15} - \frac{6}{15} = \frac{4}{15}$
2 40%
3 66.66666...%
4 a) $\frac{4}{10}$ or $\frac{2}{5}$ b) $\frac{4}{9}$ c) $\frac{5}{11}$
5 a) 0.7   b) 0.7777777...

Page 17 (Exam Questions)

2 $\frac{12}{60}$ *[1 mark]* $= \frac{1}{5}$ *[1 mark]*
   [2 marks available in total — as above]
3 $0.725 = \frac{725}{1000} = \frac{29}{40}$
   [2 marks available — 1 mark for turning into an equivalent fraction, 1 mark for the correct final answer]
4 a) $3\frac{1}{2} + 2\frac{3}{5} = \frac{7}{2} + \frac{13}{5} = \frac{35}{10} + \frac{26}{10} = \frac{35+26}{10} = \frac{61}{10}$ or $6\frac{1}{10}$
      [3 marks available — 1 mark for writing as improper fractions, 1 mark for writing over a common denominator, 1 mark for the correct answer]
   b) $3\frac{3}{4} - 2\frac{1}{3} = \frac{15}{4} - \frac{7}{3} = \frac{45}{12} - \frac{28}{12} = \frac{45-28}{12} = \frac{17}{12}$ or $1\frac{5}{12}$
      [3 marks available — 1 mark for writing as improper fractions, 1 mark for writing over a common denominator, 1 mark for the correct answer]

If you've used a different method in Q4, but still shown your working, and ended up with the same final answer, then you still get full marks.

5 a) $1\frac{2}{3} \times \frac{9}{10} = \frac{5}{3} \times \frac{9}{10} = \frac{5 \times 9}{3 \times 10} = \frac{45}{30} = \frac{3}{2}$
      [3 marks available — 1 mark for multiplying the two fractions together, 1 mark for an equivalent fraction, 1 mark for the correct final answer]
   b) $3\frac{1}{2} \div 1\frac{3}{4} = \frac{7}{2} \div \frac{7}{4} = \frac{7}{2} \times \frac{4}{7} = \frac{7 \times 4}{2 \times 7} = \frac{28}{14} = 2$
      [3 marks available — 1 mark for taking the reciprocal and multiplying the two fractions together, 1 mark for an equivalent fraction, 1 mark for the correct final answer]
6 Let $r = 1.3\dot{6}$, so $100r = 136.3\dot{6}$ *[1 mark]*
   $100r - r = 136.3\dot{6} - 1.3\dot{6}$
   $99r = 135$ *[1 mark]*
   $r = \frac{135}{99}$ *[1 mark]*
   $r = \frac{15}{11}$ *[1 mark]*
   [4 marks available in total — as above]
7 Let $10r = 5.9\dot{0}$, so $1000r = 590.9\dot{0}$ *[1 mark]*
   $990r = 585$ *[1 mark]*
   $r = \frac{585}{990} = \frac{13}{22}$ *[1 mark]*
   [3 marks available in total — as above]

Page 21 (Warm-up Questions)

1 £13.50
2 74%
3 45%
4 £208
5 £3376.53

Page 22 (Exam Questions)

2 Number of male micro pigs = $40 - 24 = 16$ *[1 mark]*
   Fraction male = $\frac{16}{40} = \frac{2}{5}$ *[1 mark]*
   So percentage male = 40% *[1 mark]*
   [3 marks available in total — as above]
3 $3.2\% = 3.2 \div 100 = 0.032$
   3.2% of £2000 = $0.032 \times £2000 = £64$
   $2 \times £64 = £128$
   [3 marks available — 1 mark for a correct method to find 3.2% of £2000, 1 mark for multiplying this by 2, 1 mark for correct answer]
4 $20\% = 20 \div 100 = 0.2$
   $0.2 \times £927 = £185.40$ *[1 mark]*
   $£927 + £185.40$ *[1 mark]* $= £1112.40$ *[1 mark]*
   [3 marks available in total — as above]
5 £15 714 = 108%
   £15 714 $\div$ 108 = £145.50 = 1% *[1 mark]*
   £145.50 $\times$ 100 = 100% *[1 mark]* = £14 550 *[1 mark]*
   [3 marks available in total — as above]
6 £120 000 $\times \left(1 + \frac{15}{100}\right)^5 = £241\,362.86... = £241\,000$
   (to nearest £1000)
   [3 marks available — 1 mark for using correct formula, 2 marks for correct answer to nearest £1000, otherwise 1 mark for an unrounded answer]
7 Let r be the interest rate.
   $£2704 = £2500 \times \left(1 + \frac{r}{100}\right)^2$ *[1 mark]*
   $\frac{£2704}{£2500} = \left(1 + \frac{r}{100}\right)^2$
   $1 + \frac{r}{100} = \sqrt{\frac{£2704}{£2500}} = 1.04$ *[1 mark]*
   interest rate = 4% *[1 mark]*
   [3 marks available in total — as above]

Page 25 (Warm-up Questions)

1 a) 1:2   b) 4:9   c) 2:9
   d) 16:7   e) 5:4
2 1:4.4
3 300 g ÷ 2 = 150 g; 150 g × 3 = 450 g of flour
4 45, 60, 75 (3 + 4 + 5 = 12 parts, so 180 ÷ 12 = 15 per part.)

Page 26 (Exam Questions)

2 a) $3\frac{3}{4} : 1\frac{1}{2}$ *[1 mark]*

   $= 4 \times 3\frac{3}{4} : 4 \times 1\frac{1}{2} = 15 : 6$ *[1 mark]*

   $= 5 : 2$ *[1 mark]*

   [3 marks available in total — as above]

   b) 1355 ml ÷ 5 = 271 ml *[1 mark]*
   271 ml × 2 = 542 ml *[1 mark]*
   [2 marks available in total — as above]
   If your answer to part a) was incorrect, but your answer to part b) was correct for your incorrect ratio, you still get the marks for part b).

3 Susan, Edmund, Peter and Lucy shared the money in the ratio
   1:2:6:3 *[1 mark for 1:2:6:3 or any four numbers in that ratio, in any order]*
   120 ÷ (1 + 2 + 6 + 3) = 10 *[1 mark]*
   Lucy got £10 × 3 = £30 *[1 mark]*
   [3 marks available in total — as above]
   You could answer this question using a formula — if you let x be the amount of money that Susan gets, then x + 2x + 6x + 3x = £120

4 Cost for 1 litre of petrol = £31.25 ÷ 25 = £1.25 *[1 mark]*
   Cost for 52 litres of petrol = £1.25 × 52 = £65 *[1 mark]*
   [2 marks available in total — as above]

5 a) $\frac{18}{12} = \frac{3}{2}$ *[1 mark]*

   $\frac{3}{2} \times 150$ g = 225 g *[1 mark]*

   [2 marks available in total — as above]

   b) 300 ÷ 75 = 4 *[1 mark]*
   4 × 12 flapjacks = 48 flapjacks *[1 mark]*
   [2 marks available in total — as above]

Page 30 (Warm-up Questions)

1 a) 40.22   b) 39.9   c) 28
2 $\frac{94 \times 1.9}{0.328 + 0.201} \approx \frac{90 \times 2}{0.3 + 0.2} = \frac{180}{0.5} = 360$
3 Upper bound = 14.5 km. Lower bound = 13.5 km
4 a) Maximum = 9.3, minimum = 9.1
   b) Maximum = 3.5, minimum = 3.3
   c) Maximum = 18.7325, minimum = 17.8125
   d) Maximum = 2.23 (to 2 d.p.), minimum = 2.12 (to 2 d.p.)

Page 31 (Exam Questions)

3 a) $\frac{197.8}{\sqrt{0.01 + 0.23}} = \frac{197.8}{\sqrt{0.24}} = \frac{197.8}{0.489897948...} = 403.757559...$

   [2 marks available — 1 mark for some correct working, 1 mark for answer correct to 4 decimal places]

   b) 404 *[1 mark]*
   In question 3, if you get part a) wrong but round your wrong answer correctly in part b) you'll still get the mark for part b).

4 $\sqrt{\frac{2321}{19.673 \times 3.81}} \approx \sqrt{\frac{2000}{20 \times 4}}$

   [1 mark for rounding at least two numbers to 1 s.f.]

   $= \sqrt{\frac{100}{4}} = \sqrt{25}$ *[1 mark for either expression]*

   $= 5$ *[1 mark]*

   [3 marks available in total — as above]

5 upper bound for x = 57.5 mm *[1 mark]*
   upper bound for y = 32.5 mm *[1 mark]*
   upper bound for area = 57.5 mm × 32.5 mm = 1868.75 mm^2
   = 1870 mm^2 to 3 s.f. *[1 mark]*
   [3 marks available in total — as above]

6 lower bound for distance = 99.5 m
   upper bound for time = 12.55 s *[1 mark for both]*

   lower bound for speed = $\frac{99.5}{12.55}$ m/s

   = 7.928... m/s *[1 mark]*
   lower bound for speed to 2 s.f. = 7.9 m/s
   lower bound for speed to 1 s.f. = 8 m/s

   upper bound for distance = 100.5 m
   lower bound for time = 12.45 s *[1 mark for both]*

   upper bound for speed = $\frac{100.5}{12.45}$ m/s

   = 8.072... m/s *[1 mark]*
   upper bound for speed to 2 s.f. = 8.1 m/s
   upper bound for speed to 1 s.f. = 8 m/s

   The lower bound to 2 s.f. does not equal the upper bound to 2 s.f., but the lower bound to 1 s.f. does equal the upper bound to 1 s.f. So Dan's speed is 8 m/s to 1 significant figure.
   [1 mark for comparing bounds to reach correct answer to 1 s.f.]
   [5 marks available in total — as above]

Page 34 (Warm-up Questions)

1 2.4×10^5 miles
2 2.7×10^{-6} seconds
3 0.00000000000000000000000027 g
4 1.2×10^8
5 a) 2.4×10^{11} b) 2×10^4
   c) 7.797×10^6 d) 3.2088×10^{12}

Page 35 (Exam Questions)

2 a) $12\,500 = 1.25 \times 10^4$ *[1 mark]*

   b) $\frac{2 \times 10^8}{8 \times 10^3} = 0.25 \times 10^5$ *[1 mark]* $= 2.5 \times 10^4$ *[1 mark]*
   [2 marks available in total — as above]

   c) $(6 \times 10^4)^2 = 36 \times 10^8$ *[1 mark]* $= 3.6 \times 10^9$ *[1 mark]*
   [2 marks available in total — as above]

3 time (s) = distance (miles) ÷ speed (miles/s)
   = $(9.3 \times 10^7) \div (1.86 \times 10^5)$ seconds *[1 mark]*
   = $(9.3 \div 1.86) \times (10^7 \div 10^5)$ seconds *[1 mark]*
   = 5×10^2 seconds *[1 mark]*
   [3 marks available in total — as above]

4 a) number of tablets = dose (grams) ÷ dose per tablet (grams)
   = $(4 \times 10^{-4}) \div (8 \times 10^{-5})$ *[1 mark]*
   = $(4 \div 8) \times (10^{-4} \div 10^{-5})$
   = 0.5×10^1 *[1 mark]*
   = 5 *[1 mark]*
   [3 marks available in total — as above]

   b) new dose = 4×10^{-4} grams + 6×10^{-5} grams *[1 mark]*
   = 4×10^{-4} grams + 0.6×10^{-4} grams *[1 mark]*
   = $(4 + 0.6) \times 10^{-4}$ grams
   = 4.6×10^{-4} grams per day *[1 mark]*
   [3 marks available in total — as above]

Page 36 (Revision Questions)

1 a) Whole numbers — either positive or negative, or zero
   b) Numbers that can be written as fractions
   c) Numbers which will only divide by themselves or 1
2 a) 169   b) 7
   c) 3   d) 125
3 a) 240 = 2 × 2 × 2 × 2 × 3 × 5
   b) 1050 = 2 × 3 × 5 × 5 × 7
4 a) 14   b) 40
5 Divide top and bottom by the same number till they won't go any further.

6 a) $8\frac{2}{9}$ b) $\frac{33}{7}$

7 Multiplying: Multiply top and bottom numbers separately.
   Dividing: Turn the second fraction upside down, then multiply.
   Adding/subtracting: Put fractions over a common denominator,
   then add/subtract the numerators.

8 a) $\frac{14}{99}$ b) $3\frac{1}{7}$ c) $\frac{11}{24}$ d) $7\frac{11}{20}$

9 a) Divide the top by the bottom.
   b) Put the digits after the decimal point on the top, and a power
       of 10 with the same number of zeros as there were decimal
       places on the bottom.

10 a) i) $\frac{4}{100} = \frac{1}{25}$ ii) 4%
    b) i) $\frac{65}{100} = \frac{13}{20}$ ii) 0.65

11 Fractions where the denominator has prime factors of only 2 or 5
    give terminating decimals. All others give recurring decimals.

12 Let $r = 0.5\dot{1}$.
    Then $100r - r = 51.5\dot{1} - 0.5\dot{1}$
    $\Rightarrow 99r = 51 \Rightarrow r = \frac{51}{99} = \frac{17}{33}$

13 To find x as a percentage of y, make sure both amounts are in the
    same units, then divide x by y and multiply by 100.

14 percentage change = (change ÷ original) × 100

15 17.6 m

16 6% simple interest pays £59.62 more (to the nearest penny)

17 240

18 1. Add up the parts
    2. Divide to find one part
    3. Multiply to find the amounts

19 600, 960, 1440

20 a) 427.96   b) 428.0
    c) 430   d) 428.0

21 Estimates should be around 20-24.

22 The upper and lower bounds are half a unit either side of the
    rounded value.

23 132.2425 m²

24 1. The front number must always be between 1 and 10.
    2. The power of 10, n, is how far the decimal point moves.
    3. n is positive for big numbers, and negative for small numbers.

25 a) 9.7×10^5 b) 3.56×10^9 c) 2.75×10^{-6}

26 a) 1.5875×10^3 b) 2.739×10^{12}

Section Two — Algebra

Page 40 (Warm-up Questions)

1 a) 8, 13, 18, 23, 28, 33
   b) 8, 11, 14, 17, 20, 23

2 a) $5n$ b) $3n + 4$

3 There is always one cross in the centre, and the number of other
   crosses is 4 times the pattern number (because there are 4 "arms"
   coming from the centre). So in the nth pattern there will be a
   total of $4n + 1$ crosses.
   This method is a kind of 'common sense method'. You can get the
   same result by finding 'a' and 'd' and then using dn + (a − d).

4 a) 4^3 b) 6^3 c) 3^{15}

5 a) 2   b) $1\frac{32}{49}$ c) 9

Page 41 (Exam Questions)

2 a) 3   8   13   18
         +5   +5   +5

   The common difference is 5, so the next two terms in the
   sequence will be $18 + 5 = 23$ and $23 + 5 = 28$. *[1 mark]*

b) The common difference is 5 so $5n$ is in the formula.

   $5n$:   5   10   15   20
            ↓−2   ↓−2   ↓−2   ↓−2
   term: 3   8   13   18

   You have to subtract 2 to get to the term, so the expression
   for the nth term is $5n - 2$.
   [2 marks available — 2 marks for correct expression,
   otherwise 1 mark for finding 5n.]
   You could also have found the nth term using the equation
   nth term = dn + (a − d), where d is the common difference
   (in this case 5) and a is the first term (in this case 3).

c) Substituting $n = 30$ into the expression for
    the nth term: $5n - 2 = (5 \times 30) - 2 = 148$. *[1 mark]*

3 a) $(9 \times 2) - 1 = 18 - 1 = 17$ *[1 mark]*
   b) $(1 \times 4) + a = 7$
       $4 + a = 7$ *[1 mark]*, so $a = 7 - 4 = 3$ *[1 mark]*
       [2 marks available in total — as above]

4 a) $\frac{1}{100} = \frac{1}{10^2} = 10^{-2}$, so $k = -2$ *[1 mark]*
   b) $\sqrt{9} = 9^{\frac{1}{2}}$, so $k = \frac{1}{2}$ or 0.5 *[1 mark]*
   c) $(3^4)^2 = 3^{4 \times 2} = 3^8$ and $\frac{3^5}{3^{11}} = 3^{5-11} = 3^{-6}$ *[1 mark]*
       so $(3^4)^2 \times \frac{3^5}{3^{11}} = 3^8 \times 3^{-6} = 3^2$ and $k = 2$ *[1 mark]*
       [2 marks available in total — as above]

Page 46 (Warm-up Questions)

1 a) $2a - 5c$ b) $7r^2 - 5r - 1$
2 a) $8p + 28$ b) $8x^2 - 2$ c) $5a^2 - 3a$
3 a) $2(3p - 6q + 2)$ b) $2cd(2d - 1 + 5cd^2)$
4 $(x + 2y)(x - 2y)$
5 $\sqrt{30}$
6 $\sqrt{36} = 6$

Page 47 (Exam Questions)

3 The perimeter of the rectangle is
   $2x + 3 + 2x + 3 + 5y - 8 + 5y - 8 = 4x + 10y - 10$ *[1 mark]*
   So $4x + 10y - 10 = 7y - 2x$. *[1 mark]*
   This rearranges to give $6x + 3y = 10$ *[1 mark]*
   [3 marks available in total — as above]

4 a) $(2t - 5)(3t + 4) = (2t \times 3t) + (2t \times 4) + (-5 \times 3t) + (-5 \times 4)$
       $= 6t^2 + 8t - 15t - 20$ *[1 mark]*
       $= 6t^2 - 7t - 20$ *[1 mark]*
       [2 marks available in total — as above]
   b) $(x + 3)^2 = (x + 3)(x + 3)$
       $= (x \times x) + (x \times 3) + (3 \times x) + (3 \times 3)$
       $= x^2 + 3x + 3x + 9$ *[1 mark]*
       $= x^2 + 6x + 9$ *[1 mark]*
       [2 marks available in total — as above]

5 a) $6x + 3 = 3(2x + 1)$ *[1 mark]*
   b) $7y - 21y^2 = 7(y - 3y^2)$ *[1 mark]*
           $= 7y(1 - 3y)$ *[1 mark]*
       [2 marks available in total — as above]
   c) $2v^3w + 8v^2w^2 = 2(v^3w + 4v^2w^2)$ *[1 mark]*
           $= 2v^2w(v + 4w)$ *[1 mark]*
       [2 marks available in total — as above]

6 $(2 + \sqrt{3})(5 - \sqrt{3})$
   $= (2 \times 5) + (2 \times -\sqrt{3}) + (\sqrt{3} \times 5) + (\sqrt{3} \times -\sqrt{3})$
   $= 10 - 2\sqrt{3} + 5\sqrt{3} - 3 = 7 + 3\sqrt{3}$
   [2 marks available — 1 mark for correct working,
   1 mark for the correct answer.]

Page 52 (Warm-up Questions)

1 a) $x = 3$ b) $x = -3$ c) $x = 5$
2 a) p b) t
3 $q = 7(p - 2r)$ or $q = 7p - 14r$
4 $z = \dfrac{3x - y}{2}$

Page 53 (Exam Questions)

3 The perimeter is $(2x - 2) + (x + 1) + (22 - x) + (3x + 2)$, so...
$(2x - 2) + (x + 1) + (22 - x) + (3x + 2) = 58$ *[1 mark]*
$2x - 2 + x + 1 + 22 - x + 3x + 2 = 58$
$2x + x - x + 3x = 58 + 2 - 1 - 22 - 2$ *[1 mark]*
$5x = 35$
$x = 7$ *[1 mark]*
[3 marks available in total — as above]

4 a) $V = \frac{1}{3}Ah$, so $3V = Ah$ and $h = \frac{3V}{A}$
   [2 marks available — 1 mark for multiplying both sides by 3, 1 mark for the correct answer.]

   b) When $V = 18$ and $A = 12$, $h = \frac{3 \times 18}{12} = \frac{54}{12} = 4.5$ cm
   [2 marks available — 1 mark for correct substitution, 1 mark for the correct answer.]

5 $\frac{8 - 2x}{3} + \frac{2x + 4}{9} = 12$

   $\frac{9(8 - 2x)}{3} + \frac{9(2x + 4)}{9} = 108$

   $3(8 - 2x) + (2x + 4) = 108$ *[1 mark]*
   $24 - 6x + 2x + 4 = 108$
   $6x - 2x = 24 + 4 - 108$ *[1 mark]*
   $4x = -80$ *[1 mark]*
   $x = -20$ *[1 mark]*
   [4 marks available in total — as above]

6 $x = \sqrt{\frac{(1 + n)}{(1 - n)}}$, so $x^2 = \frac{(1 + n)}{(1 - n)}$ *[1 mark]*, $x^2(1 - n) = 1 + n$,
   $x^2 - x^2 n = 1 + n$ *[1 mark]*, $x^2 - 1 = n + x^2 n$ *[1 mark]*,
   $x^2 - 1 = n(1 + x^2)$ *[1 mark]*,
   $n = \frac{x^2 - 1}{1 + x^2}$ *[1 mark]*
   [5 marks available in total — as above]

Page 59 (Warm-up Questions)

1 a) $(x + 4)(x + 7)$ b) $(x + 14)(x + 2)$
   c) $(x + 14)(x - 2)$.

2 a) $x = -3$ or $x = -5$ *(it factorises to $(x + 3)(x + 5) = 0$)*
   b) $x = 2$ or $x = -7$ *(it factorises to $(x - 2)(x + 7) = 0$).*
   c) $x = 3$ or $x = 4$ *(Rearrange to give $x^2 - 7x + 12 = 0$, then factorise to give $(x - 3)(x - 4) = 0$, so $x = 3$ or $x = 4$.)*

3 $(3x + 2)(x + 10)$

4 $x = -\frac{2}{5}$ or $x = 3$ *(it factorises to $(5x + 2)(x - 3) = 0$)*

5 $x = 1.46$ or $x = -0.46$ *(use the quadratic formula, with $a = 3$, $b = -3$ and $c = -2$).*

6 $(x + 4)^2 + 4$ *($(x + 4)^2 = x^2 + 8x + 16$, so $+4$ to complete the square)*

7 $x = 9$ or $x = 1$ *($(x - 5)^2$ gives $x^2 - 10x + 25$ so complete the square by subtracting 16;*
   $(x - 5)^2 - 16 = 0$
   $(x - 5)^2 = 16$
   $(x - 5) = \pm\sqrt{16}$
   $(x - 5) = 4$ or $(x - 5) = -4$
   $x = 9$ or $x = 1$.)

Page 60 (Exam Questions)

3 a) $(2x - 7)(x + 4)$
   [2 marks available — 1 mark for correct numbers in brackets, 1 mark for correct signs]

   b) $(2x - 7)(x + 4) = (2x - 7)^2$ *[1 mark]*
   $(2x - 7)(x + 4) - (2x - 7)^2 = 0$
   $(2x - 7)((x + 4) - (2x - 7)) = 0$ *[1 mark]*
   $2x - 7 = 0$ or $x + 4 - 2x + 7 = 0$ *[1 mark]*
   $x = 3.5$ or $-x + 11 = 0$
   $x = 3.5$ or $x = 11$
   [1 mark for both solutions]
   [4 marks available in total — as above]

4 $a = 1$, $b = 6$ and $c = -3$
   $x = \frac{-6 \pm \sqrt{6^2 - 4 \times 1 \times -3}}{2 \times 1} = \frac{-6 \pm \sqrt{48}}{2}$
   $x = 0.46$ or $x = -6.46$
   [3 marks available — 1 mark for correct substitution, 1 mark for each correct solution]

5 $2a = 4$, so $a = 4 \div 2 = 2$ *[1 mark]*
   $-b = 6$, so $b = -6$ *[1 mark]*
   $4ac = 24$, so $c = 24 \div 4 \div 2 = 3$ *[1 mark]*
   [3 marks available in total — as above]

6 $-6 \div 2 = -3$, so $a = -3$ and the bit in brackets is $(x - 3)^2$.
   Expanding the brackets: $(x - 3)^2 = x^2 - 6x + 9$. *[1 mark]*
   To complete the square: $3 - 9 = -6$, so $b = -6$. *[1 mark]*
   $x^2 - 6x + 3 = (x - 3)^2 - 6$ *[1 mark]*
   [3 marks available in total — as above]

7 $(x + 2)^2 - 9 = x^2 + 4x + 4 - 9$ *[1 mark]* $= x^2 + 4x - 5$
   $a = 4$ and $b = -5$ *[1 mark]*
   [2 marks available in total — as above]

Page 67 (Warm-up Questions)

1 a) $\frac{11x}{10}$ b) $\frac{ac^2}{b}$
   (For b), turn the 2nd fraction upside down and multiply)

2 $x = 13, 14, 15, 16$.

3 $n = -3, -2, -1, 0, 1, 2, 3$.

4 Dividing by 4 gives $2 < x < 5$,
   but x must be an integer so $x = 3, 4$.

5 $2q + 2 \leq 12 \Rightarrow 2q \leq 10 \Rightarrow q \leq 5$.

6 $4p + 12 > 30 \Rightarrow 4p > 18 \Rightarrow p > 4\frac{1}{2}$.

7
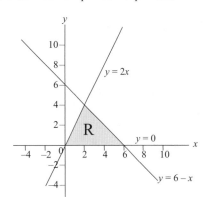

8 $x^3 + 6x = 69$

x	$x^3 + 6x$	
3	45	Too small
4	88	Too big
3.5	63.875	Too small
3.6	68.256	Too small
3.7	72.853	Too big
3.65	70.527125	Too big

$x = 3.6$ to 1 d.p.

9 $x^3 - 12x = 100$

x	$x^3 - 12x$	
5	65	Too small
6	144	Too big
5.5	100.375	Too big
5.4	92.664	Too small
5.45	96.478625	Too small

$x = 5.5$ to 1 d.p.

Page 68 (Exam Questions)

3

x	$x^2(x + 1)$	Notes
3	36	too small
4	80	too big
3.5	55.125	too small
3.7	64.343	too big
3.6	59.616	too small
3.65	61.949...	too small

$x = 3.7$

[4 marks available — 1 mark for any trial between 3 and 4, 1 mark for any trial between 3.5 and 4, 1 mark for an appropriate trial to 2 d.p., 1 mark for the correct answer]

4 a) $4q - 5 < 23$, so $4q < 28$ *[1 mark]* and $q < 7$ *[1 mark]*
[2 marks available in total — as above]

b) $\frac{2x}{5} \leq 3$, so $2x \leq 15$ *[1 mark]* and $x \leq 7.5$ *[1 mark]*
[2 marks available in total — as above]

c) $4x + 1 > x - 5$, so $3x > -6$ *[1 mark]* and $x > -2$ *[1 mark]*
[2 marks available in total — as above]

5

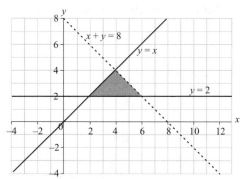

[4 marks available — 1 mark for drawing each line correctly, 1 mark for shading the correct region]

6 $\frac{16}{2x + 5} - \frac{1}{x} = 6$

$\frac{16x - (2x + 5)}{(2x + 5)x} = 6$ *[1 mark]*

$14x - 5 = 6(2x^2 + 5x)$ *[1 mark]*

$0 = 12x^2 + 30x - 14x + 5$

$0 = 12x^2 + 16x + 5$ *[1 mark]*

$(2x + 1)(6x + 5) = 0$ *[1 mark]*

$x = -\frac{1}{2}$ or $x = -\frac{5}{6}$ *[1 mark]*

[5 marks available — as above]

Page 74 (Warm-up Questions)

1 a) $x = 6, y = 6$. b) $x = 2, y = 4$. c) $x = 4, y = 3$.
Just read off the x- and y-values where the lines cross... erm, that's it.

2

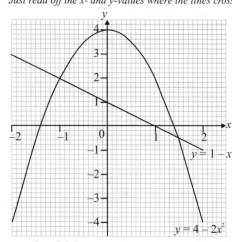

$x = -1$ and 1.5.
(The solution is just where the two graphs cross.)

3 $y = 5 - x$.
(This is like the reverse process of question 2. You need to think which equation you can combine with the one given to get to the one you want.
$y = 5 - x$ meets $y = x^2 - 3x + 2$ when $5 - x = x^2 - 3x + 2$, i.e. $x^2 - 2x - 3 = 0$ as required.)

4 $x = 2, y = 5$
(Subtract the equations to give $2y = 10$, therefore $y = 5$. Substitute $y = 5$ into the second equation to give $2x + 5 = 9$, therefore $x = 2$.)

5 $x = 4, y = 4$
(Add the equations to give $4x = 16$, therefore $x = 4$. Substitute $x = 4$ into the first equation to give $12 + 2y = 20$, giving $y = 4$.)

6 a) $A = kr^2$
b) $D = k/R$
c) $H = k/D^3$
d) $V = kS^3$

Page 75 (Exam Questions)

2 $x + 3y = 11 \xrightarrow{\times 3} 3x + 9y = 33$ *[1 mark]*

$3x + 9y = 33$ $x + 3y = 11$
$\underline{3x + \ y = 9 -}$ $x + (3 \times 3) = 11$
    $8y = 24$ $x = 11 - 9$
     $y = 3$ *[1 mark]* $x = 2$ *[1 mark]*
[3 marks available in total — as above]

3 a) $c \propto \frac{1}{d^2}$, so $c = \frac{k}{d^2}$ *[1 mark]*
When $c = 2$ and $d = 3$, $2 = \frac{k}{3^2}$, so $k = 2 \times 3^2 = 18$ *[1 mark]*
So $c = \frac{18}{d^2}$ *[1 mark]*
[3 marks available in total — as above]

b) $c = \frac{18}{d^2}$ so when $c = 0.5$, $0.5 = \frac{18}{d^2}$, $d = \pm\sqrt{\frac{18}{0.5}}$ *[1 mark]*
$= \pm 6$ *[1 mark]*
[2 marks available in total — as above]

4 $x^2 + y = 4$, so $y = 4 - x^2$
$4x - 1 = 4 - x^2$ *[1 mark]*
$x^2 + 4x - 5 = 0$ *[1 mark]*
$(x + 5)(x - 1) = 0$ *[1 mark]*
$x = -5$ or $x = 1$ *[1 mark]*

When $x = 1$, $y = (4 \times 1) - 1 = 3$
When $x = -5$, $y = (4 \times -5) - 1 = -21$

So the solutions are $x = 1, y = 3$ and $x = -5, y = -21$ *[1 mark]*
[5 marks available in total — as above]

5 n is an integer. $2n$ represents any even number, so the difference between the squares of two consecutive even numbers will be given by $(2n + 2)^2 - (2n)^2$. *[1 mark]*
$(2n + 2)^2 - (2n)^2 = (4n^2 + 8n + 4) - 4n^2 = 8n + 4 = 4(2n + 1)$
$= 4x$ (where $x = 2n + 1$) *[1 mark]*
Any integer multiplied by 4 is a multiple of 4, so $4x$ must be a multiple of 4 and therefore the difference between the squares of two consecutive even numbers will always be a multiple of 4.
[1 mark]
[3 marks available in total — as above]

6

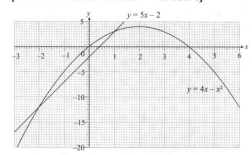

$x = 1, y = 3$ and $x = -2, y = -12$
[3 marks available — 1 mark for correctly drawing the line $y = 5x - 2$, 1 mark for each correct solution]

Page 76 (Revision Questions)

1 a) $2n + 5$ b) $-3n + 14$

2 Yes, it's the 5th term.

3 a) x^9 b) y^2 c) z^{12}

4 $5x - 4y - 5$

5 a) $6x + 3$ b) $x^2 - x - 6$

6 a) $(x + 4y)(x - 4y)$ b) $(7 + 9pq)(7 - 9pq)$
   c) $12(x + 2y)(x - 2y)$

7 a) $3\sqrt{3}$ b) 5

8 a) $x = 2$ b) $x = \pm 3$

9 a) $p = -\dfrac{4y}{3}$ b) $p = \dfrac{qr}{q + r}$

10 a) $x = -3$ and $x = -6$
   b) $x = 4$ and $x = -\dfrac{3}{5}$

11 $x = \dfrac{-b \pm \sqrt{b^2 - 4ac}}{2a}$

12 a) $x = 1.56$ and $x = -2.56$
   b) $x = 0.27$ and $x = -1.47$
   c) $x = 0.44$ and $x = -3.44$

13 a) $x = -6 \pm \sqrt{21}$ b) $x = 3 \pm \sqrt{11}$

14 $\dfrac{3x + 1}{(x + 3)(x - 1)}$

15 $x \geq -2$

16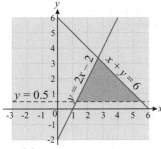

17 $x = 4.1$

18 Sketch the graphs and find the coordinates of the points where the graphs cross.

19 $x = -2$, $y = -2$ and $x = -4$, $y = -8$

20 $y = kx^2$

21 $p = 72$

22 Take an even number, $2p$, and an odd number, $2q + 1$. Their product is $2p \times (2q + 1) = 4pq + 2p = 2(2pq + p)$, which is even.

Section Three — Graphs

Page 84 (Warm-up Questions)

1 a) $y = x$.
  b) Horizontal line ($y = 4$).
  c) Vertical line ($x = -1$).
  d) $y = -x$.

2 Positive: C, E. Negative: A, D. No gradient: B.

3 a)

x	0	2	3
y	-4	2	5

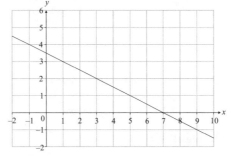

b) $y = 3x + 2$ will be parallel to $y = 3x - 4$ and will pass through the point $(0, 2)$ on the y axis.

4 a) $y = 2x + 4$
  b) $-\dfrac{1}{2}$

Page 85 (Exam Questions)

2 Using $y = mx + c$, where m is the gradient, and c is the y-intercept: Find the gradient, m:
Using the points $(0.2, 0.1)$ and $(-0.2, 0)$,
$m = \dfrac{(0.1 - 0)}{(0.2 - (-0.2))} = 0.25$
Find c:
When $x = 0$, $y = 0.05$, so $c = 0.05$
So, $y = 0.25x + 0.05$
[3 marks available — 1 mark for a correct method to find the gradient, 1 mark for a correct method to find the y-intercept, 1 mark for the correct final answer]

3

[3 marks available — 1 mark for plotting any point on the line (e.g. (0, 3.5)), 1 mark for plotting a second correct point (e.g. (7, 0)), 1 mark for the correct line extending between $x = -2$ and $x = 10$]
To draw these graphs, you could either create a table of values and plot the points, or you could set $y = 0$ and $x = 0$ and join up the points.

4 $3x + 4 = 2x + 6$ *[1 mark]*
$x = 2$ *[1 mark]*
so, $y = 10$ and point M is $(2, 10)$ *[1 mark]*
gradient of perpendicular line $= \dfrac{-1}{2} = -0.5$,
so, $y = -0.5x + c$ *[1 mark]*
$10 = -0.5 \times 2 + c$, so $c = 10 + 1 = 11$
$y = -0.5x + 11$ *[1 mark]*
[5 marks available in total — as above]

220

Page 90 (Warm-up Questions)

1 a)

x	–2	–1	0	1	2	3	4	5
y	7	2	–1	–2	–1	2	7	14

b)

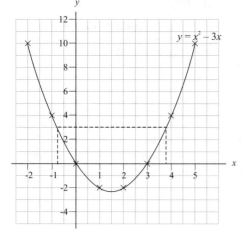

$y = x^2 - 2x - 1$

c) 4.25 (a value between 4 and 4.5 is acceptable).

d) $x = -1.65$ and 3.65 (values between –1.6 and –1.7 and between 3.6 and 3.7 are acceptable).

2

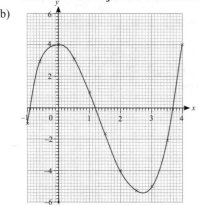

$y = x^2 - 3x$

a) $x = 0$ and 3.

b) $x = -0.8$ and 3.8 *(anything from –0.9 to –0.6 and from 3.6 to 3.9 is acceptable)*

3 $x = 310°$ *(anything from 308° – 312° is acceptable)*

Page 91 (Exam Questions)

2 a)

x	2.5	3	3.5	4
y	–5.375	–5	–2.125	4

[2 marks available — 2 marks for all answers correct, otherwise 1 mark for two correct answers]

b)

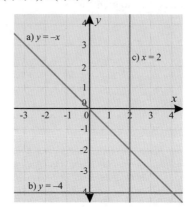

[2 marks available — 1 mark for plotting correct points, 1 mark for joining them with a smooth curve]

c) Reading off the graph, where the line intersects the x-axis, $x = -0.9$, $x = 1.2$ and $x = 3.7$ *[1 mark]*
    You'll still get the mark if your answers are within 0.1 of the answer.

3 a) F *[1 mark]*

   b) A *[1 mark]*

   c) B *[1 mark]*

Page 95 (Warm-up Questions)

1 Both graphs have the same shape, but the second is shifted up the y-axis by 2 units.

2 Graph A and 2, Graph B and 3
   Graph C and 4, Graph D and 1

Page 96 (Exam Questions)

2 a) Plan A: £25 *[1 mark]*
       Plan B: £28 *[1 mark]*
       [2 marks available in total — as above]

   b) Mr Barker should use Plan A because it is cheaper. Using 85 units with Plan A would cost £26.50. 85 units with Plan B would cost £34. *[2 marks available — 1 mark for correctly stating which plan, 1 mark for giving a reason]*

3 a) $y = f(x) - 4$ *[1 mark]*

   b) (–2, 1) *[2 marks available — 1 mark for each correct coordinate, up to a maximum of 2]*

   c) (4, 2) *[2 marks available — 1 mark for each correct coordinate, up to a maximum of 2]*

   d)

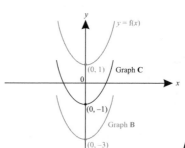

[1 mark]

   e)

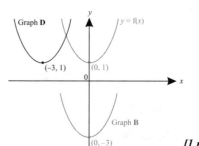

[1 mark]

Page 97 (Revision Questions)

1 (2.5, –0.5)

2 A(4, 5, 0), B(4, 5, 5)

3

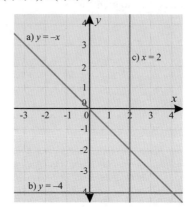

ANSWERS

4 Straight-line equations just contain something *x*, something *y* and a number. They don't contain any powers of *x* or *y*, *xy*, 1/*x* or 1/*y*.

5
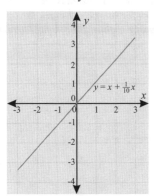

6
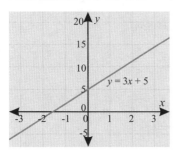

7 A line with a negative gradient slopes 'downhill' from left to right.

8 Gradient = –0.75

9 'm' is the gradient and 'c' is the *y*-intercept.

10
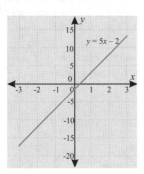

11 $y = 2x + 10$

12 The gradients of two perpendicular lines multiply together to give –1. The gradients of parallel lines are the same as each other.

13 $y = -\frac{1}{2}x + 4$

14 They are both symmetrical "bucket shaped" graphs. $y = x^2 + 2x - 8$ is like a "u" whereas $y = -x^2 + 2x - 8$ is like an "n" (or an upturned bucket).

15
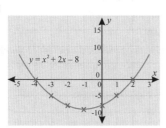

$x = -3.6$ or 1.6 (both ±0.2)

16 a) A graph with a "wiggle" in the middle. E.g.
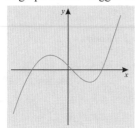

b) A graph made up of two curves in diagonally opposite quadrants. The graph is symmetrical about the lines $y = x$ and $y = -x$. E.g.
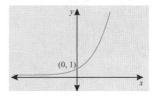

c) A graph which curves rapidly upwards. E.g.
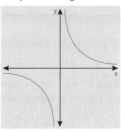

17 $b = 0.25, c = 8$

18 *y*-stretch ($y = k \times f(x)$)
y-shift ($y = f(x) + a$)
x-shift ($y = f(x - a)$)
x-stretch ($y = f(kx)$)
reflection ($y = -f(x)$ or $y = f(-x)$)

19 a) $y = (-x)^3 + 1$ is the original graph reflected in *y*-axis.
b) $y = (x + 2)^3 + 1$ is the original graph shifted by 2 units in the negative *x*-direction.
c) $y = (3x)^3 + 1$ is the original graph scrunched up horizontally by a factor of 3.
d) $y = x^3 - 1$ is the original graph shifted downwards by 2 units.

20
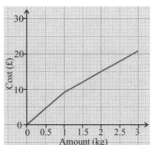

Section Four — Geometry and Measures

Page 103 (Warm-up Questions)

1 180°

2 $a = 115°$, angles on a line add to 180°, so $a = 180° - 65°$.
$b = 115°$, *a* and *b* are corresponding angles, so $a = b$.
$c = 65°$, *c* and 65° are also corresponding angles.
$d = 115°$, angles on a line add to 180°, so $d = 180 - c$.
There are often different ways of going about angle questions. Just keep scribbling down angles as you find them. It can make it easier to get the angle you want.

3 6 sides

4 Pentagon

5 Number of sides = 360° ÷ 24° = 15

Page 104 (Exam Questions)

2 a)

[2 marks available — 2 marks if all four lines of symmetry correctly drawn, otherwise 1 mark if two out of four lines of symmetry correctly drawn]

b) 4 *[1 mark]*

3 Angle BCA = angle BAC *[1 mark]*
Angle BCA = (180° – 48°) ÷ 2 = 66° *[1 mark]*
Angle BCD = 180° – 66° = 114° *[1 mark]*
[3 marks available in total — as above]

4 5x + (4x – 9°) = 180° *[1 mark]*
Rearranging this: 9x = 189°
Therefore x = 21° *[1 mark]*
(4y – 12°) + 2y = 180° *[1 mark]*
Rearranging this: 6y = 192°
Therefore y = 32° *[1 mark]*
[4 marks available in total — as above]

5 a) x is the same as an exterior angle, so x = 360° ÷ 8 *[1 mark]*
x = 45° *[1 mark]*
[2 marks available in total — as above]
b) y = (180° – 45°) ÷ 2 *[1 mark]*
y = 67.5° *[1 mark]*
[2 marks available in total — as above]

Page 108 (Warm-up Question)

1 M = N = 64°
(Angles M and N are equal to the 64° angle given, using the alternate segment theorem)
L = 52° (Angles in a triangle add to 180°, so 180° – 64° – 64° = 52°.)

Page 109 (Exam Questions)

2 a) Angle BCD = 150° ÷ 2 = 75° *[1 mark]*
(Angle at the centre is 2 × angle at circumference.) *[1 mark]*
[2 marks available in total — as above]
b) Opposite angles in a cyclic quadrilateral sum to 180°.
[1 mark]

3 Angle DBC = 62° *[1 mark]*
Angle ABC = 90° *[1 mark]*
Angle x = 90° – 62° = 28° *[1 mark]*
[3 marks available in total — as above]

4 a) Angle QPR = 90° *[1 mark]*
Angle QPT = 180° – 90° – 52° = 38° *[1 mark]*
[2 marks available in total — as above]
b) Using the alternate segment theorem, angles in opposite segments are equal, so angle QRP = angle QPT = 38°.
[1 mark]
The angle between a chord and a tangent is equal to the angle made at the circumference of the circle by two lines drawn from the ends of the chord.

Page 115 (Warm-up Questions)

1 $\begin{pmatrix} -3 \\ 3 \end{pmatrix}$

2 64 m²

3 a) A and E   b) B and F

4 a) 0.222 or $\frac{2}{9}$
Note that the enlargement scale factor is less than one — so the 'enlargement' actually makes the shape smaller.
b) 2.6 cm

Pages 116-117 (Exam Questions)

2 a) Rotation 90° anti-clockwise around the point (0, 0)
[3 marks available — 1 mark for rotation, 1 mark for correct angle and direction of rotation, 1 mark for correct centre of rotation]
b)

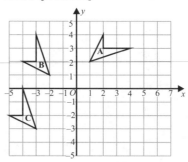

[1 mark for correct translation]

3 a) and b)

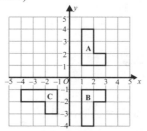

[2 marks available for part a) — 2 marks if shape correctly reflected and in the right place on the grid, otherwise 1 mark if shape correctly reflected but in wrong location]
[2 marks available for part b) — 1 mark for a rotation of 90° clockwise around any point, 1 mark for the correct centre of rotation]
c) Reflection in the line y = –x *[2 marks available — 1 mark for reflection, 1 mark for correct line of reflection]*

4

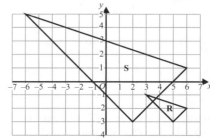

[3 marks available — 1 mark for any enlargement, 1 mark for enlarging by scale factor 4, 1 mark for correct position]

5 a) Scale factor from EFGH to ABCD = 9 ÷ 6 = 1.5 *[1 mark]*
EF = 6 ÷ 1.5 = 4 cm *[1 mark]*
[2 marks available in total — as above]
b) BC = 4 × 1.5 = 6 cm *[1 mark]*

6 Scale factor = 16 ÷ 4 = 4 *[1 mark]*

7 KP = OL (since they are diameters of identical circles) *[1 mark]*
Angle KMP = angle ONL (since angles in a semicircle = 90°)
[1 mark]
Angle MKO = angle NLP (since alternate angles are equal)
[1 mark]
Satisfies condition AAS so triangles are congruent. *[1 mark]*
[4 marks available in total — as above]

8 a) Scale factor from **A** to **C**:
$n^2 = 108\pi \div 12\pi = 9$ *[1 mark]*
n = 3 *[1 mark]*
Volume of **A** = 135π cm³ ÷ 3³ *[1 mark]*
= 5π cm³ *[1 mark]*
[4 marks available in total — as above]

b) Scale factor from **A** to **B**:
$m^2 = 48\pi \div 12\pi = 4$ *[1 mark]*
$m = 2$ *[1 mark]*
Perpendicular height of B = 4 cm × 2 *[1 mark]*
= 8 cm *[1 mark]*
[4 marks available in total — as above]

Page 124 (Warm-up Questions)

1 a)   b)   c)

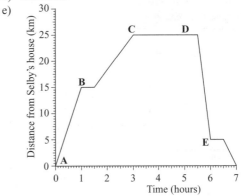

2 a) 1963.5 mm² *($\pi r^2 = 25^2 \times \pi$)*

   b) 37 146 mm² *(area of rectangle minus area of four circles)*

   c) 148 584 mm³ *(volume = area × thickness)*

3   672 cm³ *(area of triangle × length = ½ × 12 × 8 × 14)*

4   268 m³ *(volume of a sphere = $\frac{4}{3}\pi r^3$)*

Pages 125-126 (Exam Questions)

2   Area of field = ½ × (105 + 80) × 60 = 5550 m² *[1 mark]*
Price of weed killer per m² = 0.27 ÷ 10 = £0.027 *[1 mark]*
Cost = area × price per square metre = 5550 × 0.027 *[1 mark]*
     = £149.85 *[1 mark]*
[4 marks available in total — as above]

3   Area of triangle = ½ × 6.0 × 5.2 = 15.6 cm²
Area of whole octahedron = 8 × 15.6 = 124.8 cm²
[3 marks available — 1 mark for a correct method for finding the area of the triangle, 1 mark for the correct triangle area, 1 mark for the correct final answer]

4   A regular hexagon is made up of 6 identical triangles.
Area of triangle = ½ × 8 × 7 = 28 cm² *[1 mark]*
Area of whole hexagon cross-section = 28 × 6 = 168 cm²
[1 mark]
Volume of prism = cross-sectional area × length =
168 × 6 = 1008 cm³ *[1 mark]*
[3 marks available in total — as above]

5   Area of pool base = π × (2 ÷ 2)² = π m² *[1 mark]*
Volume of pool = π × 0.4 = 0.4π m³ *[1 mark]*
Volume of water Amy should use = $0.4\pi \times \frac{3}{4}$ *[1 mark]*
= 0.94 m³ (to 2 d.p.) *[1 mark]*
[4 marks available in total — as above]

6   Area of full circle = π × 12² = 144π cm²
Area of sector = (50 ÷ 360) × area of circle
= (50 ÷ 360) × 144π cm²
= 62.831... cm² = 62.8 cm² (3 s.f.)
[4 marks available — 1 mark for a correct method for finding the area of the full circle, 1 mark for correct area of the full circle, 1 mark for a correct method for calculating the area of the sector, and 1 mark for the correct answer]

7   Surface area of curved part of hemisphere =
½ × surface area of a sphere = ½ × 4 × π × 7² *[1 mark]*
= 307.876... cm² *[1 mark]*
Surface area of curved part of cone = π × 2 × 12 *[1 mark]*
= 75.398... cm² *[1 mark]*
Surface area of flat top of hemisphere = (π × 7²) − (π × 2²)
= 141.371... cm² *[1 mark]*
Total surface area = 307.876... + 75.398... + 141.371...
= 525 cm² (to 3 s.f.) *[1 mark]*
[6 marks available in total — as above]

Page 131 (Warm-up Questions)

1   11.3 g/cm³ *(density = mass ÷ volume)*

2   96 g *(Volume = 5 × 4 × 6 = 120 cm³.*
Then use mass = density × volume.)

3   90 km/h *(Speed in m/s = 100 ÷ 4 = 25 m/s.*
Multiply by 3600 to get m/h, then divide by 1000 to get km/h.)

4   9 km *(distance = speed × time)*

5 a)   15

   b)   The speed at which Selby is travelling.

   c)   3 hours
(As he was at point A at 0 hours, all you have to do is read off the x-value at point C to see how long Selby's journey was.)

   d)   2.5 hours

   e)

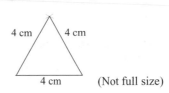

   f)   7 − 0.5 − 2.5 − 0.5 = 3.5 hours
(Selby isn't cycling whenever the graph shows a horizontal line. So, subtract these times from the total amount of time he is out.)

6 a)   12.7 × 1000 = 12 700 g   b)   1430 ÷ 100 = 14.3 m

7   10 kg.
(If you can't remember whether to multiply or divide, do both and see which answer is more sensible)

8   3 000 000 000 mm³

Page 132 (Exam Questions)

2 a)   10 °C *[1 mark]*

   b)   Temperature at noon = 10 °C + 15 °C = 25 °C
From graph, 25 °C = 77 °F
Increase in temperature = 77 °F − 50 °F = 27 °F
5 hours between 7 o'clock and 12 o'clock,
so average hourly increase = 27 ÷ 5 = 5.4 °F
[3 marks available — 1 mark for finding 25 °C in °F from graph, 1 mark for dividing change in temperature by change in time, 1 mark for correct answer]

3   39 200 ÷ 10 000 *[1 mark]*
= 3.92 m² *[1 mark]*
[2 marks available in total — as above]

4 a)   E.g. 2500 m = 2.5 km. 2.5 km = 2.5 ÷ 1.6 = 1.5625 miles.
102 s ÷ 60 = 1.7 minutes ÷ 60 = 0.02833... hours.
Speed = 1.5625 miles ÷ 0.02833... hours
= 55 mph (to nearest mph)
[3 marks available — 1 mark for converting 2500 metres to miles, 1 mark for converting 102 seconds into hours, 1 mark for the correct final answer]
It doesn't matter whether you do the conversion to miles per hour at the start or the end of the calculation — you could find the speed in m/s, km/h or km/h, and then change it to mph. Whichever way, you should get the same answer.

   b)   E.g. time = 1.5625 miles ÷ 50 mph = 0.03125 hours
0.03125 hours × 60 × 60 = 113 s (to nearest second)
[2 marks available — 1 mark for dividing the distance by the speed limit, 1 mark for the correct answer]

Page 138 (Warm-up Questions)

1

2

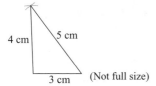

(Not full size)

3 Shaded area = where public can go

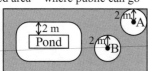

4

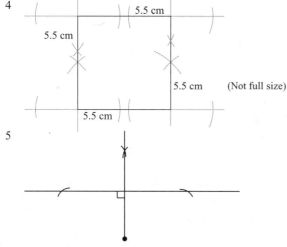

(Not full size)

5

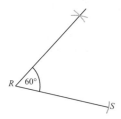

6 29.2 km

(Use the cosine rule ($a^2 = b^2 + c^2 - 2bc \, cosA$) with $A = 130°$, $b = 12$ km and $c = 20$ km. You have to draw yourself a diagram to find the angle A — you need to use angle rules to work it out.)

Page 139 (Exam Questions)

2 a)

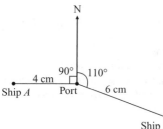

[4 marks available — 1 mark for Ship A 4 cm from the port, 1 mark for correct bearing for ship A, 1 mark for ship B 6 cm from the port, 1 mark for correct bearing for Ship B]
This diagram has been drawn a bit smaller to make it fit — your measurements should match the labels given on the diagram here.

b) 102° (accept answers between 100° and 104°) *[1 mark]*

c) 180° − 102° = 78°
360 − 78 = 282° (accept answers between 280° and 284°)
[2 marks available — 1 mark for correctly using 102°, 1 mark for correct answer]
You could also do this by adding 180° to 102°.

3

[2 marks available — 1 mark for intersecting arcs, 1 mark for line drawn through intersection]

4

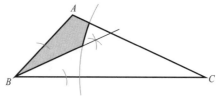

[4 marks available — 1 mark for radius of 6.5 cm with centre at C, 1 mark for construction arcs on AB and BC for angle bisector at ABC, 1 mark for correct angle bisector at ABC, and 1 mark for the correct shading]
You'll only get all four marks if you show the examiner you've constructed both the bisector of the angle and the arc from point C. So make sure you remember to leave in your construction lines.

Pages 140-141 (Revision Questions)

1 360°

2 a) $x = 154°$ b) $y = 112°$ c) $z = 58°$

3 60°

4 lines of symmetry = 3
order of rotational symmetry = 3

5 90°

6 a) $x = 53°$ b) $y = 69°$ c) $z = 33°$

7 a) Translation by vector $\left(\begin{smallmatrix} -2 \\ -4 \end{smallmatrix}\right)$
b) Reflection in the y-axis

8

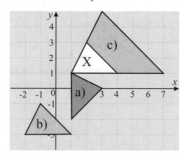

9 80 cm²

10 SSS, AAS, SAS, RHS

11 E.g. angles ACB and ACD are right angles (as it's a perpendicular bisector of a chord)
AB = AD (they're both radii)
CB = CD (as the chord is bisected)
So the condition RHS holds and the triangles are congruent.

12 $x = 2.5$ cm

13 The view from directly above an object.

14

15 $A = \frac{1}{2}(a + b) \times h_v$

16 220 cm²

17 Circumference = 16π cm,
area = 64π cm²

18 39.27 cm²

19 Surface area = $4\pi r^2$

20 75π cm²

21 396 cm³

22 129.85 cm³ (2 d.p.)

23 12 500 cm³

24 42 mph

25 The object has stopped.

26 36 mph

27 a) 5600 cm³   b) 3.6 kg
    c) 10.8 km/h   d) 5 690 000 cm²

28 7.5 miles

29
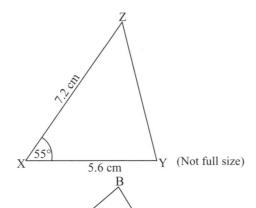
(Not full size)

30
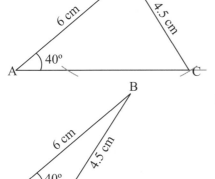
(Not full size)

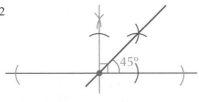

31 A circle

32
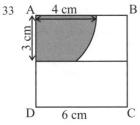

33
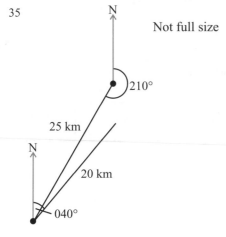

34 Put your pencil on the diagram at the point you're going FROM. Draw a north line at this point. Draw in the angle clockwise from the north line — this is the bearing you want.

35
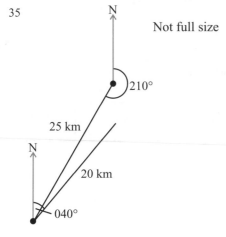
Not full size

Section Five — Pythagoras and Trigonometry

Page 145 (Warm-up Questions)

1 a) 13.1 cm *(by Pythagoras)*
   b) 40° *(tan x = 8.4 ÷ 10)*

2 3 cm

Page 146 (Exam Questions)

3 *Find the height by splitting the triangle into two right-angled triangles.*
   Let h be the height of the triangle:
   $13^2 = 5^2 + h^2$ *[1 mark]*
   $h = \sqrt{169 - 25} = \sqrt{144}$ *[1 mark]*
   $h = 12$ cm *[1 mark]*
   Area, $A = \frac{1}{2} \times 10 \times 12 = 60$ cm² *[1 mark]*
   [4 marks available in total — as above]

4 *Split ABC into two right-angled triangles, and find half of AC (call it x)*
   a) $\cos 34° = \frac{x}{10}$ *[1 mark]*
       $x = 10 \times \cos 34°$ *[1 mark]*
       $x = 8.29...$
       $AC = 8.29... \times 2 = 16.58$ m (2 d.p) *[1 mark]*
       [3 marks available in total — as above]
   b) $\sin 34° = \frac{h}{10}$ *[1 mark]*
       $h = 10 \times \sin 34°$ *[1 mark]*
       $h = 5.59$ m (2 d.p) *[1 mark]*
       [3 marks available in total — as above]
       You could also use $\tan 34° = \frac{h}{8.29}$ to work out the answer.

5 a) $\tan x = \frac{6}{9}$ *[1 mark]*
       $x = \tan^{-1}\left(\frac{6}{9}\right)$ *[1 mark]*
       $x = 33.7°$ (1.d.p) *[1 mark]*
       [3 marks available in total — as above.]
   b) *EG bisects the angle FEH, so find angle FEM:*
       $\tan x = \frac{6}{5}$ *[1 mark]*
       $x = \tan^{-1}\left(\frac{6}{5}\right)$ *[1 mark]*
       $x = 50.19...°$
       $FEH = 50.19... \times 2 = 100.4°$ (1 d.p) *[1 mark]*
       [3 marks available in total — as above]

Page 153 (Warm-up Questions)

1 $AC = 9.6$ cm

2 104.5°

3 $FDG = 31°$ (2 s.f.)

4 a) $\overrightarrow{CD} = -2\mathbf{a}$ *(since ABCD is a parallelogram, AB = DC)*
   b) $\overrightarrow{AC} = 2\mathbf{d} + 2\mathbf{a}$ *(because you know that AD = BC)*
   c) $\overrightarrow{BL} = \mathbf{d} - \mathbf{a}$ *(you could find this in a few different ways — for example $\overrightarrow{BL} = \overrightarrow{BC} + \frac{1}{2}\overrightarrow{CA} = 2\mathbf{d} - (\mathbf{d} + \mathbf{a}) = \mathbf{d} - \mathbf{a}$)*

Pages 154-155 (Exam Questions)

2 a) $\frac{BD}{\sin 30°} = \frac{8}{\sin 70°}$ *[1 mark]*
       $BD = \frac{8}{\sin 70°} \times \sin 30°$ *[1 mark]*
       $BD = 4.26$ m (3 s.f) *[1 mark]*
       [3 marks available in total — as above]
   b) $\frac{4}{\sin BDC} = \frac{4.26}{\sin 60°}$ *[1 mark]*
       $\sin BDC = \frac{\sin 60°}{4.26} \times 4$
       Angle $BDC = \sin^{-1}(0.813...)$ *[1 mark]*
       Angle $BDC = 54.4°$ (3 s.f) *[1 mark]*
       [3 marks available in total — as above]
       If you'd used the exact answer to part a) as the length of BD in this calculation, you'd have got 54.5° as your final answer.

3 *First you need to find one angle using the cosine rule.*
   E.g. use angle CAB.

   $\cos A = \dfrac{14^2 + 12^2 - 19^2}{2 \times 14 \times 12}$ *[1 mark]*

   $A = \cos^{-1}\left(\dfrac{-21}{336}\right)$ *[1 mark]*

   $A = 93.58...°$ *[1 mark]*

   Area $= \dfrac{1}{2} \times 14 \times 12 \times \sin 93.58...°$ *[1 mark]*

   Area $= 83.84$ cm² (2.d.p) *[1 mark]*
   [5 marks available in total — as above]

4 $BH^2 = 6^2 + 3^2 + 4^2$ *[1 mark]*
   $BH = \sqrt{61}$ *[1 mark]*
   $BH = 7.81$ cm (3 s.f) *[1 mark]*
   [3 marks available in total — as above]

5 a) $\overrightarrow{CD} = -2\mathbf{a}$ *[1 mark]*
   b) $\overrightarrow{AC} = 2\mathbf{d} + 2\mathbf{a}$ *[1 mark]*
   c) $\overrightarrow{BL} = \mathbf{d} - \mathbf{a}$ *[1 mark]*

6 First, split $ABCD$ into two triangles, ABC and ACD.

   $\dfrac{55}{\sin ACB} = \dfrac{93}{\sin 116°}$ *[1 mark]*

   $\sin ACB = \dfrac{\sin 116°}{93} \times 55$ *[1 mark]*

   Angle $ACB = \sin^{-1}(0.531...) = 32.109...°$ *[1 mark]*
   Angle $BAC = 180° - 116° - 32.109...°$ so,

   Area of $ABC = \dfrac{1}{2} \times 93 \times 55 \times \sin(180 - 116 - 32.10...)°$ *[1 mark]*
   Area of $ABC = 1351.106...$cm² *[1 mark]*

   Angle $ACD = 78° - 32.109...°$ so

   Area of $ACD = \dfrac{1}{2} \times 93 \times 84 \times \sin(78 - 32.10...)°$ *[1 mark]*
   Area of $ACD = 2804.531...$cm² *[1 mark]*
   Area of $ABCD = 1351.106... + 2804.531... = 4160$ cm² *[1 mark]*
   [8 marks available in total — as above]

7 a) $\overrightarrow{BX} = \overrightarrow{BC} + \overrightarrow{CX} = \overrightarrow{BC} - \overrightarrow{XC}$
       $\overrightarrow{BC} = 6\overrightarrow{BW} = 6\mathbf{b}$ *[1 mark]*
       As AX = 2XC, CX must be one third of AC, so:
       $\overrightarrow{CX} = -\overrightarrow{XC} = -\dfrac{1}{3}\overrightarrow{AC}$ (or $\overrightarrow{CX} = \dfrac{1}{3}\overrightarrow{CA}$) *[1 mark]*
       $\overrightarrow{AC} = \overrightarrow{AB} + \overrightarrow{BC} = 3\mathbf{a} + 6\mathbf{b}$ (or $\overrightarrow{CA} = -3\mathbf{a} - 6\mathbf{b}$) *[1 mark]*
       $\overrightarrow{CX} = -\dfrac{1}{3}(3\mathbf{a} + 6\mathbf{b}) = -\mathbf{a} - 2\mathbf{b}$

       $\overrightarrow{BX} = 6\mathbf{b} - \mathbf{a} - 2\mathbf{b} = 4\mathbf{b} - \mathbf{a}$ *[1 mark]*
       [4 marks available in total — as above.]
       You could have solved this a little differently, for instance starting
       by writing $\overrightarrow{BX} = \overrightarrow{BA} + \overrightarrow{AX}$ ...
   b) *From part a)* $\overrightarrow{BX} = 4\mathbf{b} - \mathbf{a}$
       ABCD is a parallelogram, so:
       $\overrightarrow{CD} = \overrightarrow{BA} = -\overrightarrow{AB} = -3\mathbf{a}$ *[1 mark]*
       $\overrightarrow{CM} = \dfrac{1}{2}\overrightarrow{CD} = -\dfrac{3}{2}\mathbf{a}$ *[1 mark]*
       $\overrightarrow{BM} = \overrightarrow{BC} + \overrightarrow{CM}$
       $= 6\mathbf{b} - \dfrac{3}{2}\mathbf{a} = \dfrac{3}{2}(4\mathbf{b} - \mathbf{a})$ *[1 mark]*

       B, X and M must be three points on a straight line because
       the lines BM and BX are both scalar multiples of the vector
       $4\mathbf{b} - \mathbf{a}$. *[1 mark]*
       [4 marks available in total — as above]

Page 156 (Revision Questions)

1 $a^2 + b^2 = c^2$

   You use Pythagoras' theorem to find the missing side of a
   right-angled triangle.

2 4.72 m

3 7.8

4

   O over S × H   A over C × H   O over T × A

5 33.4°

6 5.77 cm

7 21.5°

8 Sine rule: $\dfrac{a}{\sin A} = \dfrac{b}{\sin B} = \dfrac{c}{\sin C}$
   Cosine rule: $a^2 = b^2 + c^2 - 2bc \cos A$
   Area $= \dfrac{1}{2}ab \sin C$

9 Two angles given plus any side — sine rule.
   Two sides given plus an angle not enclosed by them — sine rule.
   Two sides given plus the angle enclosed by them — cosine rule.
   All three sides given but no angles — cosine rule.

10 56.4° (3 s.f.)

11 6.84 cm (3 s.f.)

12 48.1 cm² (3 s.f.)

13 $a^2 + b^2 + c^2 = d^2$

14 11.9 m (3 s.f.)

15 15.2° (3 s.f.)

16 54°

17 Multiplying by a scalar changes the size of a vector but not its
    direction (unless the scalar is negative).

18 a) $\overrightarrow{AX} = \dfrac{1}{3}\mathbf{a}$
    b) $\overrightarrow{DX} = \dfrac{4}{3}\mathbf{a} - \mathbf{b}$
        $\overrightarrow{XB} = \dfrac{8}{3}\mathbf{a} - 2\mathbf{b}$
    c) $\overrightarrow{XB} = 2\overrightarrow{DX}$, so DXB is a straight line.

Section Six — Statistics and Probability

Page 160 (Warm-up Questions)

1 a) Stratified sampling.   b) 18

2 The population is all Birmingham households. The sample is
   made up of 600 residential addresses in Birmingham.
   The results obtained are likely to be biased as the interview
   timing will exclude households where the occupants are at
   work during normal working hours.

Page 161 (Exam Questions)

2 a) E.g. no time frame is specified, so the response boxes are
       vague and could be interpreted differently by different
       people. *[1 mark]*
   b) E.g. Mike could assign a number to each person in his year
       group, generate a list of random numbers using a calculator/
       computer/random number table. *[1 mark]*
       He should then match these two sets of numbers up to create
       the sample. *[1 mark]*
       [2 marks available in total — as above]

3 $(116 \div 720) \times 75$ *[1 mark]* $= 12.083... = 12$ *[1 mark]*
   [2 marks available in total — as above]

4 $(487 \div 2033) \times 150$ *[1 mark]* $= 35.932... = 36$ *[1 mark]*
   [2 marks available in total — as above]

Page 168 (Warm-up Questions)

1 Mode = most common.   Median = middle value.
   Mean = total of items ÷ number of items
   Range = difference between the highest and the lowest values.

2

Number of cars	0	1	2	3	4	5	6	Total
Frequency	1	24	36	31	22	9	1	124
No. of cars × F	0	24	72	93	88	45	6	328

   a) Mean $= 328 \div 124 = 2.645$
   b) Median is half-way between the 62nd and 63rd values,
       so median $= 3$
   c) Mode $= 2$ d) Range $= 6 - 0 = 6$.

3

Height (cm)	$145 \leq x < 155$	$155 \leq x < 165$	$165 \leq x < 175$	$175 \leq x < 185$	Total
Frequency	18	22	24	15	79
Midpoint	150	160	170	180	
Midpoint × F	2700	3520	4080	2700	13 000

a) Mean = $13000 \div 79 = 164.56$

b) Median is in the group containing the 40th value, so the median group is $155 \leq x < 165$.

c) Modal Group = $165 \leq x < 175$

Pages 169-170 (Exam Questions)

2 a) $8 + 3 + 5 + 8 + 4 + 1 = 29$
[2 marks available — 1 mark for the correct calculation, 1 mark for the correct answer]

b) $(0 \times 8) + (1 \times 3) + (2 \times 5) + (3 \times 8) + (4 \times 4) + (5 \times 1) = 58$
[2 marks available — 1 mark for the correct calculation, 1 mark for the correct answer]

c) $58 \div 29 = 2$
[2 marks available — 1 mark for the correct calculation, 1 mark for the correct answer]

3 Total running time for first 20 days = $20 \times 56.2 = 1124$
Total running time for all 30 days = $30 \times 54.4 = 1632$
Total running time for last 10 days = $1632 - 1124 = 508$
Mean running time for last 10 days = $508 \div 10 = 50.8$ minutes
[3 marks available — 1 mark for calculating the total running time for the first 20 days OR for all 30 days, 1 mark for calculating the total running time for the last 10 days, 1 mark for the correct answer]

4 a)
```
0 | 3 4 4 5 5 7 8 8 9
1 | 0 1 2
```
Key: 0 | 3 = 3

[3 marks available — 1 mark for correct entries, 1 mark for correct order, 1 mark for key]

b) E.g. the interquartile range will remain the same, as all the values have decreased by 50p. This 50p will cancel out when you subtract the lower quartile from the upper quartile.
[1 mark]

5 a)
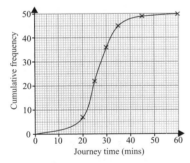

[2 marks available — 1 mark for plotting points correctly, 1 mark for joining them with a smooth curve or straight lines]

b) Number of journeys between 27 and 47 minutes
= $49 - 28 = 21$
[2 marks available — 1 mark for reading the cumulative frequencies off at 27 and 47 minutes, 1 mark for correct answer, accept answers ± 3]

c) 48 journeys took less than 40 mins so 2 journeys took longer.
Percentage of total number = $(2 \div 50) \times 100 = 4\%$
[2 marks available — 1 mark for correct method, 1 mark for correct answer, accept answers ± 2%]

d)
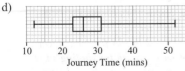

[3 marks available — 1 mark for plotting end points correctly, 1 mark for plotting median correctly (± 1), 1 mark for plotting lower and upper quartiles correctly (± 1)]

Page 174 (Warm-up Questions)

1 a) Graph 1 — (Moderate) positive correlation.
b) Graph 2 — (Weak) negative correlation.

2 21

Page 175 (Exam Questions)

2 $(15 \times 1) + (7 \times 3) + (5 \times 5) + (3 \times 7)$ *[1 mark]*
$= 15 + 21 + 25 + 21 = 82$
$82 \div (15 + 7 + 5 + 3)$ *[1 mark]*
$= 82 \div 30 = 2.733... = 2.7$ hours (to 1 d.p.) *[1 mark]*
[3 marks available in total — as above]

3 a)
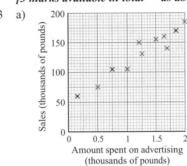

[1 mark if all three points are plotted correctly]

b) Positive correlation *[1 mark]*

c) £1150
[3 marks available — 1 mark for a line of best fit, 1 mark for indicating 125 on the y-axis, 1 mark for correctly reading off from your line of best fit, allow answers ± £100]

Page 182 (Warm-up Questions)

1 $\frac{1}{216}$ or 0.0046. ($\frac{1}{6} \times \frac{1}{6} \times \frac{1}{6}$)

2 $\frac{16}{49}$ or 0.33. ($\frac{4}{7} \times \frac{4}{7}$)

3 $\frac{1}{8}$ or 0.125. ($\frac{1}{2} \times \frac{1}{2} \times \frac{1}{2}$)

4 $\frac{6}{7}$ or 0.86. *(prob at least one of each colour
$= 1 - $ prob all blue $- $ prob all red
$= 1 - (\frac{3}{7} \times \frac{2}{6} \times \frac{1}{5}) - (\frac{4}{7} \times \frac{3}{6} \times \frac{2}{5}) = \frac{6}{7}$.)*

Pages 183-184 (Exam Questions)

2 a) Number of red counters = $10 - 4 = 6$ *[1 mark]*
Probability of getting a red counter = $\frac{6}{10} = \frac{3}{5}$ *[1 mark]*
[2 marks available in total — as above]

b) No green counters so probability of getting a green = 0
[1 mark]

3 a)

		2	4	6	8	10
					Cards	
	1	3	5	7	9	11
	2	4	6	8	10	12
Dice	3	5	7	9	11	13
	4	6	8	10	12	14
	5	7	9	11	13	15
	6	8	10	12	14	16

[2 marks available — 2 marks for all numbers correct, otherwise 1 mark for at least 5 numbers correct]

b) 3 ways of scoring exactly 9 *[1 mark]* . They are (1,8), (3,6) and (5,4). Total number of possible outcomes $6 \times 5 = 30$
Probability of scoring exactly 9 = $\frac{3}{30} = \frac{1}{10}$ *[1 mark]*
[2 marks available in total — as above]

c) Zynah wins if the score is between 8 and 11 (including 8 and 11). There are 12 ways of scoring between 8 and 11 *[1 mark]*. They are (1,8), (1,10), (2,6), (2,8), (3,6), (3,8), (4,4), (4,6), (5,4), (5,6), (6,2) and (6,4).

Probability that Zynah wins = $\frac{12}{30} = \frac{2}{5}$ *[1 mark]*

[2 marks available in total — as above]

4 a)

Number on counter	1	2	3	4	5
Frequency	23	25	22	21	9
Relative Frequency	0.23	0.25	0.22	0.21	0.09

[2 marks available — 2 marks for all correct answers, otherwise 1 mark for any frequency ÷ 100]

b) Elvin is likely to be wrong. The bag seems to contain fewer counters numbered 5. *[1 mark]*

c) P(odd number) = (0.23 + 0.22 + 0.09) *[1 mark]* = 0.54 *[1 mark]*
[2 marks available in total — as above]

5 E.g. use a probability tree diagram:

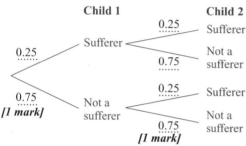

P(at least one of them has the disease)
= 1 – P(neither have the disease) = 1 – (0.75 × 0.75) *[1 mark]*
= 1 – 0.5625 = 0.4375 *[1 mark]*

[4 marks available in total — as above]

6 P(2 orange and a brown) = P(orange then orange then brown)
+ P(orange then brown then orange)
+ P(brown then orange then orange)

$$= \left(\frac{12}{20} \times \frac{11}{19} \times \frac{8}{18}\right) + \left(\frac{12}{20} \times \frac{8}{19} \times \frac{11}{18}\right) + \left(\frac{8}{20} \times \frac{12}{19} \times \frac{11}{18}\right)$$

$$= 3 \times \frac{12 \times 11 \times 8}{20 \times 19 \times 18} = \frac{44}{95}$$

[4 marks available — 1 mark for the correct probability for picking each bead, 1 mark for multiplying the probabilities of the three beads together, 1 mark for adding the probabilities for each possible case together, 1 mark for the correct final answer]

Page 185 (Revision Questions)

1 A sample is part of a population. Samples need to be representative so that conclusions drawn from sample data can be applied to the whole population.

2 A random sample is one where every member of the population has an equal chance of being in it.

3 20

4 Questions need to be:
   (i) clear and easy to understand
   (ii) easy to answer
   (iii) fair (i.e. not leading or biased)
   (iv) easy to analyse afterwards

5 The <u>mode</u> is the most common value. The <u>median</u> is the middle value when the data has been arranged in order of size. The <u>mean</u> is the total of the data values divided by the number of data values. The <u>range</u> is the difference between the highest and lowest data values.

6 a) Mode = 31, Median = 24, Mean = 22, Range = 39
   b) Lower quartile = 11, Upper quartile = 31
      Interquartile range = 20

7 The median time in winter is lower than the median time in summer, so it generally took longer to get to work in the summer. The range and the IQR for the summer are smaller than those for the winter, so there is less variation in journey times in the summer.

8 a) Modal class is: $1.5 \leq y < 1.6$.
   b) Class containing median is: $1.5 \leq y < 1.6$
   c) Estimated mean = 1.58 m (to 2 d.p.)

9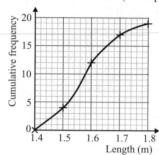

10 Calculate the bar's area or use the formula:
   frequency = frequency density × class width.

11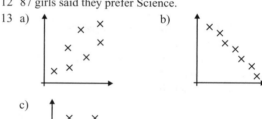

12 87 girls said they prefer Science.

13 a) 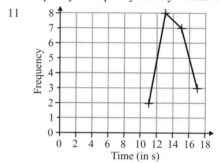 b)

   c)

14 $\frac{4}{25}$

15 1

16 Expected times outcome will happen = probability × n

17 $\frac{1}{12}$

18 $\frac{1}{2}$

19 $\frac{1}{221}$

20 When you can't tell what the probabilities of different outcomes are 'just by looking', e.g. when you have a biased dice/spinner etc.

Practice Paper 1

1 a) (i) The common difference is 11 so $11n$ is in the expression.

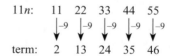

To get each term you need to subtract 9, so the expression for the nth term is $11n - 9$.
[2 marks available — 2 marks for the correct expression, otherwise 1 mark for finding 11n]
If you enjoy learning formulas, you could do this question using the formula nth term = dn + (a – d), where d is the common difference and a is the first term.

(ii) Substituting $n = 8$ into the expression for the nth term:
$11n - 9 = (11 \times 8) - 9 = 88 - 9 = 79$ *[1 mark]*
[3 marks available in total — as above]

b) Set the expression for the nth term equal to 65 and solve for n. If n is a whole number, then 65 will be in the sequence. If $2n + 2 = 65$, then $2n = 63$ and $n = 31.5$. Since n is not a whole number, 65 will not be in the sequence.
[2 marks available — 2 marks for saying that 65 will not be in the sequence, with a correct explanation, otherwise 1 mark for setting the expression equal to 65]
You could also answer part (b) by saying that all multiples of 2 are even numbers, and an even number plus 2 is also an even number — so all the terms in the sequence will be even numbers. Since 65 is an odd number, it can't be in the sequence.

2 a) Sum of exterior angles = 360° *[1 mark]*
b) Sum of interior angles = $(7 - 2) \times 180°$ *[1 mark]*
= 900° *[1 mark]*
[2 marks available in total — as above]

3 Let the number of people going be n. Then the total cost of the trip will be $100 + 15n$ *[1 mark]*. The youth centre will charge £23 per person, which is $23n$ in total.
To cover the cost, $23n$ must equal $100 + 15n$.
So $23n = 100 + 15n$ *[1 mark]*
$8n = 100$
$n = 12.5$ *[1 mark]*
So there need to be 13 people on the trip for the Youth Centre to cover its costs. *[1 mark]*.
[4 marks available in total — as above]
You have to round up here — if only 12 people went, 23n would be less than 100 + 15n so the Youth Centre wouldn't make enough money.

4 $3\frac{3}{7} - 2\frac{1}{5} = \frac{24}{7} - \frac{11}{5} = \frac{120}{35} - \frac{77}{35} = \frac{43}{35}$
[3 marks available — 1 mark for writing as improper fractions, 1 mark for writing over a common denominator, 1 mark for the correct answer]

5 a) E.g. this is a leading question because it's encouraging you to agree with the statement.
[1 mark]
b) E.g. 'Do you think that Digton needs a new supermarket?'
[1 mark]
c) E.g. the response boxes are very vague, so they could be interpreted differently by different people.
[1 mark]
d) E.g. 'How many miles are you willing to travel to buy your food shopping each week?'

 less than 5 5 to 10 ☐ over 10

[2 marks available — 1 mark for a more specific question, 1 mark for at least 3 non-overlapping response options, with the units specified]

6 a) $4e - 6ef = 2e(2 - 3f)$ *[1 mark]*
b) $g^2 - 16 = g^2 - 4^2 = (g + 4)(g - 4)$ *[1 mark]*

7 Cost of 2 steaks at 'The Big Grill':
£16 + (£16 ÷ 2) = £16 + £8 = £24
Cost of 2 steaks at 'Steak 'a' Lot':
2 × £18 = £36
20% of £36 = 0.2 × £36 = £7.20
£36 − £7.20 = £28.80
Cost of 2 steaks at 'Danny's Steak House':
2 × £21 = £42
⅓ × £42 = £14
£42 − £14 = £28
So 'The Big Grill' is the cheapest.
Michael and Jojo should go to 'The Big Grill' for the best deal.
[5 marks available in total — 1 mark for each of three correct methods for finding the costs, 1 mark for all three costs correct, 1 mark for the correct answer]

8 a) E.g.

So $56 = 2 \times 2 \times 2 \times 7$
$56^2 = (2 \times 2 \times 2 \times 7)^2$
$= 2 \times 2 \times 2 \times 2 \times 2 \times 2 \times 7 \times 7$ (or $2^6 \times 7^2$)
[2 marks available — 1 mark for a correct method, 1 mark for all prime factors correct]

b) E.g.

So $72 = 2 \times 2 \times 2 \times 3 \times 3$
$2 \times 2 \times 2$ is common to both 56 and 72, so the highest common factor is $2 \times 2 \times 2 = 8$ *[1 mark]*
Another way to tackle this sort of question is to list all the factors of each number, then the HCF is the highest number that appears in both lists. If you're not completely happy with finding prime factors, it'd be safer to do it this way.

9 E.g. As RS and VT are parallel, angle URS = angle UTV (alternate angles). Similarly angle USR = angle UVT (alternate angles). Angle RUS = angle TUV (vertically opposite angles are equal). Triangles RSU and TVU have all three angles the same so are similar. *[3 marks available — 1 mark for showing one angle is the same, 1 mark for showing that the rest are the same (the third angle can be implied from 2 angles the same), 1 mark for stating that the triangles are similar because their angles are the same]*

10 a) Rotation of 90° clockwise about the point (−1, −1).
[3 marks available — 1 mark for rotation of 90°, 1 mark for the correct direction of rotation, 1 mark for the correct centre of rotation]
Using tracing paper is the easiest way to make sure you get the centre of rotation correct.

b)

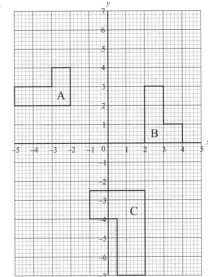

[3 marks available — 1 mark for any enlargement, 1 mark for enlarging by the scale factor −1.5 and 1 mark for the correct position]

11 a) Area of side = 5 cm × 12 cm = 60 cm².
        Area of base = 6 cm × 12 cm = 72 cm².
        Area of triangular end = ½ × b × h.
        Splitting the triangle into 2 right-angled triangles:

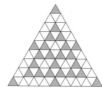

        By Pythagoras' Theorem, $h^2 + 3^2 = 5^2$
        $h^2 = 25 - 9 = 16$
        $h = 4$ cm.
        Area of triangular end = ½ × 6 cm × 4 cm = 12 cm².
        So total surface area = (2 × 60 cm²) + 72 cm² + (2 × 12 cm²)
        = 120 cm² + 72 cm² + 24 cm² = 216 cm²
        [3 marks available — 1 mark for finding the area of the triangular face, 1 mark for finding the area of at least one rectangular face, 1 mark for finding the surface area of the whole shape]

    b) Area of cross section = area of triangle = ½ × 6 × 4 = 12 cm²
        (from above).
        Volume = area of cross section × length = 12 × 12 = 144 cm³.
        [2 marks available — 1 mark for a correct method and 1 mark for the correct answer]

12 $5y + 6x = 7$ (1)
    $4y - 3x = 16$ (2)
    (2) × 2: $8y - 6x = 32$ (3) *[1 mark]*
    (1) + (3):
    $5y + 6x = 7$
    $\underline{8y - 6x = 32}$ +
    $13y\quad = 39$
    $\quad y\quad = 3$ *[1 mark]*
    Substituting $y = 3$ in (1):
    (5 × 3) + 6x = 7
    15 + 6x = 7
    6x = –8
    $x = -\dfrac{8}{6} = -\dfrac{4}{3}$ *[1 mark]*
    [3 marks available in total — as above]

13 a) $\dfrac{4x + 10}{6x + 14} = \dfrac{2(2x + 5)}{2(3x + 7)} = \dfrac{2x + 5}{3x + 7}$
        [2 marks available — 1 mark for correctly factorising at least one of the numerator and denominator, 1 mark for the correct answer]

    b) $\dfrac{x^2 - 2x - 15}{x^2 + 10x + 21} = \dfrac{(x - 5)(x + 3)}{(x + 7)(x + 3)} = \dfrac{x - 5}{x + 7}$
        [3 marks available — 1 mark for correctly factorising the numerator, 1 mark for correctly factorising the denominator, 1 mark for the correct answer]

14 Area = length × width
    $= \sqrt{6}(\sqrt{2} + \sqrt{3})$ *[1 mark]*
    $= \sqrt{6}\sqrt{2} + \sqrt{6}\sqrt{3}$
    $= \sqrt{3}\sqrt{2}\sqrt{2} + \sqrt{2}\sqrt{3}\sqrt{3}$ *[1 mark]*
    $= \sqrt{3} \times 2 + \sqrt{2} \times 3$
    $= (2\sqrt{3} + 3\sqrt{2})$ cm² *[1 mark]*
    [3 marks available in total — as above]

15 a) The angle at the centre is twice the angle at the circumference, so: $b = a \div 2 = 36° \div 2 = 18°$ *[1 mark]*

    b) Area of sector = $\dfrac{a}{360}$ × area of circle
        Area of full circle = $\pi r^2 = \pi \times 3^2 = 9\pi$ cm² *[1 mark]*
        Area of sector = $\dfrac{36}{360} \times 9\pi$ *[1 mark]*
        $= \dfrac{1}{10} \times 9\pi = \dfrac{9\pi}{10}$ cm² *[1 mark]*
        [3 marks available in total — as above]

    c) Length of arc = $\dfrac{a}{360}$ × circumference
        Circumference of full circle = $\pi \times d = 6\pi$ cm *[1 mark]*
        Length of arc = $\dfrac{36}{360} \times 6\pi$ *[1 mark]*
        $= \dfrac{1}{10} \times 6\pi = \dfrac{6\pi}{10} = \dfrac{3\pi}{5}$ cm *[1 mark]*
        [3 marks available in total — as above]

16 $(x^2 + 6x + 9) - 9 - 8$ *[1 mark]*
    $(x + 3)^2 - 9 - 8$ *[1 mark]*
    $(x + 3)^2 - 17$ *[1 mark]*
    [3 marks available in total — as above]

17 a) PQD and ACD are similar, and $AD:PD = 5:3$,
        so $\overrightarrow{CA} = \dfrac{5}{3} \times \overrightarrow{QP} = \dfrac{5}{3}\mathbf{b}$ *[1 mark]*

    b) $\overrightarrow{PR} = \overrightarrow{PA} + \overrightarrow{AR}$
        $\overrightarrow{PA} = \dfrac{2}{3}\overrightarrow{DP} = \dfrac{2}{3}(-\mathbf{a} + \mathbf{b}) = -\dfrac{2}{3}\mathbf{a} + \dfrac{2}{3}\mathbf{b}$ *[1 mark]*
        $\overrightarrow{AR} = \dfrac{2}{5}\overrightarrow{AC} = -\dfrac{2}{5}\overrightarrow{CA} = -\dfrac{2}{5} \times \dfrac{5}{3}\mathbf{b} = -\dfrac{2}{3}\mathbf{b}$ *[1 mark]*
        $\overrightarrow{PR} = -\dfrac{2}{3}\mathbf{a} + \dfrac{2}{3}\mathbf{b} - \dfrac{2}{3}\mathbf{b} = -\dfrac{2}{3}\mathbf{a}$ *[1 mark]*
        $\overrightarrow{PR}$ is a scalar multiple of $\overrightarrow{DQ} (= -\mathbf{a})$, so $\overrightarrow{PR}$ and $\overrightarrow{DQ}$ are parallel. *[1 mark]*
        [4 marks available in total — as above]

Practice Paper 2

1

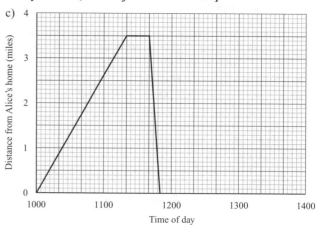

    [3 marks available — 3 marks if all twelve triangles are correctly shaded, otherwise 2 marks if eight out of twelve triangles are correctly shaded, otherwise 1 mark if four out of twelve triangles are correctly shaded]

2 a) 12 boys and 26 – 12 = 14 girls. *[1 mark]*
       Ratio of boys to girls is 12 : 14 = 6 : 7 *[1 mark]*
       [2 marks available in total — as above]

    b) 25 ÷ (2 + 3) = 5 *[1 mark]*
       Number of girls is 5 × 3 = 15 *[1 mark]*
       [2 marks available in total — as above]

3 a) 3.5 miles *[1 mark]*

    b) Speed = distance ÷ time = $3\dfrac{1}{2} \div 1\dfrac{1}{3} = 2.625$ mph
       [2 marks available — 1 mark for dividing the distance by the time, 1 mark for correct answer.]

    c) *[3 marks available — 1 mark for a flat line from 11:20 to 11:40, 2 marks for straight line from 11:40 to 11:50.]*

    d) 1 hour 50 minutes *[1 mark]*

4 Area of outside walls = $2(15 \times 3) + 2(12 \times 3) = 162$ m²
Area of windows = $5(2 \times 1) = 10$ m²
Area of door = $3 \times 2.5 = 7.5$ m²
Area to paint = $162 - 10 - 7.5 = 144.5$ m²
Number of litres needed = $144.5 \div 13 = 11.115...$ litres
Minimum number of tins needed = $(2 \times 5 \text{ litres}) + (1 \times 2.5 \text{ litres})$
Cost = $(2 \times 20.99) + 12.99 = £54.97$
[6 marks available — 1 mark for finding the area of outside walls, 1 mark for finding the area of the windows and door, 1 mark for finding the area to paint, 1 mark for working out how many litres of paint are needed, 1 mark for working out how many tins are needed, 1 mark for cost.]

5 E.g.

x	$x^3 - x - 4$	Comment
1	−4	too small
2	2	too big
1.5	−2.125	too small
1.7	−0.787	too small
1.8	0.032	too big
1.75	−0.390625	too small

So $x = 1.8$ (to 1 d.p.)
[4 marks available — 1 mark for any trial between 1 and 2, 1 mark for any trial between 1.5 and 2, 1 mark for a trial to 2 d.p., 1 mark for the correct answer.]

6 a) $a = \frac{1}{2}bc^2$
$2a = bc^2$
$b = \frac{2a}{c^2}$
[2 marks available — 1 mark for multiplying both sides by 2, 1 mark for the correct answer]

b) $12 = \frac{bx + 8}{by - 4}$
$12(by - 4) = bx + 8$ *[1 mark]*
$12by - 48 = bx + 8$
$12by - bx = 56$
$b(12y - x) = 56$ *[1 mark]*
$b = \frac{56}{12y - x}$ *[1 mark]*
[3 marks available in total — as above]

7 a) Eva's chance of winning = $\frac{1}{6}$,
Finn's chance of winning = $\frac{1}{3} \times \frac{1}{3} = \frac{1}{9}$,
so Eva is more likely to win.
[2 marks available — 1 mark for calculating both probabilities, 1 mark for conclusion.]
To score 6, Finn has to spin a 3 on his first spin then a 3 on his second spin and P(getting a 3) = $\frac{1}{3}$ for each spin — so you multiply the probabilities.

b) Eva: rolling a 5 or rolling a 6 = $\frac{1}{6} + \frac{1}{6} = \frac{1}{3}$
Finn: spinning 3 then 2 or spinning 2 then 3 or spinning 3 then 3 = $(\frac{1}{3} \times \frac{1}{3}) + (\frac{1}{3} \times \frac{1}{3}) + (\frac{1}{3} \times \frac{1}{3}) = \frac{1}{9} + \frac{1}{9} + \frac{1}{9} = \frac{1}{3}$
Both scoring 5 or more = $\frac{1}{3} \times \frac{1}{3} = \frac{1}{9}$
In 54 games, $54 \times \frac{1}{9} = 6$
[3 marks available — 1 mark for finding Eva's chance of scoring 5 or more, 1 mark for finding Finn's chance of scoring 5 or more, 1 mark for correct answer.]

8 a) Selling price = 90% of £190 000 = $0.9 \times 190\,000 = £171\,000$
Tibbersons' fees:
1.95% of £171 000 = $0.0195 \times 171\,000 = £3334.50$
As Shirleys' fees are £3700, it will be cheaper to use Tibbersons if the house sells for 10% below the asking price.
[3 marks available — 1 mark for calculating selling price, 1 mark for calculating Tibbersons' fees, 1 mark for conclusion.]

b) £212 500 = 85% of original price
1% of original price = $212\,500 \div 85 = £2500$
original price = $2500 \times 100 = £250\,000$
[3 marks available — 1 mark for writing 85% or 0.85, 1 mark for dividing 212 500 by 85 then multiplying by 100 or equivalent, 1 mark for correct final answer.]
You could have divided 212 500 by 0.85 instead of dividing by 85 and multiplying by 100 — you'd get the same answer.

9 a)

Height in cm (h)	Frequency	Mid-interval value	Frequency × mid-interval value
$130 \leq h < 140$	5	$(130 + 140) / 2 = 135$	$5 \times 135 = 675$
$140 \leq h < 150$	10	$(140 + 150) / 2 = 145$	$10 \times 145 = 1450$
$150 \leq h < 160$	14	$(150 + 160) / 2 = 155$	$14 \times 155 = 2170$
$160 \leq h < 170$	8	$(160 + 170) / 2 = 165$	$8 \times 165 = 1320$
$170 \leq h < 180$	3	$(170 + 180) / 2 = 175$	$3 \times 175 = 525$

Total number of children = $5 + 10 + 14 + 8 + 3 = 40$
Mean = $(675 + 1450 + 2170 + 1320 + 525) \div 40 = 6140 \div 40$
$= 153.5$ cm
[4 marks available — 1 mark for all mid-interval values, 1 mark for calculation of frequency × mid-interval value, 1 mark for adding these up and dividing by 40, 1 mark for the correct answer.]

b) E.g. The modal class for Class A is $150 \leq h < 160$, whereas the modal class for Class B is $160 \leq h < 170$, so the modal height of Class B is taller than the modal height of Class A. For Class A, the median is in $150 \leq h < 160$, and for Class B the median is in $160 \leq h < 170$, so the median height is taller in Class B.
There are more students with heights less than 160 cm in Class A than Class B. There are more students with heights greater than 160 cm in Class B than Class A, so students in Class B are generally taller.
[3 marks available — 1 mark for comparing modal classes, 1 mark for comparing median classes and 1 mark for comparing overall distributions.]
You don't need to have written exactly what's written here, just some sensible comments comparing the distributions — including their medians and modes.

10 Account 1: 2% of £4500 = $£4500 \times 0.02 = £90$
Amount in Account 1 after 1 year = $£4500 + £90 = £4590$
Account 2: 1 year is 12 months. So using the formula
$N = N_0\left(1 + \frac{r}{100}\right)^n$, where N is the amount after 1 year, N_0 is the original amount, r is the interest rate and n is the number of months, the amount in Account 2 after 1 year is:
$£4500\left(1 + \frac{0.4}{100}\right)^{12} = £4500 \times 1.004^{12} = £4720.82$ (2 d.p.)
So the savings will increase the most in Account 2.
[5 marks available — 1 mark for using a correct method to find the amount in Account 1 after one year, 1 mark for finding the correct amount in Account 1 after one year, 1 mark for using a correct method to find the amount in Account 2 after one year, 1 mark for finding the correct amount in Account 2 after one year and 1 mark for the correct conclusion]
To find the amount in Account 1, you could multiply by 1.02 instead of finding the interest then adding it on — you'd get the same answer.

11

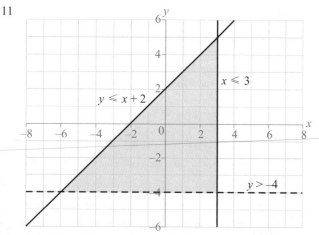

[4 marks available — 1 mark for showing each inequality correctly, 1 mark for shading the correct region]

12 Volume of cylinder = $\pi r^2 h = \pi \times (3.8 \div 2)^2 \times 4.9 = 55.57...$ cm³
Weight of sherbet = $55.57... \times 0.63 = 35.010... = 35.01$ g (2 d.p.)
[3 marks available — 1 mark for finding the volume of the cylinder using the formula, 1 mark for multiplying the volume by the weight, 1 mark for correct final answer.]

13 a) Add a cumulative frequency column to the table:

BMI (b)	Frequency	Cumulative Frequency
$15 < b \leq 20$	4	4
$20 < b \leq 25$	14	18
$25 < b \leq 30$	12	30
$30 < b \leq 35$	5	35
$35 < b \leq 40$	3	38
$40 < b \leq 45$	2	40

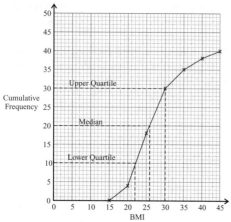

[2 marks available — 1 mark for plotting the points correctly, 1 mark for joining them with straight lines or a smooth curve]
You're asked to draw a cumulative frequency graph, so you can choose whether to join the points with a curve or straight lines.

b) Median BMI = 26 (see graph)
[1 mark, accept answers ±1]

c) Lower quartile: BMI = 22 (see graph)
Upper quartile: BMI = 30 (see graph)
Interquartile range = 30 – 22 = 8
[2 marks available — 1 mark for correct method, 1 mark for correct answer, accept answers ±2]

d) For the men: median = 28 and IQR = 34 – 22 = 12.
The median BMI for the men is higher, so the men have a higher BMI on average *[1 mark]*. The interquartile range for the men is bigger, so there is more variation in their BMI values *[1 mark]*.
[2 marks available in total — as above]

14 $62\,000\,000 = 6.2 \times 10^7$
Debt per person = debt ÷ population
= $(8.494 \times 10^{11}) \div (6.2 \times 10^7) = (8.494 \div 6.2) \times (10^{11} \div 10^7)$
= £1.37×10^4
[2 marks available — 1 mark for calculation, 1 mark for correct answer in standard form]

15 a) i) $3y - 6y^2z = 3y(1 - 2yz)$ *[1 mark]*
ii) $6x^2 - 8x - 8 = 2(3x^2 - 4x - 4)$ *[1 mark]*
= $2(3x + 2)(x - 2)$ *[1 mark]*
[3 marks available in total — as above.]

b) $x = \dfrac{-b \pm \sqrt{b^2 - 4ac}}{2a}$

$= \dfrac{-(-8) \pm \sqrt{(-8)^2 - (4 \times 1 \times 3)}}{2 \times 1}$ *[1 mark]*

$= \dfrac{8 \pm \sqrt{64 - 12}}{2} = \dfrac{8 \pm \sqrt{52}}{2}$ *[1 mark]*

$= \dfrac{8 \pm 2\sqrt{13}}{2} = 4 \pm \sqrt{13}$ *[1 mark]*

[3 marks available in total — as above.]
The mention of surd form in the question is a big hint that you're going to need to use the quadratic formula here.

16 a) $y \propto \dfrac{1}{x^3}$ so $y = \dfrac{k}{x^3}$ *[1 mark]*. When $y = 60$, $x = 2$,
so $60 = \dfrac{k}{2^3} = \dfrac{k}{8}$.
$k = 60 \times 8 = 480$ *[1 mark]*, so $y = \dfrac{480}{x^3}$ *[1 mark]*
[3 marks available in total — as above.]

b) $100 = \dfrac{480}{x^3}$
$x^3 = \dfrac{480}{100} = 4.8$ *[1 mark]*,
so $x = 1.6868... = 1.69$ (to 2 d.p.) *[1 mark]*
[2 marks available in total — as above]

17 a) $(10 \times 0.6) + (40 \times 0.1)$ *[1 mark]* = $6 + 4 = 10$ cars *[1 mark]*
[2 marks available in total — as above]
The (10 × 0.6) comes from splitting the 60-80 interval in half — you're looking for cars parked for longer than 70 minutes, so you need the bit of the bar which covers 70-80 mins, and then the whole of the bar for 80-120 mins.

b) Frequencies: 0-20 = $20 \times 1.2 = 24$,
20-30 = $10 \times 2.4 = 24$,
30-40 = $10 \times 1.6 = 16$,
40-60 = $20 \times 1.0 = 20$,
60-80 = $20 \times 0.6 = 12$,
80-120 = $40 \times 0.1 = 4$
Mean
= sum of (frequency × mid-interval value) ÷ number of cars

$= \dfrac{\left[\begin{array}{l}(24 \times 10) + (24 \times 25) + (16 \times 35) + \\ (20 \times 50) + (12 \times 70) + (4 \times 100)\end{array}\right]}{100}$

$= \dfrac{3640}{100} = 36.4$ minutes
[3 marks available — 1 mark for finding frequencies, 1 mark for the working to find the mean, 1 mark for correct answer]

18 a)

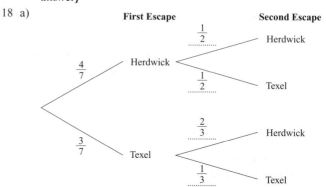

[2 marks for all four probabilities correct, otherwise 1 mark for at least two correct probabilities]

b) P(two Herdwicks) = $\frac{4}{7} \times \frac{1}{2}$ *[1 mark]* = $\frac{4}{14} = \frac{2}{7}$ *[1 mark]*
[2 marks available in total — as above]

c) P(one Herdwick and one Texel)
= P(Herdwick then Texel) + P(Texel then Herdwick)

$= \left(\frac{4}{7} \times \frac{1}{2}\right) + \left(\frac{3}{7} \times \frac{2}{3}\right)$ *[1 mark]*

$= \frac{4}{14} + \frac{6}{21} = \frac{2}{7} + \frac{2}{7} = \frac{4}{7}$ *[1 mark]*

[2 marks available in total — as above]
You could have done this one by finding the probability that both escaped sheep are the same then subtracting this from 1 instead.

19 a)
d	0	20	40	50	60	80	100
h	0	32	48	50	48	32	0

[2 marks available — 1 mark for each correct entry.]

b)
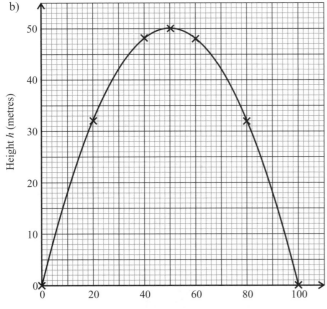

[2 marks available — 1 mark for plotting points correctly, 1 mark for joining points with a smooth curve.]

c)
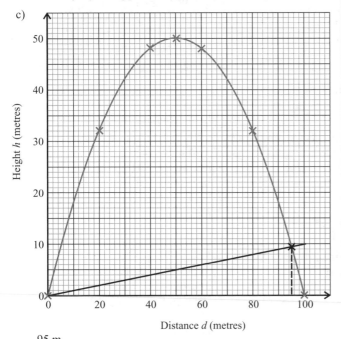

95 m
[3 marks available — 1 mark for drawing a line with gradient 0.1, 1 mark for showing line intersecting with curve, 1 mark for correct answer within 1 m.]

20 *PRT* is a triangular plane:

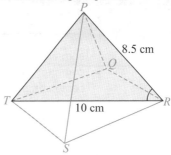

Area = ½ × *PR* × *RT* × sin*PRT*, so 35 = ½(8.5 × 10) sin*PRT*
[1 mark]

sin*PRT* = $\frac{35 \times 2}{8.5 \times 10}$ = 0.823... *[1 mark]*

PRT = sin⁻¹ 0.823... = 55.4° (1 d.p.) *[1 mark]*
[3 marks available in total — as above.]

21 Take two consecutive numbers, n and $n + 1$.
Then $3n$ and $3(n + 1) = 3n + 3$ are two consecutive multiples of 3 *[1 mark]*. Their squares are $(3n)^2 = 9n^2$ *[1 mark]* and $(3n + 3)^2 = 9n^2 + 18n + 9$ *[1 mark]*.
The sum of these two squares is $9n^2 + (9n^2 + 18n + 9)$ $= 18n^2 + 18n + 9$ *[1 mark]*, which can be written as $9(2n^2 + 2n + 1)$, which is a multiple of 9 *[1 mark]*.
[5 marks available in total — as above.]

Index